VIOLATION OF TABOO

Violation of Taboo

INCEST IN THE GREAT LITERATURE
OF THE PAST AND PRESENT

Donald Webster Cory & R. E. L. Masters

THE JULIAN PRESS, INC. *Publishers*

New York

Published by The Julian Press, Inc.
80 East 11th Street, New York 3
© Copyright 1963 by The Julian Press, Inc.
Library of Congress Catalog Card Number 63–13188
Manufactured in the United States of America
by H. Wolff, New York
Design: Marshall Lee

ACKNOWLEDGMENTS:

THE BOOK BAG by W. Somerset Maugham Copyright 1932 by Doubleday & Company, Inc. Reprinted by permission of the publisher.

THE BURNING BABY by Dylan Thomas. Copyright 1955 by New Directions. Reprinted by permission of New Directions, Publishers.

EUGENIE DE FRANVAL and PHILOSOPHY IN THEIR BOUDOIR, by Marquis de Sade. Copyright 1953 by Grove Press, Inc. From THE MARQUIS DE SADE: SELECTIONS FROM HIS WRITINGS, compiled and translated by Paul Dinnage, and a study by Simone de Beauvoir.

PIERRE by Herman Melville. Reprinted from The Grove Press Edition, with permission from Grove Press, Inc.

THE BLOOD OF THE WALSUNGS by Thomas Mann. Reprinted from STORIES OF THREE DECADES by Thomas Mann, by permission of Alfred A. Knopf, Inc. Copyright 1936 by Alfred A. Knopf, Inc.

A TALE OF INCEST by Margaret of Navarre, reprinted from THE PALACE OF PLEASURE, copyright by G. P. Putnam's Sons. Reprinted with permission.

CONFESSIONS OF A YOUNG WOMAN, by Pierre Louys, appears in a new translation by Donald Webster Cory, and is protected by copyright.

Contents

VIOLATION OF TABOO

INTRODUCTION

This book presents a cross-section of literary works—fiction and drama—on incest. For the most part the selections have considerable merit; the authors are well-known. Thus, on a literary basis, the volume is justified.

Our intentions, however, are different from those of the typical anthologist. We are offering this collection to the scientist as well as to the general reader.

Here are different perspectives on incest than those to be found in the clinical reports, the anthropological surveys, the sociological studies.[1] The authors of the selections are not "incest offenders" under arrest or in therapy. Neither are they members of primitive (or preliterate) societies. We find in these selections the creative imagination and intellect at grips with a subject that has always fascinated, appalled, and perplexed mankind.

Incest is one of the most ancient of human problems and preoccupations. It is customary to say that the thought of incest arouses only horror and revulsion in all peoples. That such is not the case, the selections in this volume eloquently demonstrate.

Isabel Drummond has remarked that incest "has touched the extremes in sanction and denunciation. It fluctuates in degree of illegality with the times." Similarly, Guyon observes that "the conception of incest current in the Western world seems to vary from one age to another." Some readers will be less than happy to learn that such has been the case.

Ambivalence, not unvacillating outrage and censure, has typically characterized human responses to the idea and practice of incest. The incestuous union ordinarily both attracts and repels.

1 The reader interested in these and other aspects of incest is referred to the companion volume, R. E. L. Masters' *Patterns of Incest,* Julian Press, New York, 1963.

At various places and times, and in countless individual cases, the element of attraction has been the stronger; more often, however, incestuous relationships have been viewed *mainly* with disapproval and even horror.

Both primitive and civilized societies have had incest taboos. The reader should remember here that a taboo is not necessarily, as in popular usage, a total prohibition. A tabooed act, such as incest, may be prohibited altogether; but it may also be sacred, and thus reserved to particular persons, or for special occasions.

Thus, among the rulers of some ancient peoples, fathers married daughters, mothers married sons, and sisters had union with their brothers. Also among ancient peoples (and some modern ones), incestuous unions were reserved for occasions of sacred significance. On such occasions, incest was not merely tolerated, but might be obligatory.

Additionally, incest has been, for some peoples, a therapeutic practice. Victims of plague and of syphilis have believed that incestuous intercourse would remedy the maladies that beset them.

Incestuous marriages and extramarital copulations were commonplace among the gods of ancient peoples. In the case of the Egyptians, the incest of the gods was paralleled by brother-sister marriages of their rulers. Later, the people generally adopted the practice. The complicated and numerous incestuous relationships of the gods of the Greeks were accompanied, early in Greek history, by a tolerance for similar human relationships. Later, incestuous marriages were condemned; apparently by popular opinion, rather than by law. And despite this opinion, reflecting an "official" moral position, much tolerance remained for the marriage of siblings.

What must have been an early Greek inclination to incest is evidenced by the Homeric version of the Oedipus myth. In that version, neither Oedipus nor his mother, Jocasta, is penalized for having consummated an incestuous marriage. But in the later version of Sophocles—the version used by Freud to elaborate his Oedipus complex—calamity follows the incestuous union.

The incest behavior of the gods of mythology, along with the gods' other sexual practices, reflects human appetites and deeds. So, too, do the sexual practices of the heroes and heroines of legend and Scripture.

In the *Old Testament* of the Hebrews, various of God's favorites become involved in incestuous unions: Lot (with his daughters); Noah (with his son); Abraham (with his half-sister), etc. Like the Greeks, the Hebrews seem gradually to have abandoned a tolerance for incestuous practices. Gradually, they tightened their enforcement of old and neglected interdictions, arriving at last at the total prohibition with which we are presently familiar.

Christians, regarding intercourse within marriage as a regrettable necessity, and rigidly adhering to the Mosaic prohibitions, abominated incest. Under the domination of the Roman Catholic Church, Christianity extended its definition of incestuous relationships to preposterous lengths. At some periods in Europe, even sixth cousins were forbidden to marry. But such excesses encouraged, rather than inhibited, incestuous connections. In small villages, which the residents were often not permitted to leave, and where almost everyone was to some degree related, marriage became impossible for most. The result was incest, necessarily furtive, and mainly of the mother with her sons.

The incestuous behavior of the French clergy in the Middle Ages at times was open and notorious. A decree of 1208 forbade sisters and mothers to share dwellings with their clergymen-brothers and sons—precisely for that reason. But such laxity was succeeded, once the witchcraft epidemic had begun, and for a long while thereafter, by a horror of incest. Incestuous unions were regarded as the ultimate abomination; and at the Sabbats of the Witches, those most damnable of conclaves, incestuous couplings were mandatory. The very same practices, inspired or commanded by the Devil, were attributed to a variety of heretical sects (recalling identical accusations from a much earlier time).

Also during the Italian Renaissance, incest prohibitions were often ignored; and not infrequently, openly flouted. Incestuous behavior was attributed to popes, and to many of the nobles and

Church dignitaries of the period. This was paralleled by a literature in which incest is taken lightly, and sometimes regarded as
humorous.

From the eighteenth century on, the incest theme in literature sent delicious shivers of horror up the spines of European
and American readers. Sometimes a young couple, betrothed
and about to be wed, discovered at the very last moment (i.e.,
before consummation) that they were brother and sister. If
Providence spared them their incestuous coupling, a sin ir-
remediable, the reader was reassured—God's goodness was demonstrated. But the devil was also abroad. He brought brother
and sister, mother and son, father and daughter, together upon
couches of lust. He stirred in these couples, often separated for
many years and unaware of their blood-bonds, the most damnable ardors. Then, when consummation had occurred, the devil
revealed the incest. Suicides might follow; or one or both of the
victims of the satanic machinations might be carried off directly
to hell.

The extent of present-day incestuous behavior, most carefully
guarded of all sexual secrets, is not known. Kinsey, on the basis
of his interviews—and quite possibly too trustful of his data in
this case—thought such unions very rare. Some psychoanalysts,
on the other hand, regard them as commonplace. The truth
probably lies somewhere in between; but recent scientific writings suggest that the incidence is greater than is usually supposed.

Incest is much more overt in Africa, among both Negroes and
Arabs, and in areas of the East, than in Europe or North America. Sexual intercourse between young Muslim siblings, both
heterosexual and homosexual, is frequent; and parents often
display a marked tolerance for such practices, which have also
been their own. No doubt as a consequence of this adult permissiveness, serious traumas due to incest seem but rarely to occur.
If that is the case, the situation is quite different from what one
finds in the West. In Christian countries, the incest experience
is believed to spawn neuroses, sexual deviations, and even psy-
choses.

The average American man or woman professes revulsion at

the thought of an incestuous relationship—and may advance this "instinctive abhorrence" as the basis for incest prohibitions. (A strange argument, one notes, since what is instinctively abhorred should not have to be prohibited.) Such strong negative reactions almost certainly derive in our society from religious interdictions. To these, too, the average person appeals. Laws prohibiting incest are regarded as in accord with the will of the Creator.

Scientific justifications for the incest prohibitions are less arbitrary and lay claim to an empirical basis; and much evidence has been gathered to support the necessity for prohibiting both marriage and extramarital intercourse between persons who are closely related. This evidence is most persuasive regarding incest relationships within the immediate family, and in the home.

When incest occurs between members of the family within the home, family organization may be disrupted or destroyed. If the incest is between siblings, one or both may be driven from the home by the parents. When the incest is between parent and child, arrest, divorce, and other calamities may follow. When the incest is more or less tolerated, the family's power structure changes. The daughter having relations with her father, may usurp her mother's role. The son having relations with his mother, may displace his father as head of the household. In either case, the situation is likely to become intolerable for the person displaced.

(Primitive peoples, too, it may be noted, have a "sociological argument" against incest relationships. They note that the incest taboo has a socializing influence—enlarging the family and its contacts and preventing too narrow and withdrawn social units.)

Incest is "scientifically" condemned not only as a threat to the family, and so to society, but on genetic grounds. Children of incestuous unions are held to have a higher mortality, and to be more susceptible to congenital defects, than are other children. This argument, however, is of dubious value as a basis for the incest prohibitions. First of all, the results of inbreeding are not necessarily bad. They may also be good or indifferent. Secondly, our society shows little interest in improving the species

—or in preventing its deterioration. Thus, a prohibition based on genetic grounds smacks of hypocrisy. And third, procreation need not be involved in incestuous unions. A couple wishing to marry might submit voluntarily to sterilization. In such a case, the genetic argument would be meaningless.

A great many factors have been designated as conducive to incest behavior. Among them are broken homes, drunkenness, poverty and overcrowding, lack of adequate moral training, feeblemindedness, drug addiction, frigidity or impotence of spouse, promiscuity of mother or daughter, breakdown of father's authority, etc., etc.

Those are the factors most often cited by sociologists. Psychologists add: Oedipus complexes (male and female), witnessing of the primal scene, pedophilia, nymphomania, satyriasis, homosexuality, and other aberrations, illnesses, and traumas.

Writers of fiction have long noted the occurrence of incestuous desires between parents and children, and still more commonly siblings, reunited after long separations. Clinical literature also has its quota of such cases. Nothing is less difficult to understand than the occurrence of incestuous desires under such circumstance.

When male and female are so reunited, and if discrepancies of age are not too great, the love that they feel for one another has not been purged, by daily association, of conscious erotic elements. Roles are not clearly defined, as occurs within the family in the course of day-to-day living. The blood-bond is conducive, for psychological reasons, to love. But the love is then that of male and female, not of parent and child, or of brother and sister. When sexual intimacies develop there is certainly no cause for surprise.

Many peoples have taken note of the powerful bond that sometimes exists between twins. In Bali, recognition of this bond resulted in allowance for twin sister-brother marriages. Twins, said the Balinese, by way of explanation, must certainly have been intimate in the womb. This being the case, why should they not marry? Whether twins are, in fact, especially subject to incestuous cravings, we are not able to say. But it is plain that romantic imagination would have such to be the case.

We should not ignore the attraction of the *idea* of incest, as it appeals to the sophisticated, creative imagination. This appeal may be bound up with a desire to do evil (with which incest is equated); with a wish to revolt against taboo or prohibition (incest seeming to be a particularly appropriate vehicle), or with a craving to engage in what may seem the most intimate of all possible unions (a craving supposed to be especially intense in the case of identical twins). All of these motives have been explored by novelists, dramatists, and poets—with and without condemnation.

It is said that the force of the incest prohibition is proved by the psychical catastrophes which may follow violation of the prohibition. Murders, suicides, and neurotic and psychotic breakdowns are known to have followed incestuous behavior—and are attributed to the incest. (That the incest is *causal* in such cases does not necessarily follow. It may be, like murder, for example, symptomatic behavior; and it may be an effect of the same cause that results in the breakdown. Moreover, relationships between incest and calamities are more often assumed than conclusively demonstrated.) Some recent writers suggest a high incidence of incest experience in the backgrounds of delinquents and prostitutes. Deviations including homosexuality, fetichism, coprophilia, and others, are said to have resulted from incestuous traumas. A similar origin is attributed to a variety of other psychical disturbances.

There is reason to doubt the accuracy of a good many "memories" of incest experiences; that is, they may be phantasies based on real wishes or products of the analytic situation. But despite all objections one may raise to the findings of some psychotherapists, it seems certain that the incest experience may be seriously traumatic. The savage, having violated a tribal taboo, may quickly sicken and die. His civilized counterpart who has violated the incest or some other powerful prohibition may become neurotic.

The moral argument is one of the strongest which may be mustered against certain incestuous unions. Exploitation of his or her own child by a parent, or exploitation of a sibling by another much older, is a betrayal of the trust a child rightfully reposes in parents and elder siblings. When the siblings are of about equal age, or after the children are adults, this moral argument loses much, if not all, of its force.

Whatever may be said for the necessity of the incest prohibition, it claims a high toll—not just among violators, but also among those whose incestuous cravings give rise to maiming guilt. This guilt, self-perpetuating, is instilled in successive generations by (guilty) parents, who themselves are in one way or another victims of the prohibition.

The popular acquaintance with the Oedipus complex has probably not improved the situation. Parents have learned to look for their own, often faint, incestuous desires and to magnify these beyond reasonable proportion. Too often, the most natural parental affections have been twisted by suspicions and fears into incest desires. This is an area psychology has largely ignored. But the withholding of tangible evidences of affection may also have damaging effects. And if parents, fearful of stimulating incestuous cravings (in the child or—but seldom admitted—in themselves), withhold their affection and caresses, the results may be equally unfortunate.

Here, as elsewhere, in the area of sexual relationships, the situation is thoroughly muddled, with lamentable consequences. A generally desirable objective—prevention of intercourse between young siblings, and between parents and children, within the home—has never been the real aim. The taboos and interdictions have been otherwise motivated, and have not improved with refinement. Instead, down the centuries, we have modified our prohibitions to bring out what is worst and most destructive in human beings.

The incest prohibition, as it exists in the Judeo-Christian West, consciously derives not from taboo but from religious interdiction. What God has forbidden, the society and its laws will vigorously punish. Violations provoke outrage—and a clamor that the culprit(s) must suffer. Moral condemnation, handed down from generation to generation, sustained by emotion rather than by reason, aims at insuring that in the absence of detection, self-punishment occurs. And self-punishment should occur whether the *act* occurs or not; desire for the act is sufficient to bring retributive suffering.

Some have sensed or understood that there is evil in a prohibition which has such harmful effects. There has been some recognition that this evil may be greater than any that might reside in what is prohibited and that the solution to the problems incest poses may not lie in a rigid, neurosis-spawning "Thou Shalt Not."

Neither is there any practical solution in blanket permissiveness. Rather, what we must find is a more rational and less damaging method of accomplishing our legitimate objectives.

Meanwhile, those who note the evil harvest we are reaping, not infrequently rebel. Their rebellion may lead them to romanticize or glamorize incest; or to make of incest a symbol for the expression of a larger rebellion.

The serious author is likely to be sympathetic to the plight of incestuous lovers. In many cases, to be sure, he punishes, finally, the offending couple. But it is plain that this is often a bow to custom, and a means of achieving publication, rather than a genuine conviction that punishment (by self, society, calamity, or whatever) should occur. And the fact of the punishment may point up the stupidity and savagery of the society and its standards.

2

Central in the incest literature is, of course, *Oedipus Rex,* in which Oedipus kills his father and marries Jocasta, his mother —each act having been predicted by an oracle and having been performed by Oedipus without knowledge or suspicion of his relationship to the other persons. For Sophocles, man travels inevitably toward his foredoomed tragedy; even the warnings of what may lie ahead cannot divert man from the path along which he is fated to wander. And what could be more tragic than this double crime? What man is able to look without horror into his own soul after having committed patricide (albeit unwittingly) in order to pave the way for copulation with his mother? Man is doomed, and incest (particularly between mother and son) has enormity about it so unmatched that it can dramatize and epitomize that doom.

But Oedipus courted and married Jocasta ignorant of his relationship to her. That each man might have an overwhelming unconscious drive to remove from the scene his father in order that he might become the lover of his mother—this remained inherent in the Sophocles tragedy for many centuries, but was not made explicit as an interpretation of this literature until the age of Freud. Following Sophocles, the incestuous relationship between two people unaware of their kinship bond continued to provide a variation on this theme for novelists, dramatists, and poets.

In the literature of the Medieval period and during the Renaissance, the incest theme is occasionally found. It is present in the little sketch of Margaret of Navarre, "A Tale of Incest," and it seems, according to a note made by Havelock Ellis, to have been mentioned, if not discussed, in 1615 by one Rosset, in a work entitled *Histoire Tragique de Nostre Temps*.

However, it was probably not until John Ford's drama, *'Tis Pity She's a Whore,* that the theme of incest was approached in a forthright manner by a serious writer in the English language. Acted for the first time in approximately 1626, the play has since been revived from time to time, has been deliberately omitted from many otherwise complete editions of the works of Ford, and has been the subject of critical studies by Charles Algernon Swinburne, John Addington Symonds, Havelock Ellis, and many others.

A drama of love between a brother and sister, this play, like *Oedipus Rex,* illustrates the helplessness of man before the onsweep of fate. "The sin once committed," wrote Swinburne, "there is no more wavering or flinching possible to him, who has fought so hard against the demoniac possession; while she who resigned body and soul to the tempter, almost at a word, remains liable to the influences of religion and remorse." In a critique of this play, Dr. A. W. Ward stated: "This different treatment shows the feeling of the poet—the feeling for which he seeks to evoke our inmost sympathy—to oscillate between

the belief that an awful crime brings with it its lawful punishment . . . and the notion that there is something fatal, something irresistible, and therefore in a sense self-justified, in so
dominant a passion."

If Ford failed to delve into the motivation that permits Giovanni to express his passion for Annabella, despite the strength
of the cultural prohibitions, he nevertheless captured the conflict and the guilt that haunt those who violate so strong a norm,
and the sense of fatalistic doom that is all-pervasive, as in a
Greek tragedy, and that must follow the perpetrators of the
incestuous act.

In the picaresque novel of the 17th and 18th centuries, the
references to incest are not numerous. The Marquis de Sade in-
cluded it, repeatedly though usually briefly, among the situations that he depicted, and occasionally another reference, usually minor, is encountered, but the subject was for the most
part as taboo as the act. It remained for nineteenth century
American novelists, deeply involved with the grotesque and the
macabre, to turn again to incest as a theme: particularly Nathaniel Hawthorne, in "Alice Doane's Appeal," and Herman
Melville, in *Pierre, or the Ambiguities*.

Pierre is a full-length novel, a brief part of which is here reprinted. Its major theme is a variation of the *Oedipus Rex* story,
a variation that one finds recurring with ever-greater frequency
as this literature develops. Melville's characters, Pierre and Isabel, are brother and sister who have been separated from in-
fancy. They meet again in adulthood, but are aware of their
relationship. From the first, their meeting is charged with passion:

> He stands before the door; the house is steeped in silence; he
> knocks; the casement light flickers for a moment, and then moves
> away; within, he hears a door creak on its hinges; then his whole
> heart beats wildly as the outer latch is lifted; and holding the light
> above her supernatural head, Isabel stands before him. It is herself.
> No word is spoken; no other soul is seen. They enter the room of
> the double-casement; and Pierre sits down, overpowered with bodily
> faintness and spiritual awe. He lifts his eyes to Isabel's gaze of

loveliness and loneliness; and then a low, sweet, half-sobbing voice
of more than natural musicalness is heard:—
    'And so, thou art my brother;—shall I call thee Pierre?'

Pierre devotes his life to his sister, but he is aware of the great
conflict within himself, and poses to himself the question of
why he cannot defy his society and his culture. Finally, defiance
triumphs, but in a moment of doom.

The brother and sister in the work of Melville, like the
mother and son in the tragedy of Sophocles, were brought together after many years of absence. But Melville's characters
knew of their kinship ties before they met, while in the Sophocles drama only after they had consummated their relationship.
In Melville, there is an *a priori* awareness, with all of the anxiety, guilt, jealousy, and conflict that it arouses; in Sophocles, it
is all *a posteriori*.

These seem to be two of the major bifurcations that the literature of incest follows, and in dealing with separated kin who
are reunited with a full knowledge of the relationship, Somerset Maugham has developed the brother-sister tie in his story,
"The Book-Bag." Entering here is a factor that is to crop up
with frequency in several later writers: the desire of one of the
actors to break the bond, and of the other to continue it, with
concomitant jealousy often leading to doom.

In Isak Dinesen's Gothic-like tale, "The Caryatids," separation of brother and sister (or, more exactly, half-brother and
half-sister) takes place for a lengthy period, and they are
brought together, unaware of their relationship. On the other
hand, the separation between brother and sister is rather brief
in *Black Grapes,* a novel by L. de Stefani, for the youths are
brought out of their respective foster homes while in their very
tender years, and they turn to each other, yearning for affection
and for sex, because of a deepgoing anguish born of their hatred
for their father.

In an American novel, *The Closest Kin There Is,* by Clara
Winston, the brother and sister are reunited after a lengthy sep-
aration, but there is no lack of knowledge of the relationship.
However, their turn to each other is a result of their common

loneliness, their unwillingness and inability to develop relationships outside of their circle of two. And in another work, *Equi-
nox* by Allan Seager, a similar attraction develops when father
and daughter meet again after many years of separation.

The moment of revelation, the discovery that there is a kinship bond in addition to the sexual one, has had numerous vari-
ations since Sophocles. In *Brother and Sister* by Leonhard Frank,
there is the simplest variation of the Greek tragedy; it is Sophocles without patricide, and as it turns out, it is Greek drama
without tragedy. Despite the contrived situation which the author so painstakingly creates in order that the reader might believe that the brother and sister do not know that they are
related, the work is remarkable on one account: the incest-
participants are not doomed.

In an earlier novel, *The Monster* by Edgar Saltus, one of the
central characters discovers that her father, who had vigorously
opposed her marriage to a young man, had done so because she
and the groom were half-siblings. From the specter of incest,
the woman flees in panic. Saltus portrays the guilt and despair
that might be expected to grip people under such circumstances.

A contemporary variation on this theme is depicted in a German novel, *Homo Faber,* by Max Frisch, in which the father
discovers his relationship to the youthful girl after their affair
has been consummated, and, in fact, after the girl had died in
an accident. How far did you go with her, the mother, in her
moment of anguish, asks of the man whom she meets again
after an absence of some two decades, and who still is unaware
that he had fathered a child with this woman. How far did you
go with her? The question contains within it the despairing
cry of one who suspects that the incest taboo has been broken,
and that her daughter has been a participant in an incestuous
act.

Often classified as part of the literature of incest, and having
certain similarities to it, are various tales and dramas in which
the relationship is one that exists between a foster- or a step-
parent and child, or between step-siblings. While it is likely
(as O'Neill demonstrates in *Desire Under the Elms*) that such
a situation would create intrafamilial jealousy, the fear of which

may have been a causative factor in the development of the incest taboo, nevertheless, in our society, a relationship between step-siblings, step-parent and child, foster-siblings or foster-parent and child, does not awaken the sense of horror and repulsion that characterizes incest. No matter how such a situation may be defined legally, and no matter how much it may be strongly tabooed in certain societies, it patently does not excite a strong negative reaction of horror and repulsion in these societies whose morals are derived largely from the Judeo-Christian tradition.

It is entirely possible, for example, that in many societies there might be as strong a repulsion, internalized in the individuals as if it were natural, at the thought of adultery of a man with his mother-in-law as with his mother. No Western society defines incest in this manner, so far as social sanctions are concerned, no matter what the legal definition may be.

Nevertheless, the intrafamilial jealousies that are aroused when forbidden (but not incest-tabooed) relationships take place have often been discussed as if these were incestuous situations. The theme is found in *A Tribe of Women,* by H. Bazin, in which a mother brings to her home, and to her very lovely daughters, a new husband, and the ensuing triangle is not difficult to predict.

The theme has a variation found when the parties engaging in sexual relations are believed to be bound by strong kinship ties, but it develops that they are not. In the Italian novel, *Perdu,* by Paride Bombi, the youthful protagonist comes to suspect that his grandfather is also his father. It is the story of a search for identity, in which the youth finally confronts the older man, who unravels a tangled and woeful tale. There had been no incest, but the fear of it, the belief that he might be progeny issued from it, overwhelms the boy.

The daughter and step-father scene, to which rape is added, is found in the popular novel *Peyton Place,* by Grace Metalious; in another popular novel, *The Carpetbaggers,* by Harold Robbins, intercourse is between a youth and a girl who has been raised with him as his sister, but who was adopted by his parents; and even Nabokov's *Lolita* might be considered an account of an incest relationship, since the relationship would be so defined by the statutes of some states.

Most of the literary excursions into incest stem from Sophocles. The couple had been separated and learn of their kinship rather late; sometimes the revelation takes place before, sometimes after, the sexual act has been consummated. There are numerous examples that one may continue to cite. In *Brothers and Sisters* by Ivy Compton-Burnett, Christian learns that Sophia, to whom he has been married for twenty-seven years and whom he had thought was his adopted sister, is actually his half-sister. Already suffering from a heart ailment, Christian dies while reading the letter in which he learns the truth. As in the work by Edgar Saltus, *The Monster,* it is clear that our society defines a single common parent as sufficient to constitute a bond tabooed as strongly by the unwritten and written laws covering incest as if both parents were shared.

Miss Compton-Burnett has developed a variation in her novel: Sophia and Christian had been brought up in the same house as brother and sister, but had been aware of themselves in a foster-relationship. They had been subjected to all the closeness of a small group where intimacy of a sexual nature is forbidden, but they had learned (falsely, as it turns out) that love, sex, and marriage would not be barred to them because there was no common parent.

In another novel by the same author, *A Heritage and Its History,* Naomi and Hamish, who had been brought up as cousins, are told that they are brother and sister, to stop their forthcoming marriage. Again, it is common fatherhood that binds them.

Another development of what might be termed a pseudo-incestuous situation is described by Pamela Frankau in *Ask Me No More,* where there is an involvement between a woman and her ex-husband's son. A brother-sister love (with but one parent in common, however) in which the participants are unaware of the kinship bond is the theme of Edmund Keeley's *The Libation.* In *Madame Solario,* a novel published anonymously, the brother-sister kinship is not revealed until after the two have met and have become committed to each other. And *Carlotta*

McBride, by Charles O. Gorham, is a story that a young actress narrates to a psychoanalyst, in which she reveals that she had been seduced by a man whom she believed, at the time, to be her father. Although the seduction had a disastrous effect upon her, Carlotta had not been a participant, even unwillingly or unwittingly, in an incestuous relationship but she suffered because she believed that she had been.

We are not, at this time, focusing attention on what might be the most universal and in many respects the most profound aspect of the literature of incest, namely, on the great unconscious drives, frequently overwhelming, suppressed, sublimated into socially-acceptable channels, and unrecognized by the very people who harbor them. The vast literature of exploration of the unconscious, which grew up in the wake of the Freudian revolution, would include a great many of the modern works dealing with the Oedipus myth; among them, D. H. Lawrence's *Sons and Lovers,* Eugene O'Neill's *Mourning Becomes Electra,* and several works of Tennessee Williams.

On rare occasions (as in "Pages from Cold Point" by Paul Bowles), a homosexual-incest relationship has been described. There is little in scientific literature on this subject, and only rarely has it been alluded to in fiction. It would seem, however, that the overwhelming horror that men and women feel at the very thought of carnal contact between brother and sister, father and daughter, or mother and son, does not prevail when the contact is between similarly close kin of the same sex. In this instance, it is the homosexuality which offends or disgusts, as the case may be, but not the kinship closeness. If incest is defined in terms of such acts as are so strongly interdicted as to produce this type of revulsion, then one would not include a brother-brother or a father-son situation within its area. It is possible, merely as a matter of conjecture, that because homosexuality cannot result in conception, mankind has not been as stern in its attitudes as in the case of heterosexual incest.

Most of the situations we have described have involved either a separation or a lack of knowledge of the relationship, or both; nevertheless, there is considerable literature on incest in which the participants have not been separated, and are fully aware of their common parenthood. A small novel published in Germany in the late 1920's, *A Room in Berlin* by Gunther Birkenfeld, places the protagonists not only in one home, but in one room. They are drawn together by their physical proximity as well as by their anguish born of poverty and unemployment, and their relationship becomes a search for meaningful expression in the atmosphere of personal and social disorganization. The disorganization and social degeneration found in William Faulkner's South, with its incestuous backdrop for *The Sound and the Fury,* is again found in the internal loves and hatreds of the world of Robinson Jeffers, when Tamar says to her father: "Tell God we have revoked relationship in the house; he is not your son nor you my father."

Awareness of the relationship between the participants in incest is the theme of *Ask My Brother* by Constance R. Wagner, in which the woman is the aggressor in the act; in *Own Wilderness,* by Nina Warner Hooke, again the participants being related as half-brother and half-sister; and in *Gemini,* by Theodora Keogh, in which the brother and sister meet after being parted for twelve years. It is a story that had an interesting and original variation in *Thunder Without Rain* by Clifton Cuthbert (reprinted under the title *The Shame of Mary Quinn*), in which the brother is a seminary student preparing himself for the priesthood. Surely no writer has presented himself with a situation more fraught with the burden of guilt. And in a recent novel, *A Severed Head* by Iris Murdoch, there is knowledge of the brother-sister kinship, no separation, and no atmosphere of social and personal disintegration that so many authors have imposed upon the incest situation.

All of this might seem like a vast literature, and if one mentions several other names that have here been omitted (some of them are found in this collection) it appears even greater in scope and quantity. One might add here Thomas Mann's "The Blood of the Walsungs," where incest is the medium whereby the brother and sister exclude from their inner circle the vast world without; it is almost a glorification that is revealed, rather than a prohibition, somewhat reminiscent of the manner in which the institution was viewed in the royal families of

Egypt and of Hawaii (for the latter, see James Michener's
novel, *Hawaii*). For Mann's characters, their blood was superior, and all others must be excluded; no relationship could
unite two people so strongly, against the world of strangers, as
that of brother and sister, if they were Walsungs. He deals with
incest again in *The Holy Sinner*.

Yet, extensive as this literature seems, there were only slight
references to incest in literary media that Albert Ellis found
when he made his study, *The Folklore of Sex*, in the early
1950's, and several more when he studied what had happened
in an intervening decade at the time of the revision of his work.
In the earlier period, he cited Taylor Caldwell's *Let Love Come
Last*, and one minor short story, presumably of an autobio-
graphical nature. And, in the 1960's, there was *Peyton Place*,
references to incest in *The Cave* by Robert Penn Warren, a remark on the fear and shame of a young man upon seeing his
mother undress, in *The Devil's Advocate* by Morris L. West, and
some passages in *A Loss of Roses*, a play by William Inge.
Finally, there was *Lolita*. But in none of these works, however,
was incest a central theme.

Despite the many authors who appear in this volume and
several others mentioned here but whose works we have not
reprinted, despite a list that includes Sophocles, John Ford, the
Marquis de Sade, Nathaniel Hawthorne, Herman Melville, Pierre Louÿs, Maxim Gorky, Thomas Mann, Robinson Jeffers,
Somerset Maugham, Isak Dinesen, William Faulkner, and Dylan Thomas, among others, the possibilities for utilization of
the incest theme to penetrate the mysteries of the human condition have only begun to be exploited. That incest will have a
greater place in literature in the years ahead seems apparent.
It is our hope that by bringing together some of the highlights
of this literature and by calling attention to certain other
phases of it in these introductory words, we will contribute to
an understanding of the phenomenon of the incest prohibition
itself and to the better utilization of this theme by men of letters in the future.

D.W.C. and R.E.L.M.

New York City

Thomas Mann
THE BLOOD OF THE WALSUNGS

THOMAS MANN, German novelist and Nobel Prize winner (1875-1955), has left a literary heritage whose importance is matched by few writers of this century. Among his best-known works are *The Magic Mountain, Buddenbrooks, Joseph and His Brethren,* and *Death in Venice.* The latter, together with *Tonio Kruger, The Blood of the Walsungs,* and numerous other tales, appears in the Mann collection, entitled *Stories of Three Decades.* Mann left Germany after Hitler came to power in 1933, and thereafter was one of the most powerful anti-Nazi voices in the world. He became a citizen of the United States in 1944.

It was seven minutes to twelve. Wendelin came into the first floor entrance-hall and sounded the gong. He straddled in his violet knee-breeches on a prayer-rug pale with age and belabored with his drumstick the metal disk. The brazen din, savage and primitive out of all proportion to its purport, resounded through the drawing-rooms to left and right, the billiard-room, the library, the winter garden, up and down through the house; it vibrated through the warm and even atmosphere, heavy and exotic perfume. At last the sound ceased, and for another seven minutes Wendelin went about his business while Florian in the dining room gave the last touches to the table. But on the stroke of twelve the cannibalistic summons sounded a second time. And the family appeared.

Herr Aarenhold came in his little toddle out of the library where he had been busy with his old editions. He was continually acquiring old books, first editions, in many languages, costly and crumbling trifles. Gently rubbing his hands he asked in his slightly plaintive way:

"Beckerath not here yet?"

"No, but he will be. Why shouldn't he? He will be saving a

meal in a restaurant," answered Frau Aarenhold, coming noiselessly up the thick-carpeted stairs, on the landing of which stood
a small, very ancient church organ.

Herr Aarenhold blinked. His wife was impossible. She was
small, ugly, prematurely aged, and shrivelled as though by
tropic suns. A necklace of brilliants rested upon her shrunken
breast. She wore her hair in complicated twists and knots to
form a lofty pile, in which, somewhere on one side, sat a great
jeweled brooch, adorned in its turn with a bunch of white ai-
grettes. Herr Aarenhold and the children had more than once,
as diplomatically as possible, advised against this style of coif-
fure. But Frau Aarenhold clung stoutly to her own taste.

The children came: Kunz and Marit, Siegmund and Sieglinde. Kunz was in a braided uniform, a stunning tanned creature with curling lips and a killing scar. He was doing six weeks'
service with his regiment of hussars. Marit made her appearance in an uncorseted garment. She was an ashen, austere blonde
of twenty-eight, with a hooked nose, grey eyes like a falcon's,
and a bitter, contemptuous mouth. She was studying law and
went entirely her own way in life.

Siegmund and Sieglinde came last, hand in hand, from the
second floor. They were twins, graceful as young fawns, and
with immature figures despite their nineteen years. She wore a
Florentine cinquecento frock of claret-colored velvet, too heavy
for her slight body. Siegmund had on a green jacket suit with a
tie of raspberry shantung, patent leather shoes on his narrow
feet, and cuff-buttons set with small diamonds. He had a strong
growth of black beard but kept it so close-shaven that his sallow
face with the heavy gathered brows looked no less boyish than
his figure. His head was covered with thick black locks parted
far down on one side and growing low on his temples. Her dark
brown hair was waved in long, smooth undulations over her
ears, confined by a gold circlet. A large pearl—his gift—hung
down upon her brow. Round one of his boyish wrists was a
heavy gold chain—a gift from her. They were very like each
other, with the same slightly drooping nose, the same full lips
lying softly together, the same prominent cheekbones and black,
bright eyes. Likest of all were their long slim hands, his no

more masculine than hers, save that they were slightly redder. And they went always hand in hand, heedless that the hands of both inclined to moisture.

The family stood about awhile in the lobby, scarcely speaking. Then Beckerath appeared. He was engaged to Sieglinde. Wendelin opened the door to him and as he entered in his black frock-coat he excused himself for his tardiness. He was a government official and came of a good family. He was short of stature, with a pointed beard and a very yellow complexion, like a canary. His manners were punctilious. He began every sentence by drawing his breath in quickly through his mouth and pressing his chin on his chest.

He kissed Sieglinde's hand and said:

"And you must excuse me too, Sieglinde—it is so far from the Ministry to the Zoo—"

He was not allowed to say thou to her—she did not like it. She answered briskly:

"Very far. Supposing that, in consideration of the fact, you left your office a bit earlier."

Kunz seconded her, his black eyes narrowing to glittering cracks:

"It would no doubt have a most beneficial effect upon our household economy."

"Oh, well—business, you know what it is," von Beckerath said dully. He was thirty-five years old.

The brother and sister had spoken glibly and with point. They may have attacked out of a habitual inward posture of self-defence; perhaps they deliberately meant to wound—perhaps again their words were due to the sheer pleasure of turning a phrase. It would have been unreasonable to feel annoyed. They let his feeble answer pass, as though they found it in character; as though cleverness in him would have been out of place. They went to table; Herr Aarenhold led the way, eager to let von Beckerath see that he was hungry.

They sat down, they unfolded their stiff table napkins. The immense room was carpeted, the walls were covered with eighteenth-century panelling, and three electric lusters hung from the ceiling. The family table, with its seven places, was lost in the void. It was drawn up close to the large French window, beneath which a dainty little fountain spread its silver spray behind a low lattice. Outside was an extended view of the still wintry garden. Tapestries with pastoral scenes covered the upper part of the walls; they, like the panelling, had been part of the furnishings of a French chateau. The dining-chairs were low and soft and cushioned with tapestry. A tapering glass vase holding two orchids stood at each place, on the glistening, spotless, faultlessly ironed damask cloth. With careful, skinny hands Herr Aarenhold settled the pince-nez half-way down his nose and with a mistrustful air read the menu, three copies of which lay on the table. He suffered from a weakness of the solar plexus, that nerve center which lies at the pit of the stomach and may give rise to serious distress. He was obliged to be very careful what he ate.

There was bouillon with beef marrow, sole au vin blanc, pheasant, and pineapple.

Nothing else. It was a simple family meal. But it satisfied Herr Aarenhold. It was good, light, nourishing food. The soup was served: a dumb-waiter above the sideboard brought it noiselessly down from the kitchen and the servants handed it around, bending over assiduously, in a very passion of service. The tiny cups were of translucent porcelain, whitish morsels of marrow floated in the hot golden liquid.

Herr Aarenhold felt himself moved to expand a little in the comfortable warmth thus purveyed. He carried his napkin cautiously to his mouth and cast after a means of clothing his thought in words.

"Have another cup, Beckerath," said he. "A working-man has a right to his comforts and his pleasures. Do you really like to eat—really enjoy it, I mean? If not, so much the worse for you. To me every meal is a little celebration. Somebody said that life is pretty nice after all—being arranged so that we can eat four times a day. He's my man! But to do justice to the arrangement one has to preserve one's youthful receptivity—and not everybody can do that. We get old—well, we can't help it. But the thing is to keep things fresh and not get used to them. For instance," he went on, putting a bit of marrow on a piece of roll and sprinkling salt on it, "you are about to change your estate, the plane on which you live is going to be a good deal elevated" (von Beckerath smiled), "and if you want to enjoy your new life, really enjoy it, consciously and artistically, you must take care never to get used to your new situation. Getting used to things is death. It is ennui. Don't live into it, don't let anything become a matter of course, preserve a childlike taste for the sweets of life. You see . . . for some years now I have been able to command some of the amenities of life" (von Beckerath smiled), "and yet I assure you, every morning that God lets me wake up I have a little thrill because my bed-cover is made of silk. That is what it is to be young. I know perfectly well how I did it; and yet I can look around me and feel like an enchanted prince."

The children exchanged looks, so openly that Herr Aaren-hold could not help seeing it; he became visibly embarrassed. He knew that they were united against him, that they despised him: for his origins, for the blood which flowed in his veins and through him in theirs; for the way he had earned his money; for his fads, which in their eyes were unbecoming: for his valetudinarianism, which they found equally annoying; for his weak and whimsical loquacity, which in their eyes traversed the bounds of good taste. He knew all this—and in a way con-ceded that they were right. But after all he had to assert his per-sonality, he had to lead his own life; and above all he had to be able to talk about it. That was only fair—he had proved that it was worth talking about. He had been a worm, a louse if you like. But just his capacity to realize it so fully, with such vivid self-contempt, had become the ground of that persistent, pain-ful, never-satisfied striving which had made him great. Herr Aarenhold had been born in a remote village in East Prussia, had married the daughter of a well-to-do tradesman, and by means of a bold and shrewd enterprise, of large-scale schemings which had as their object a new and productive coal-bed, he had diverted a large and inexhaustible stream of gold into his cof-fers.

The fish course came on. The servants hurried with it from the sideboard through the length of the room. They handed

around with it a creamy sauce and poured out a Rhine wine that prickled on the tongue. The conversation turned to the approaching wedding.

It was very near, it was to take place in the following week. They talked about the dowry, about plans for the wedding journey to Spain. Actually it was only Herr Aarenhold who talked about them, supported by von Beckerath's polite acquiescence. Frau Aarenhold ate greedily, and as usual contributed nothing to the conversation save some rather pointless questions. Her speech was interlarded with guttural words and phrases from the dialect of her childhood days. Marit was full of silent opposition to the church ceremony which they planned to have; it affronted her highly enlightened convictions. Herr Aarenhold also was privately opposed to the ceremony. Von Beckerath was a Protestant and in Herr Aarenhold's view Protestant ceremonial was without any aesthetic value. It would be different if von Beckerath belonged to the Roman confession. Kunz said nothing, because when von Beckerath was present he always felt annoyed with his mother. And neither Siegmund nor Sieglinde displayed any interest. They held each other's narrow hands between their chairs. Sometimes their gaze sought each other's, melting together in an understanding from which everybody else was shut out. Von Beckerath sat next to Sieglinde on the other side.

"Fifty hours," said Herr Aarenhold, "and you are in Madrid, if you like. That is progress. It took me sixty by the shortest way. I assume that you prefer the train to the sea route via Rotterdam?"

Von Beckerath hastily expressed his preference for the overland route.

"But you won't leave Paris out. Of course, you could go direct to Lyons. And Sieglinde knows Paris. But you should not neglect the opportunity . . . I leave it to you whether or not to stop before that. The choice of the place where the honeymoon begins should certainly be left to you."

Sieglinde turned her head, turned it for the first time toward her betrothed, quite openly and unembarrassed, careless of the lookers-on. For quite three seconds she bent upon the courte-

ous face beside her the wide-eyed, questioning, expectant gaze
of her sparkling black eyes—a gaze as vacant of thought as any
animal's. Between their chairs she was holding the slender hand
of her twin; and Siegmund drew his brows together till they
formed two black folds at the base of his nose.

The conversation veered and tacked to and fro. They talked
of a consignment of cigars which had just come by Herr Aarenhold's order from Havana, packed in zinc. Then it circled
around a point of purely abstract interest, brought up by Kunz:
namely, whether, if a were the necessary and sufficient condition for b, b must also be the necessary and sufficient condition
for a. They argued the matter, they analyzed it with great ingenuity, they gave examples; they talked nineteen to the dozen,
attacked each other with steely and abstract dialectic, and got
no little heated. Marit had introduced a philosophical distinc-
tion, that between the actual and the causal principle. Kunz told
her, with his nose in the air, that "causal principle" was a
pleonasm. Marit, in some annoyance, insisted upon her termi-
nology. Herr Aarenhold straightened himself, with a bit of
bread between thumb and forefinger, and prepared to elucidate
the whole matter. He suffered a complete rout, the children
joined forces to laugh him down. Even his wife jeered at him.
"What are you talking about?" she said. "Where did you learn
that—you didn't learn much!" Von Beckerath pressed his chin
on his breast, opened his mouth, and drew in breath to speak—
but they had already passed on, leaving him hanging.

Siegmund began, in a tone of ironic amusement, to speak of
an acquaintance of his, a child of nature whose simplicity was
such that he abode in ignorance of the difference between dress
clothes and dinner jacket. This Parsifal actually talked about a
checked dinner jacket. Kunz knew an even more pathetic case
—a man who went out to tea in dinner clothes.

"Dinner clothes in the afternoon!" Sieglinde said, making a
face. "It isn't even human!"

Von Beckerath laughed sedulously. But inwardly he was remembering that once he himself had worn a dinner coat before
six o'clock. And with the game course they passed on to matters
of more general cultural interest: to the plastic arts, of which

von Beckerath was an amateur, to literature and the theater, which in the Aarenhold house had the preference—though Siegmund did devote some of his leisure to painting.

The conversation was lively and general and the young people set the key. They talked well, their gestures were nervous and self-assured. They marched in the van of taste, the best was none too good for them. For the vision, the intention, the laboring will, they had no use at all; they ruthlessly insisted upon power achievement, success in the cruel trial of strength. The triumphant work of art they recognized—but they paid it no homage.

Herr Aarenhold himself said to von Beckerath, "You are very indulgent, my dear fellow; you speak up for intentions—but results, results are what we are after! You say: 'Of course his work is not much good—but he was only a peasant before he took it up, so his performance is after all astonishing.' Nothing in it. Accomplishment is absolute, not relative. There are no mitigating circumstances. Let a man do first-class work or let him shovel coals. How far should I have got with a good-natured attitude like that? I might have said to myself; 'You're only a poor fish, originally—it's wonderful if you get to be the head of your office.' Well, I'd not be sitting here! I've had to force the world to recognize me, so now I won't recognize anything unless I am forced to!"

The children laughed. At that moment they did not look down on him. They sat there at table, in their low, luxuriously cushioned chairs, with their spoiled, dissatisfied faces. They sat in splendor and security, but their words rang as sharp as though sharpness, hardness, alertness, and pitiless clarity were demanded of them as survival values. Their highest praise was a grudging acceptance, their criticism deft and ruthless; it snatched the weapons from one's hand, it paralyzed enthusiasm, made it a laughing-stock. "Very good," they would say of some masterpiece whose lofty intellectual plane would seem to have put it beyond the reach of critique. Passion was a blunder—it made them laugh. Von Beckerath, who tended to be disarmed by his enthusiasms, had hard work holding his own—also his age put him in the wrong. He got smaller and smaller in his chair, pressed his chin on his breast, and in his excitement breathed through his mouth—quite unhorsed by the brisk arrogance of youth. They contradicted everything—as though they found it impossible, discreditable, lamentable not to contradict. They contradicted most efficiently, their eyes narrowing to gleaming cracks. They fell upon a single word of his, they worried it, they tore it to bits and replaced it by another so telling and deadly that it went straight to the mark and sat in the wound with quivering shaft. Toward the end of luncheon von Beckerath's eyes were red and he looked slightly deranged.

Suddenly—they were sprinkling sugar on their slices of pineapple—Siegmund said, wrinkling up his face in the way he had, as though the sun were making him blink, "Oh, by the bye, von Beckerath, something else, before we forget it. Sieglinde and I approach you with a request—metaphorically speaking, you see us on our knees. They are giving the Walkure tonight. We should like, Sieglinde and I, to hear it once more together— may we? We are of course aware that everything depends upon your gracious favor—"

"How thoughtful!" said Herr Aarenhold.

Kunz drummed the Hunding motif on the cloth.

Von Beckerath was overcome at anybody asking his permission about anything. He answered eagerly, "But by all means, Siegmund—and you too, Sieglinde; I find your request very reasonable—do go, of course; in fact, I shall be able to go with you. There is an excellent cast tonight."

All the Aarenholds bowed over their plates to hide their laughter. Von Beckerath blinked with his effort to be one of them, to understand and share their mirth.

Siegmund hastened to say, "Oh, well, actually, it's a rather poor cast, you know. Of course, we are just as grateful to you as though it were good. But I am afraid there is a slight misunderstanding. Sieglinde and I were asking you to permit us to hear the Walkure once more alone together before the wedding. I don't know if you feel now that—"

"Oh, certainly. I quite understand. How charming! Of course you must go!"

"Thanks, we are most grateful indeed. Then I will have Percy and Leiermann put in for us. . . ."

"Perhaps I may venture to remark," said Herr Aarenhold, "that your mother and I are driving to dinner with the Erlangers and using Percy and Leiermann. You will have to condescend to the brown coupe and Baal and Lampa."

"And your box?" asked Kunz.

"I took it long ago," said Siegmund, tossing back his head.

They all laughed, all staring at the bridegroom.

Herr Aarenhold unfolded with his finger tips the paper of a belladonna powder and shook it carefully into his mouth. Then he lighted a fat cigarette, which presently spread abroad a priceless fragrance. The servants sprang forward to draw away his and Frau Aarenhold's chairs. The order was given to serve coffee in the winter garden. Kunz in a sharp voice ordered his dogcart brought around; he would drive to the barracks.

Siegmund was dressing for the opera; he had been dressing for an hour. He had so abnormal and constant a need for purification that actually he spent a considerable part of his time before the wash basin. He stood now in front of his large Empire mirror with the white enameled frame; dipped a powder puff in its embossed box and powdered his freshly shaven chin and cheeks. His beard was so strong that when he went out in the evening he was obliged to shave a second time.

He presented a colorful picture as he stood there, in rose-tinted silk drawers and socks, red morocco slippers, and a wadded house-jacket in a dark pattern with revers of grey fur. For background he had his large sleeping-chamber, full of all sorts of elegant and practical white-enameled devices. Beyond the windows was a misty view over the tree tops of the Tiergarten.

It was growing dark. He turned on the circular arrangement of electric bulbs in the white ceiling—they filled the room with soft milky light. Then he drew the velvet curtains across the darkening panes. The light was reflected from the liquid depths of the mirrors in wardrobe, washstand, and toilet table; it flashed from the polished bottles on the tile-inlaid shelves. And Siegmund continued to work on himself. Now and then some thought in his mind would draw his brows together till they formed two black folds over the base of the nose.

His day had passed as his days usually did, vacantly and swiftly. The opera began at half past six and he had begun to change at half past five, so there had not been much afternoon. He had rested on his chaise longue from two to three, then had drunk tea and employed the remaining hour sprawled in a deep leather armchair in the study which he shared with Kunz, reading a few pages in each of several new novels. He had found them pitiably weak on the whole; but he had sent a few of them to the binder's to be artistically bound in choice bindings, for his library.

But in the forenoon he had worked. He had spent the hour from ten to eleven in the atelier of his professor, an artist of European repute, who was developing Siegmund's talent for drawing and painting, and receiving from Herr Aarenhold two thousand marks a month for his services. But what Siegmund painted was absurd. He knew it himself; he was far from having any glowing expectations on the score of his talent in this line. He was too shrewd not to know that the conditions of his existence were not the most favorable in the world for the development of a creative gift. The accoutrements of life were so rich and varied, so elaborated, that almost no place at all was left for life itself. Each and every single accessory was so costly and beautiful that it had an existence above and beyond the purpose it was meant to serve—until one's attention was first confused and then exhausted. Siegmund had been born into superfluity; he was perfectly adjusted to it. And yet it was the fact that this superfluity never ceased to thrill and occupy him, to give him constant pleasure. Whether consciously or not, it was with him as with his father, who practiced the art of never getting used to anything.

Siegmund loved to read; he strove after the word and the spirit as after a tool which a profound instinct urged him to grasp. But never had he lost himself in a book as one does when that single work seems the most important in the world, unique, a little, all-embracing universe, into which one plunges and submerges oneself in order to draw nourishment out of every syllable. The books and magazines streamed in; he would buy them all; they heaped up about him and even while he read,

the number of those still to be read disturbed him. But he had
the books bound in stamped leather and labelled with Siegmund Aarenhold's beautiful book-plate; they stood in rows,
weighing down his life like a possession which he did not
succeed in subordinating to his personality.

The day was his; it was given to him as a gift with all its
hours from sunrise to sunset; and yet Siegmund found in his
heart that he had no time for a resolve, how much less then for
a deed. He was no hero; he commanded no giant powers. The
preparation, the lavish equipment for what should have been
the serious business of life used all his energy. How much mental effort had to be expended simply in making a proper toilette! How much time and attention went to his supplies of
cigarettes, soaps, and perfumes; how much occasion for making
up his mind lay in that moment, recurring two or three times
daily, when he had to select his cravat! And it was worth the
effort. It was important. The blond-haired citizenry of the
land might go about in elastic-sided boots and turnover collars,
heedless of the effect. But he—and most explicitly he—must be
unassailable and blameless of exterior from head to foot.

And in the end no one expected more of him. Sometimes
there came moments when he had a feeble misgiving about the
nature of the "actual"; sometimes he felt that this lack of expectation lamed and dislodged his sense of it.

The household arrangements were all made to the end that
the day might pass quickly and no empty hour be perceived.
The next mealtime always came promptly on. They dined before seven; the evening, when one can idle with a good conscience, was long. The days disappeared; swiftly the seasons
came and went. The family spent two summer months at their
little castle on the lake, with its large and splendid grounds and
many tennis courts, its cool paths through the parks, and shaven
lawns adorned by bronze statuettes. A third month was spent
in the mountains, in hotels where life was even more expensive
than at home. Of late, during the winter, he had had himself
driven to school to listen to a course of lectures in the history of
art which came at a convenient time. But he had had to leave

off because his sense of smell indicated that the rest of the class
did not wash often enough.

He spent the hour walking with Sieglinde instead. Always
she had been at his side since the very first; she had clung to
him since they lisped their first syllables, taken their first steps.
He had no friends, never had had one but this, his exquisitely
groomed, darkly beautiful counterpart, whose moist and slender hand he held while the richly gilded, empty-eyed hours
slipped past. They took fresh flowers with them on their walks,
a bunch of violets or lilies of the valley, smelling them in turn
or sometimes both together, with languid yet voluptuous abandon. They were like self-centered invalids who absorb themselves in trifles, as narcotics to console them for the loss of hope.
With an inward gesture of renunciation they doffed the evil-
smelling world and loved each other alone, for the priceless
sake of their own rare uselessness. But all that they uttered was
pointed, neat, and brilliant; it hit off the people they met, the
things they saw, everything done by somebody else to the end
that it might be exposed to the unerring eye, the sharp tongue,
the witty condemnation.

Then von Beckerath had appeared. He had a post in the government and came of a good family. He had proposed for Sieglinde. Frau Aarenhold had supported him; Herr Aarenhold
had displayed a benevolent neutrality; Kunz the hussar was his
zealous partisan. He had been patient, assiduous, endlessly
good-mannered and tactful. And in the end, after she had told
him often enough that she did not love him, Sieglinde had begun to look at him searchingly, expectantly, mutely, with her
sparkling black eyes—a gaze as speaking and as vacant of
thought as an animal's—and had said yes. And Siegmund, whose
will was her law, had taken a position too; slightly to his own
disgust he had not opposed the match; was not von Beckerath
in the government and a man of good family too? Sometimes he
wrinkled his brows over his toilette until they made two heavy
black folds at the base of his nose.

He stood on the white bearskin which stretched out its claws
beside the bed; his feet were lost in the long soft hair. He sprin-

kled himself lavishly with toilet water and took up his dress
shirt. The starched and shining linen glided over his yellowish
torso, which was as lean as a young boy's and yet shaggy with
black hair. He arrayed himself further in black silk drawers,
black silk socks, and heavy black silk garters with silver buckles,
put on the well-pressed trousers of silky black cloth, fastened
the white silk braces over his narrow shoulders, and with one
foot on a stool began to button his shoes. There was a knock on
the door.

"May I come in, Gigi?" asked Sieglinde.

"Yes, come in," he answered.

She was already dressed, in a frock of shimmering sea-green
silk, with a square neck outlined by a wide band of beige em-
broidery. Two embroidered peacocks facing each other above
the girdle held a garland in their beaks. Her dark brown hair
was unadorned; but a large egg-shaped precious stone hung on
a thin pearl chain against her bare skin, the color of smoked
meerschaum. Over her arm she carried a scarf heavily worked
with silver.

"I am unable to conceal from you," she said, "that the carriage is waiting."

He parried at once, "And I have no hesitation in replying
that it will have to wait patiently two minutes more." It was
at least ten. She sat down on the white velvet chaise longue
and watched him at his labors.

Out of a rich chaos of ties he selected a white pique band
and began to tie it before the glass.

"Beckerath," said she, "wears colored cravats, crossed over
the way they wore them last year."

"Beckerath," said he, "is the most trivial existence I have
ever had under my personal observation." Turning to her
quickly he added, "Moreover, you will do me the favor of not
mentioning that German's name to me again this evening."

She gave a short laugh and replied, "You may be sure it will
not be a hardship."

He put on the low-cut pique waistcoat and drew his dress
coat over it, the white silk lining caressing his hands as they
passed through the sleeves.

"Let me see which buttons you chose," said Sieglinde. They
were the amethyst ones—shirt studs, cuff links, and waistcoat
buttons, a complete set.

She looked at him admiringly, proudly, adoringly, with a
world of tenderness in her dark, shining eyes. He kissed the lips
lying so softly on each other. They spent another minute on the
chaise longue in mutual caresses.

"Quite, quite soft you are again," said she, stroking his
shaven cheeks.

"Your little arm feels like satin," said he, running his hand
down her tender forearm. He breathed in the violet odor of her
hair.

She kissed him on his closed eyelids; he kissed her on the
throat where the pendant hung. They kissed one another's
hands. They loved one another sweetly, sensually, for sheer mutual delight in their own well-groomed, pampered, expensive
smell. They played together like puppies, biting each other
with their lips. Then he got up.

"We mustn't be too late today," said he. He turned the top of
the perfume bottle upside down on his handkerchief one last
time, rubbed a drop into his narrow red hands, took his gloves,
and declared himself ready to go.

He put out the light and they went along the red-carpeted
corridor hung with dark old oil paintings and down the steps
past the little organ. In the vestibule on the ground floor Wendelin was waiting with their coats, very tall in his long yellow
paletot. They yielded their shoulders to his ministrations; Sieglinde's dark head was half lost in her collar of silver fox. Followed by the servant they passed through the stone-paved vestibule into the outer air. It was mild, and there were great ragged
flakes of snow in the pearly air. The coupe awaited them. The
coachman bent down with his hand to his cockaded hat while
Wendelin ushered the brother and sister to their seats; then the
door banged shut, he swung himself up to the box, and the carriage was at once in swift motion. It crackled over the gravel,
glided through the high, wide gate, curved smoothly to the
right, and rolled away.

The luxurious little space in which they sat was pervaded by a gentle warmth. "Shall I shut us in?" Siegmund asked. She nodded and he drew the brown silk curtains across the polished panes.

They were in the city's heart. Lights flew past behind the curtains. Their horses' hoofs rhythmically beat the ground, the carriage swayed noiselessly over the pavement, and around them roared and shrieked and thundered the machinery of urban life. Quite safe and shut away they sat among the wadded brown silk cushions, hand in hand. The carriage drew up and stopped. Wendelin was at the door to help them out. A little group of gray-faced shivering folk stood in the brilliance of the arc-lights and followed them with hostile glances as they passed through the lobby. It was already late; they were the last. They mounted the staircase, threw their cloaks over Wendelin's arms, paused a second before a high mirror, then went through the little door into their box. They were greeted by the last sounds before the hush—voices and the slamming of seats. The lackey pushed their plush-upholstered chairs beneath them; at that moment the lights went down and below their box the orchestra broke into the wild pulsating notes of the prelude.

Night, and tempest. . . . And they, who had been wafted hither on the wings of ease, with no petty annoyances on the way, were in exactly the right mood and could give all their attention at once. Storm, a raging tempest, without in the wood. The angry god's command resounded, once, twice repeated in its wrath, obediently the thunder crashed. The curtain flew up as though blown by the storm. There was the rude hall, dark save for a glow on the pagan hearth. In the center towered the trunk of the ash tree. Siegmund appeared in the doorway and leaned against the wooden post beaten and harried by the storm. Draggingly he moved forward on his sturdy legs wrapped around with hide and thongs. He was rosy-skinned, with a straw-colored beard; beneath his blond brows and the blond forelock of his wig his blue eyes were directed upon the conductor, with an imploring gaze. At last the orchestra gave way to his voice, which rang clear and metallic, though he tried to make it sound like a gasp. He sang a few bars, to the effect that no matter to whom the hearth belonged he must rest upon it; and at

the last word he let himself drop heavily on the bearskin rug
and lay there with his head cushioned on his plump arms. His
breast heaved in slumber. A minute passed, filled with the singing, speaking flow of the music, rolling its waves at the feet of
the events on the stage. . . . Sieglinde entered from the left.
She had an alabaster bosom which rose and fell marvelously
beneath her muslin robe and deerskin mantle. She displayed
surprise at sight of the strange man, pressed her chin upon her
breast until it was double, put her lips in position and expressed it, this surprise, in tones which swelled soft and warm
from her white throat and were given shape by her tongue and
her mobile lips. She tended the stranger; bending over him so
that he could see the white flower of her bosom rising from the
rough skins, she gave him with both hands the drinking-horn.
He drank. The music spoke movingly to him of cool refreshment and cherishing care. They looked at each other with the
beginning of enchantment, a first dim recognition, standing
rapt while the orchestra interpreted in a melody of profound
enchantment.

She gave him mead, first touching the horn with her lips, then
watching while he took a long draught. Again their glances
met and mingled, while below, the melody voiced their yearning. Then he rose, in deep dejection, turning away painfully,
his arms hanging at his sides, to the door, that he might remove
from her sight his affliction, his loneliness, his persecuted, hated
existence and bear it back into the wild. She called upon him
but he did not hear; heedless of self she lifted up her arms and
confessed her intolerable anguish. He stopped. Her eyes fell.
Below them the music spoke darkly of the bond of suffering
that united them. He stayed. He folded his arms and remained
by the hearth, awaiting his destiny.

Announced by his pugnacious motif, Hunding entered,
paunchy and knock-kneed, like a cow. His beard was black with
brown tufts. He stood there frowning, leaning heavily on his
spear, and staring ox-eyed at the stranger guest. But as the
primitive custom would have it he bade him welcome, in an
enormous, rusty voice.

Sieglinde laid the evening meal, Hunding's slow, suspicious

gaze moving to and fro between her and the stranger. Dull lout though he was, he saw their likeness: the selfsame breed, that odd, untrammeled rebellious stock, which he hated, to which he felt inferior. They sat down, and Hunding, in two words, introduced himself and accounted for his simple, regular, and orthodox existence. Thus he forced Siegmund to speak of himself—and that was incomparably more difficult. Yet Siegmund spoke, he sang clearly and with wonderful beauty of his life and misfortunes. He told how he had been born with a twin sister —and as people do who dare not speak out, he called himself by a false name. He gave a moving account of the hatred and envy which had been the bane of his life and his strange father's life, how their hall had been burnt, his sister carried off, how they had led in the forest a harried, presecuted, outlawed life; and how finally he had mysteriously lost his father as well. . . . And then Siegmund sang the most painful thing of all: he told of his yearning for human beings, his longing and ceaseless loneliness. He sang of men and women, of friendship and love he had sometimes won, only to be thrust back again into the dark. A curse had lain upon him forever; he was marked by the brand of his strange origins. His speech had not been as others' speech nor theirs as his. What he found good was vexation to them, he was galled by the ancient laws to which they paid honor. Always and everywhere he had lived amid anger and strife; he had borne the yoke of scorn and hatred and contempt—all because he was strange, of a breed and kind hopelessly different from them.

Hunding's reception of all this was entirely characteristic. His reply showed no sympathy and no understanding, but only a sour disgust and suspicion of all Siegmund's story. And finally understanding that the stranger standing here on his own hearth was the very man for whom the hunt had been called up today, he behaved with the four-square pedantry one would have expected of him. With a grim sort of courtesy he declared that for tonight the guest right protected the fugitive; tomorrow he would have the honor of slaying him in battle. Gruffly he commanded Sieglinde to spice his night-drink for him and to await him in bed within; then after a few more threats he fol-

lowed her, taking all his weapons with him and leaving Siegmund alone and despairing by the hearth.

Up in the box Siegmund bent over the velvet ledge and
leaned his dark boyish head on his narrow red hand. His brows
made two black furrows, and one foot, resting on the heel of
his patent leather shoe, was in constant nervous motion. But it
stopped as he heard a whisper close to him.
"Gigi!"
His mouth, as he turned, had an insolent line.
Sieglinde was holding out to him a mother-of-pearl box with
maraschino cherries.
"The brandy chocolates are underneath," she whispered. But
he accepted only a cherry, and as he took it out of the waxed
paper she said in his ear, "She will come back to him again at
once."
"I am not entirely unaware of the fact," he said, so loudly
that several heads were jerked angrily in his direction. Down
in the darkness big Siegmund was singing alone. From the
depths of his heart he cried out for the sword—for a shining
haft to swing on that day when there burst forth at last the
bright flame of his anger and rage, which so long had smoul-
dered deep in his heart. He saw the hilt glitter in the tree, saw
the embers fade on the hearth, sank back in gloomy slumber
—and started up in joyful amaze when Sieglinde glided back to
him in the darkness.
Hunding slept like a stone a deafened, drunken sleep. Together they rejoiced at the outwitting of the clod; they laughed,
and their eyes had the same way of narrowing as they laughed.
Then Sieglinde stole a look at the conductor, received her cue,
and putting her lips in position sang a long recitative. She related the heart-breaking tale of how they had forced her, forsaken, strange and wild as she was, to give herself to the crude
and savage Hunding and to count herself lucky in an honorable
marriage which might bury her dark origins in oblivion. She
sang too, sweetly and soothingly, of the strange old man in the
hat and how he had driven the sword-blade into the trunk of
the ash tree, to await the coming of him who was destined to

draw it out. Passionately she prayed in song that it might be he whom she meant, whom she knew and grievously longed for, the consoler of her sorrows, the friend who should be more than friend, the avenger of her shame, whom once she had lost, whom in her abasement she wept for, her brother in suffering, her savior, her rescuer. . . .

But at this point Siegmund flung about her his two rosy arms. He pressed her cheek against the pelt that covered his breast and, holding her so, sang above her head—sang out his exultation to the four winds, in a silver trumpeting of sound. His breast flowed hot with the oath that bound him to his mate. All the yearning of his hunted life found assuagement in her; all that love which others had repulsed, when in conscious shame of his dark origins he forced it upon them—in her it found its home. She suffered shame as did he, dishonored was she like to himself—and now, now their brother-and-sister love should be their revenge!

The storm whistled, a gust of wind burst open the door, a flood of white electric light poured into the hall. Divested of darkness they stood and sang their song of spring and spring's sister, love!

Crouching on the bearskin they looked at each other in the white light as they sang their duet of love. Their bare arms touched each other as they held each other by the temples and gazed into each other's eyes, and as they sang their mouths were very near. They compared their eyes, their foreheads, their voices—they were the same. The growing, urging recognition wrung from his breast his father's name; she called him by his: Siegmund! Siegmund! He freed the sword, he swung it above his head, and submerged in bliss, she told him in song who she was: his twin sister, Sieglinde. In ravishment he stretched out his arms to her, his bride; she sank upon his breast—the curtain fell as the music swelled into a roaring, rushing, foaming whirl-pool of passion—swirled and swirled and with one mighty throb stood still.

Rapturous applause. The lights went on. A thousand people got up, stretched unobtrusively as they clapped, then made ready to leave the hall, with heads still turned toward the stage,

where the singers appeared before the curtain, like masks hung
out in a row at a fair. Hunding too came out and smiled politely, despite all that had just been happening.

Siegmund pushed back his chair and stood up. He was hot;
little red patches showed on his cheekbones, above the lean,
sallow, shaven cheeks.

"For my part," said he, "what I want now is a breath of fresh
air. Siegmund was pretty feeble, wasn't he?"

"Yes," answered Sieglinde, "and the orchestra saw fit to drag
abominably in the Spring Song."

"Frightfully sentimental," said Siegmund, shrugging his narrow shoulders in his dress coat. "Are you coming out?" She
lingered a moment, with her elbows on the ledge, still gazing
at the stage. He looked at her as she rose and took up her silver
scarf. Her soft, full lips were quivering.

They went into the foyer and mingled with the slow-moving
throng, downstairs and up again, sometimes holding each other
by the hand.

"I should enjoy an ice," said she, "if they were not in all
probability uneatable."

"Don't think of it," said he. So they ate bonbons out of their
box—maraschino cherries and chocolate beans filled with cognac.

The bell rang and they looked on contemptuously as the
crowds rushed back to their seats, blocking the corridors. They
waited until all was quiet, regaining their places just as the
lights went down again and silence and darkness fell soothingly
upon the hall. There was another little ring, the conductor
raised his arms and summoned up anew the wave of splendid
sound.

Siegmund looked down into the orchestra. The sunken space
stood out bright against the darkness of the listening house;
hands fingered, arms drew the bows, cheeks puffed out—all
these simple folk labored zealously to bring to utterance the
work of a master who suffered and created, created the noble
and simple visions enacted above on the stage. Creation? How
did one create? Pain gnawed and burned in Siegmund's breast,
a drawing anguish which yet was somehow sweet, a yearning

—whither, for what? It was all so dark, so shamefully unclear! Two thoughts, two words he had: creation, passion. His temples glowed and throbbed, and it came to him as in a yearning vision that creation was born of passion and was reshaped anew as passion. He saw the pale, spent woman hanging on the breast of the fugitive to whom she gave herself, he saw her love and her destiny and knew that so life must be to be creative. He saw his own life, and knew its contradictions, its clear understanding and spoiled voluptuousness, its splendid security and idle spite, its weakness and wittiness, its languid contempt; his life, so full of words, so void of acts, so full of cleverness, so empty of emotion—and he felt again the burning, the drawing anguish which yet was sweet—whither, and to what end? Creation? Experience? Passion?

The finale of the act came; the curtain fell. Light, applause, general exit. Sieglinde and Siegmund spent the interval as before. They scarcely spoke, as they walked hand in hand through the corridors and up and down the steps. She offered him cherries but he took no more. She looked at him but withdrew her gaze as his rested upon her, walking rather constrainedly at his side and enduring his eye. Her childish shoulders under the silver web of her scarf looked like those of an Egyptian statue, a little too high and too square. Upon her cheeks burned the same fire he felt in his own.

Again they waited until the crowd had gone in and took their seats at the last possible moment. Storm and wind and driving cloud; wild, heathenish cries of exultation. Eight females, not exactly stars in appearance, eight untrammeled, laughing maidens of the wild, were disporting themselves amid a rocky scene. Brunnhilde broke in upon their merriment with her fears. They skimmed away in terror before the approaching wrath of Wotan, leaving her alone to face him. The angry god nearly annihilated his daughter—but his wrath roared itself out, by degrees grew gentle and dispersed into a mild melancholy, on which note it ended. A noble prospect opened out, the scene was pervaded with epic and religious splendor. Brunnhilde slept. The god mounted the rocks. Great, full-bodied flames, rising, falling, and flickering, glowed all over the boards. The

Walkure lay with her coat of mail and her shield on her mossy couch ringed around with fire and smoke, with leaping, dancing tongues, with the magic sleep-compelling fire-music. But she had saved Sieglinde, in whose womb there grew and waxed the seed of that hated unprized race, chosen of the gods, from which the twins had sprung, who had mingled their misfortunes and their afflictions in free and mutual bliss.

Siegmund and Sieglinde left their box; Wendelin was outside, towering in his yellow paletot and holding their cloaks for them to put on. Like a gigantic slave he followed the two dark, slender, fur-mantled, exotic creatures down the stairs to where the carriage waited and the pair of large finely matched glossy thoroughbreds tossed their proud heads in the winter night. Wendelin ushered the twins into their warm little silken-lined retreat, closed the door, and the coupe stood poised for yet a second, quivering slightly from the swing with which Wendelin agilely mounted the box. Then it glided swiftly away and left the theater behind. Again they rolled noiselessly and easefully to the rhythmic beat of the horses' hoofs, over all the unevenness of the road, sheltered from the shrill harshness of the bustling life through which they passed. They sat as silent and remote as they had sat in their opera box facing the stage—almost, one might say, in the same atmosphere. Nothing was there which could alienate them from that extravagant and stormily passionate world which worked upon them with its magic power to draw them to itself.

The carriage stopped; they did not at once realize where they were, or that they had arrived before the door of their parents' house. Then Wendelin appeared at the window, and the porter came out of his lodge to open the door.

"Are my father and mother at home?" Siegmund asked, looking over the porter's head and blinking as though he were staring into the sun.

No, they had not returned from dinner at the Erlangers'. Nor was Kunz at home; Marit too was out, no one knew where, for she went entirely her own way.

In the vestibule they paused to be divested of their wraps; then they went up the stairs and through the first floor hall

into the dining room. Its immense and splendid spaces lay in
darkness save at the upper end, where one luster burned above
a table and Florian waited to serve them. They moved noiselessly across the thick carpet, and Florian seated them in their
softly upholstered chairs. Then a gesture from Siegmund dismissed him; they would dispense with his services.

The table was laid with a dish of fruit, a plate of sandwiches,
and a jug of red wine. An electric teakettle hummed upon a
great silver tray, with all appliances about it.

Siegmund ate a caviar sandwich and poured out wine into a
slender glass where it glowed a dark ruby red. He drank in
quick gulps, and grumblingly stated his opinion that red wine
and caviar were a combination offensive to good taste. He drew
out his case, jerkily selected a cigarette, and began to smoke,
leaning back with his hands in his pockets, wrinkling up his
face and twitching his cigarette from one corner of his mouth
to the other. His strong growth of beard was already beginning
to show again under the high cheekbones; the two black folds
stood out on the base of his nose.

Sieglinde had brewed the tea and added a drop of burgundy.
She touched the fragile porcelain cup delicately with her full,
soft lips and as she drank she looked across at Siegmund with her
great humid black eyes.

She set down her cup and leaned her dark, sweet little head
upon her slender hand. Her eyes rested full upon him, with
such liquid, speechless eloquence that all she might have said
could be nothing beside it.

"Won't you have any more to eat, Gigi?"

"One would not draw," said he, "from the fact that I am
smoking, the conclusion that I intend to eat more."

"But you have had nothing but bonbons since tea. Take a
peach, at least."

He shrugged his shoulders—or rather he wriggled them like
a naughty child, in his dress coat.

"This is stupid. I am going upstairs. Good night."

He drank out his wine, tossed away his table napkin, and
lounged away, with his hands in his pockets, into the darkness
at the other end of the room.

He went upstairs to his room, where he turned on the light—
not much, only two or three bulbs, which made a wide white
circle on the ceiling. Then he stood considering what to do
next. The good night had not been final; this was not how they
were used to take leave of each other at the close of the day. She
was sure to come to his room. He flung off his coat, put on his
fur-trimmed house-jacket, and lighted another cigarette. He lay
down on the chaise longue; sat up again, tried another posture,
with his cheek in the pillow; threw himself on his back again
and so remained awhile, with his hands under his head.

The subtle, bitterish scent of the tobacco mingled with that
of the cosmetics, the soaps, and the toilet waters; their combined perfume hung in the tepid air of the room and Siegmund breathed it in with conscious pleasure, finding it sweeter
than ever. Closing his eyes he surrendered to this atmosphere,
as a man will console himself with some delicate pleasure of the
senses for the extraordinary harshness of his lot.

Then suddenly he started up again, tossed away his cigarette
and stood in front of the white wardrobe, which had long mirrors let into each of its three divisions. He moved very close to
the middle one and eye to eye he studied himself, conned every
feature of his face. Then he opened the two side wings and
studied both profiles as well. Long he looked at each mark of
his race: the slightly drooping nose, the full lips that rested so
softly on each other; the high cheekbones, the thick black, curling hair that grew far down on the temples and parted so
decidedly on one side: finally the eyes under the knit brows,
those large black eyes that glowed like fire and had an expression of weary sufferance.

In the mirror he saw the bearskin lying behind him, spreading out its claws beside the bed. He turned around, and there
was tragic meaning in the dragging step that bore him toward
it—until after a moment more of hesitation he lay down all its
length and buried his head in his arm.

For awhile he lay motionless, then propped his head on his
elbows, with his cheeks resting on his slim reddish hands, and
fell again into contemplation of his image opposite him in
the mirror. There was a knock on the door. He started, red-

dened, and moved as though to get up—but sank back again, his head against his outstretched arm, and stopped there, silent.

Sieglinde entered. Her eyes searched the room, without finding him at once. Then with a start she saw him lying on the rug.

"Gigi, what ever are you doing there? Are you ill?" She ran to him, bending over with her hand on his forehead, stroking his hair as she repeated: "You are not ill?"

He shook his head, looking up at her under his brow as she continued to caress him.

She was half ready for bed, having come over in slippers from her dressing-room, which was opposite to his. Her loosened hair flowed down over her open white dressing-jacket; beneath the lace of her chemise Siegmund saw her little breasts, the color of smoked meerschaum.

"You were so cross," she said. "It was beastly of you to go away like that. I thought I would not come. But then I did, because that was not a proper good night at all. . . ."

"I was waiting for you," said he.

She was still standing bent over, and made a little moue which brought out markedly the facial characteristics of her race. Then, in her ordinary tone, "Which does not prevent my present position from giving me a crick in the back."

He shook her off.

"Don't, don't—we must not talk like that—not that way, Sieglinde." His voice was strange, he himself noticed it. He felt parched with fever, his hands and feet were cold and clammy. She knelt beside him on the skin, her hand in his hair. He lifted himself a little to fling one arm around her neck and so looked at her, looked as he had just been looking at himself— at eyes and temples, brow and cheeks.

"You are just like me," said he, haltingly, and swallowed to moisten his dry throat. "Everything about you is just like me— and so—what you have—with Beckerath—the experience—is for me too. That makes things even, Sieglinde—and anyhow, after all, it is, for that matter—it is a revenge, Sieglinde—"

He was seeking to clothe in reason what he was trying to

say—yet his words sounded as though he uttered them out of some strange, rash, bewildered dream.

But to her it had no quality of strangeness. She did not blush at his half-spoken, turbid, wild imaginings; his words enveloped her senses like a mist, they drew her down whence they had come, to the borders of a kingdom she had never entered, though sometimes, since her betrothal, she had been carried thither in expectant dreams.

She kissed him on his closed eyelids; he kissed her on her throat, beneath the lace she wore. They kissed each other's hands. They loved each other with all the sweetness of the senses, each for the other's spoiled and costly well-being and delicious fragrance. They breathed it in, this fragrance, with languid and voluptuous abandon, like self-centered invalids, consoling themselves for the loss of hope. They forgot themselves in caresses, which took the upper hand, passing over into a tumult of passion, dying away into a sobbing. . . .

She sat there on the bearskin, with parted lips, supporting herself with one hand, and brushed the hair out of her eyes. He leaned back on his hands against the white dressing chest, rocked to and fro on his hips, and gazed into the air.

"But Beckerath," said she, seeking to find some order in her thoughts, "Beckerath, Gigi . . . what about him, now?"

"Oh," he said—and for a second the marks of his race stood out strong upon his face—"he ought to be grateful to us. His existence will be a little less trivial, from now on."

W. Somerset Maugham
THE BOOK BAG

W. SOMERSET MAUGHAM, author of *The Book Bag*, (1874-   )
is one of the most prominent and versatile contemporary British writers.
He has written scores of novels, plays, short stories, and other literary
works, of which the semiautobiographical novel, *Of Human Bondage,* is
probably best known. *The Book Bag* appeared in a volume entitled *East
and West: The Collected Short Stories of W. Somerset Maugham,* and in
his own preface to that collection, the author wrote: "Three of the stories
in this volume were told me and I had nothing to do but make them
probable, coherent and dramatic," and he then mentions the story reprinted here as one that had been narrated to him.

Some people read for instruction, which is laudable, and some
for pleasure, which is innocent, but not a few read from habit,
and I suppose this is neither innocent nor praiseworthy. Of this
lamentable company am I. Conversation after a time bores me,
games tire me and my own thoughts, which we are told are the
unfailing resource of a sensible man, have a tendency to run dry.
Then I fly to my book as the opium smoker to his pipe. I would
sooner read the catalog of the Army and Navy Stores or Brad-
shaw's Guide than nothing at all, and indeed I have spent
many delightful hours over both these works. At one time I
never went out without a second-hand bookseller's list in my
pocket. I know no reading that is more fruity. Of course to read
in this way is as reprehensible as drug taking, and I never cease
to wonder at the impertinence of great readers who, because
they are such, look down on the illiterate. From the standpoint
of what eternity is, is it better to have read a thousand books
than to have ploughed a million furrows? Let us admit that reading with us is just a drug that we cannot do without—who of
this band does not know the restlessness that attacks him when

he has been severed from reading too long, the apprehension, the irritability, and the sigh of relief which the sight of a printed page extracts from him?—and so let us be no more vainglorious than the poor slaves of the hypodermic needle or the pint pot.

And, like the dope fiend who cannot move from place to place without taking with him a plentiful supply of his deadly balm, I never venture far without a sufficiency of reading matter. Books are so necessary to me that when in a railway train I have become aware that fellow-travelers have come away without a single one I have been seized with a veritable dismay. But when I am starting on a long journey the problem is formidable. I have learned my lesson. Once, imprisoned by illness for three months in a hilltown in Java, I came to the end of all the books I had brought with me, and knowing no Dutch was obliged to buy the school books from which intelligent Javanese, I suppose, acquired knowledge of French and German. So I read again after five and twenty years the frigid plays of Goethe, the sonorous tragedies of Corneille and the tender Racine. I have the greatest admiration for Racine, but I admit that to read his plays one after the other requires a certain effort in a person who is suffering from colitis. Since then I have made a point of traveling with the largest sack made for carrying soiled linen and filling it to the brim with books to suit every possible occasion and every mood. It weighs a ton and strong porters reel under its weight. Customhouse officials look at it askance, but recoil from it in consternation when I give them my word that it contains nothing but books. Its inconvenience is that the particular work I suddenly hanker to read is always at the bottom and it is impossible for me to get it without emptying the book bag's entire contents upon the floor. Except for this however I should perhaps never have heard the singular history of Olive Hardy.

I was wandering about Malaya, staying here and there, a week or two if there was a resthouse or a hotel, and a day or so if I was obliged to inflict myself on a planter or a district officer whose hospitality I had no wish to abuse; and at the moment I happened to be at Penang. It is a pleasant little town, with a hotel that has always seemed to me very agreeable, but the stranger finds little to do there and time hung a trifle heavily on my hands. One morning I received a letter from a man I knew only by name. This was Mark Featherstone. He was Acting Resident, in the absence on leave of the Resident, at a place called Tenggarah. There was a sultan there and it appeared that a water festival of some sort was to take place which Featherstone thought would interest me. He said that he would be glad if I would come and stay with him for a few days. I wired to tell him that I should be delighted and next day took the train to Tenggarah. Featherstone met me at the station. He was a man of about thirty-five, I should think, tall and handsome, with fine eyes and a strong, stern face. He had a wiry black mustache and bushy eyebrows. He looked more like a soldier than a government official. He was very smart in white ducks, with a white topi, and he wore his clothes with elegance. He was a little shy, which seemed odd in a strapping fellow of resolute mien, but I surmised that this was only because he was unused to the society of that strange fish, a writer, and I hoped in a little while to put him at his ease.

"My boys'll look after your *barang*," he said. "We'll go down to the club. Give them your keys and they'll unpack before we get back."

I told him that I had a good deal of luggage and thought it better to leave everything at the station but what I particularly wanted. He would not hear of it.

"It doesn't matter a bit. It'll be safer at my house. It's always better to have one's *barang* with one."

"All right."

I gave my keys and the ticket for my trunk and my book bag to a Chinese boy who stood at my host's elbow. Outside the station a car was waiting for us and we stepped in.

"Do you play bridge?" asked Featherstone.

"I do."

"I thought most writers didn't."

"They don't," I said. "It's generally considered among authors a sign of deficient intelligence to play cards."

The club was a bungalow, pleasing but unpretentious; it had a large reading room, a billiard room with one table, and a small card room. When we arrived it was empty but for one or two persons reading the English weeklies, and we walked through to the tennis courts where a couple of sets were being played. A number of people were sitting on the veranda, looking on, smoking and sipping long drinks. I was introduced to one or two of them. But the light was failing and soon the players could hardly see the ball. Featherstone asked one of the men I had been introduced to if he would like a rubber. He said he would. Featherstone looked about for a fourth. He caught sight of a man sitting a little by himself, paused for a second, and went up to him. The two exchanged a few words and then came toward us. We strolled in to the card room. We had a very nice game. I did not pay much attention to the two men who made up the four. They stood me drinks and I, temporary member of the club, returned the compliment. The drinks were very small, quarter whiskies, and in the two hours we played, each of us was able to show his openhandedness without an excessive consumption of alcohol. When the advancing hour suggested that the next rubber must be the last we changed from whisky to gin *pahits.* The rubber came to an end. Featherstone called for the book and the winnings and losings of each one of us were set down. One of the men got up.

"Well, I must be going," he said.

"Going back to the estate?" asked Featherstone.

"Yes," he nodded. He turned to me. "Shall you be here tomorrow?"

"I hope so."

He went out of the room.

"I'll collect my mem and get along home to dinner," said the other.

"We might be going too," said Featherstone.

"I'm ready whenever you are," I replied.

We got into the car and drove to his house. It was a longish drive. In the darkness I could see nothing much, but presently I realized that we were going up a rather steep hill. We reached the Residency.

It had been an evening like any other, pleasant, but not at all exciting, and I had spent I don't know how many just like it. I did not expect it to leave any sort of ımpression on me.

Featherstone led me into his sitting room. It looked comfortable, but it was a trifle ordinary. It had large basket armchairs covered with cretonne and on the walls were a great many framed photographs; the tables were littered with papers, magazines and official reports, with pipes, yellow tins of straight-cut cigarettes and pink tins of tobacco. In a row of shelves were untidily stacked a good many books, their bindings stained with damp and ravages of white ants. Featherstone showed me my room and left me with the words, "Shall you be ready for a gin *pahit* in ten minutes?"

"Easily," I said.

I took a bath and changed and went downstairs. Featherstone, ready before me, mixed our drink as he heard me clatter down the wooden staircase. We dined. We talked. The festival which I had been invited to see was the next day but one, but Featherstone told me he had arranged for me before that to be received by the sultan.

"He's a jolly old boy," he said. "And the palace is a sight for sore eyes."

After dinner we talked a little more, Featherstone put on the gramophone, and we looked at the latest illustrated papers that had arrived from England. Then we went to bed. Featherstone came to my room to see that I had everything I wanted.

"I suppose you haven't got any books with you," he said. "I haven't got a thing to read."

"Books?" I cried.

I pointed to my book bag. It stood upright, bulging oddly, so that it looked like a humpbacked gnome somewhat the worse for liquor.

"Have you got books in there? I thought that was your dirty linen or a camp bed or something. Is there anything you can lend me?"

"Look for yourself."

Featherstone's boys had unlocked the bag, but quailing before the sight that then discovered itself had done no more. I knew from long experience how to unpack it. I threw it over on its side, seized its leather bottom and, walking backwards, dragged the sack away from its contents. A river of books poured onto the floor. A look of stupefaction came upon Featherstone's face.

"You don't mean to say you travel with as many books as that? By George, what a snip."

He bent down and turning them over rapidly looked at the titles. There were books of all kinds: volumes of verse, novels, philosophical works, critical studies, (they say books about books are profitless, but they certainly make very pleasant reading), biographies, history; there were books to read when you were ill and books to read when your brain, all alert, craved for something to grapple with; there were books that you had always wanted to read but in the hurry of life at home had never found time to; there were books to read at sea when you were meandering through narrow waters on a leisurely tramp steamer and there were books for bad weather when everything in your cabin creaked and you had to wedge yourself in your bunk in order not to fall out; there were books chosen solely for their length, which you took with you when on some expedition you had to travel light, and there were the books you could read when you could read nothing else. Finally Featherstone picked out a life of Byron that had recently appeared.

"Hello, what's this?" he said. "I read a review of it some time ago."

"I believe it's very good," I replied. "I haven't read it yet."

"May I take it? It'll do me for tonight at all events."

"Of course. Take anything you like."

"No, that's enough. Well, good night. Breakfast at 8:30."

When I came down next morning the head boy told me that Featherstone, who had been at work since six, would be in shortly. While I waited for him I glanced at his shelves.

"I see you've got a grand library of books on bridge," I remarked as we sat down to breakfast.

"Yes, I get every one that comes out. I'm very keen on it."

"That fellow we were playing with yesterday plays a good game."

"Which? Hardy?"

"I don't know. Not the one who said he was going to collect his wife. The other."

"Yes, that was Hardy. That was why I asked him to play. He doesn't come to the club very often."

"I hope he will tonight."

"I wouldn't bank on it. He has an estate about thirty miles away. It's a longish ride to come just for a rubber of bridge."

"Is he married?"

"No. Well, yes. But his wife is in England."

"It must be awfully lonely for those men who live by themselves on those estates," I said.

"Oh, he's not so badly off as some. I don't think he much cares about seeing people. I think he'd be just as lonely in London."

There was something in the way Featherstone spoke that struck me as a little strange. His voice had what I can only describe as a shuttered tone. He seemed suddenly to have moved away from me. It was as though one were passing along a street at night and paused for a second to look in at a lighted window that showed a comfortable room, and suddenly an invisible hand pulled down a blind. His eyes, which habitually met those of the person he was talking to with frankness, now avoided mine and I had a notion that it was not only my fancy that read in his face an expression of pain. It was drawn for a moment as it might be by a twinge of neuralgia. I could not think of anything to say and Featherstone did not speak. I was conscious that his thoughts, withdrawn from me and what we were about, were turned upon a subject unknown to me. Presently he gave a little sigh, very slight, but unmistakable, and seemed with a deliberate effort to pull himself together.

"I'm going down to the office immediately after breakfast," he said. "What are you going to do with yourself?"

"Oh, don't bother about me. I shall slack around. I'll stroll down and look at the town."

"There's not much to see."

"All the better. I'm fed up with sights."

I found that Featherstone's veranda gave me sufficient entertainment for the morning. It had one of the most enchanting

views I had seen in the F.M.S. The Residency was built on the
top of a hill and the garden was large and well cared for. Its
great trees gave it somewhat the look of an English park. It had
vast lawns and there Tamils, black and emaciated, were scything
with deliberate and beautiful gestures. Beyond and below, the
jungle grew thickly to the bank of a broad, winding and swiftly
flowing river, and on the other side of this, as far as the eye could
reach, stretched the wooded hills of Tenggarah. The contrast
between the trim lawns, so strangely English, and the savage
growth of the jungle beyond pleasantly titillated the fancy. I sat
and read and smoked. It is my business to be curious about people and I asked myself how the peace of this scene, charged
nevertheless with a tremulous and dark significance, affected
Featherstone who lived beholding it month in, month out. He
knew it under every aspect, at dawn when the mist rising from
the river shrouded it with a ghostly pall, in the splendor of
noon, and at last when the shadowy gloaming crept softly out of
the jungle, like an army cautiously making its way in unknown
country, and presently enveloped the green lawns and the great
flowering trees and the flaunting cassias in the silent night. I
wondered whether, unbeknownst to him, the tender and yet
strangely sinister aspect of the scene, acting on his nerves and
his loneliness, imbued him with some mystical quality so that
the life he led, the life of the capable administrator, the sports-
man and the good fellow, on occasion seemed to him not quite
real. I smiled at my own fancies, for certainly the conversation
we had had the night before had not indicated in him any stir-
rings of the soul. I had thought him quite nice. He had been at
Oxford and was a member of a good London club. He seemed to
attach a good deal of importance to social things. He was a gentleman and slightly conscious of the fact that he belonged to a
better class than most of the Englishmen his life brought him
in contact with. I gathered from the various silver pots that
adorned his dining room that he excelled in games. He played
tennis and billiards. When he went on leave he hunted and, anxious to keep his weight down, he dieted carefully. He talked a
good deal of what he would do when he retired. He hankered
after the life of a country gentleman, a little house in Leicester-

shire, a couple of hunters and neighbors to play bridge with. He would have his pension and he had a little money of his own. But meanwhile he worked hard and did his work, if not brilliantly, certainly with competence. I have no doubt that he was looked upon by his superiors as a reliable officer. He was cut upon a pattern that I knew too well to find very interesting. He was like a novel that is careful, honest and workmanlike, but a little ordinary, so that you seem to have read it all before, and you turn the pages listlessly knowing that it will never afford you a surprise or move you to excitement.

But human beings are incalculable and he is a fool who tells himself that he knows what a man is capable of.

In the afternoon Featherstone took me to see the sultan. We were received by one of his sons, a shy, smiling youth who acted as his A.D.C. He was dressed in a neat blue suit, but round his waist he wore a sarong, white flowers on a yellow ground, on his head a red fez and on his feet very knobby American shoes. The palace, built in the Moorish style, was like a very big doll's house and it was painted bright yellow, which is the royal color. We were led into a spacious room, furnished with the sort of furniture you would find in an English lodging house at the seaside, but all the chairs were covered with yellow silk. On the floor was a Brussels carpet and on the walls photographs in very grand gilt frames of the sultan at various state functions. In a cabinet was a large collection of all kinds of fruit done entirely in crochet work. The sultan came in with several attendants. He was a man of fifty, perhaps, short and stout, dressed in trousers and tunic of a white and yellow check; round his middle he wore a very beautiful yellow sarong and on his head a white fez. He had large, handsome, friendly eyes. He gave us coffee to drink, sweet cakes to eat and cheroots to smoke. Conversation was not difficult, for he was affable, and he told me that he had never been to a theater or played cards, for he was very religious, and that he had four wives and twenty-four children. The only bar to the happiness of his life seemed to be that common decency obliged him to divide his time equally between his four wives. He said that an hour with one was a month and with another five minutes. I remarked that Professor Einstein—or was

it Bergson?—had made similar observations upon time and indeed on this question had given the world much to ponder over.
Presently we took our leave and the sultan presented me with
some beautiful white Malaccas.

In the evening we went to the Club. One of the men we had
played with the day before got up from his chair as we entered.

"Ready for a rubber?" he said.

"Where's our fourth?" I asked.

"Oh, there are several fellows here who'll be glad to play."

"What about that man we played with yesterday?" I had forgotten his name.

"Hardy? He's not here."

"It's not worth while waiting for him," said Featherstone.

"He very seldom comes to the club. I was surprised to see him
last night."

I did not know why I had the impression that behind the very
ordinary words of these two men there was an odd sense of embarrassment. Hardy had made no impression on me and I did
not even remember what he looked like. He was just a fourth at
the bridge table. I had a feeling that they had something against
him. It was no business of mine and I was quite content to play
with a man who at that moment joined us. We certainly had a
more cheerful game than before. A good deal of chaff passed
from one side of the table to the other. We played less serious
bridge. We laughed. I wondered if it was only that they were
less shy of the stranger who had happened in upon them or if
the presence of Hardy had caused in the other two a certain con-
straint. At half past eight we broke up and Featherstone and I
went back to dine at his house.

After dinner we lounged in armchairs and smoked cheroots.
For some reason our conversation did not flow easily. I tried
topic after topic, but could not get Featherstone to interest himself in any of them. I began to think that in the last twenty-four
hours he had said all he had to say. I fell somewhat discouraged
into silence. It prolonged itself and again, I did not know why,
I had a faint sensation that it was charged with a significance
that escaped me. I felt slightly uncomfortable. I had that queer
feeling that one sometimes has when sitting in an empty room

that one is not by oneself. Presently I was conscious that Featherstone was steadily looking at me. I was sitting by a lamp, but he
was in shadows so that the play of his features was hidden from
me. But he had very large brilliant eyes and in the half darkness
they seemed to shine dimly. They were like new boot buttons
that caught a reflected light. I wondered why he looked at me
like that. I gave him a glance and catching his eyes insistently
fixed upon me faintly smiled.

"Interesting book that one you lent me last night," he said
suddenly, and I could not help thinking his voice did not sound
quite natural. The words issued from his lips as though they
were pushed from behind.

"Oh, the *Life of Byron?*" I said breezily. "Have you read it
already?"

"A good deal of it. I read till three."

"I've heard it's very well done. I'm not sure that Byron inter-
ests me so much as all that. There was so much in him that was
so frightfully second-rate. It makes one rather uncomfortable."

"What do you think is the real truth of that story about him
and his sister?"

"Augusta Leigh? I don't know very much about it. I've never
read Astarte."

"Do you think they were really in love with one another?"

"I suppose so. Isn't it generally believed that she was the only
woman he ever genuinely loved?"

"Can you understand it?"

"I can't really. It doesn't particularly shock me. It just seems
to me very unnatural. Perhaps unnatural isn't the right word.
It's incomprehensible to me. I can't throw myself into the state
of feeling in which such a thing seems possible. You know, that's
how a writer gets to know the people he writes about, by standing himself in their shoes and feeling with their hearts."

I knew I did not make myself very clear, but I was trying to
describe a sensation, an action of the subconscious, which from
experience was perfectly familiar to me, but which no words I
knew could precisely indicate. I went on.

"Of course she was only his half-sister, but just as habit kills
love I should have thought habit would prevent its arising.

When two persons have known one another all their lives and lived together in close contact I can't imagine how or why that sudden spark should flash that results in love. The probabilities are that they would be joined by mutual affection and I don't know anything that is more contrary to love than affection."

I could just see in the dimness the outline of a smile flicker for a moment on my host's heavy and, it seemed to me then, somewhat saturnine face.

"You only believe in love at first sight?"

"Well, I suppose I do, but with the proviso that people may have met twenty times before seeing one another. Seeing has an active side and a passive side. Most people we run across mean so little to us that we never bestir ourselves to look at them. We just suffer the impression they make on us."

"Oh, but one's often heard of couples who've known one another for years and it's never occurred to one they cared two straws for each other and suddenly they go and get married. How do you explain that?"

"Well, if you're going to bully me into being logical and consistent I should suggest that their love is of a different kind. After all, passion isn't the only reason for marriage. It may not even be the best one. Two people may marry because they're lonely or because they're good friends or for convenience sake. Though I said that affection was the greatest enemy of love I would never deny that it's a very good substitute. I'm not sure that a marriage founded on it isn't the happiest."

"What did you think of Tim Hardy?"

I was a little surprised at the sudden question which seemed to have nothing to do with the subject of our conversation.

"I didn't think of him very much. He seemed quite nice. Why?"

"Did he seem to you just like everybody else?"

"Yes. Is there anything peculiar about him? If you'd told me that I'd have paid more attention to him."

"He's very quiet, isn't he? I suppose no one who knew nothing about him would give him a second thought."

I tried to remember what he looked like. The only thing that had struck me when we were playing cards was that he had fine hands. It passed idly through my mind that they were not the sort of hands I should have expected a planter to have. But why a planter should have different hands from anybody else I did not trouble to ask myself. His were somewhat large, but very well formed, with peculiarly long fingers, and the nails were of an admirable shape. They were virile and yet oddly sensitive hands. I noticed this and thought no more about it. But if you are a writer, instinct and the habit of years enable you to store up impressions that you are not aware of. Sometimes of course they do not correspond with the facts and a woman, for example, may remain in your subconsciousness as a dark, massive and ox-eyed creature when she is indeed rather small and of a non-descript coloring. But that is of no consequence. The impression may very well be more exact than the sober truth. And now, seeking to call up from the depths of me a picture of this man I had a feeling of some ambiguity. He was clean-shaven and his face, oval but not thin, seemed strangely pale under the tan of long exposure to the tropical sun. His features were vague. I did not know whether I remembered it or only imagined now that his rounded chin gave one the impression of a certain weakness. He had thick brown hair, just turning gray, and a long wisp fell down constantly over his forehead. He pushed it back with a gesture that long years had rendered habitual. His brown eyes were rather large, and gentle, but perhaps a little sad; they had a melting softness which, I could imagine, might be very appealing.

After a pause Featherstone continued.

"It's rather strange that I should run across Tim Hardy here after all these years. But that's the way of the F.M.S. People move about and you find yourself in the same place as a man you'd known years before in another part of the country. I first knew Tim when he had an estate near Sibuku. Have you ever been there?"

"No. Where is it?"

"Oh, it's up North. Towards Siam. It wouldn't be worth your while to go. It's just like every other place in the F.M.S. But it was rather nice. It had a very jolly little club and there were some quite decent people. There was the schoolmaster and the head of the police, the doctor, the padre and the government engineer. The usual lot, you know. A few planters. Three or four women. I was A.D.O. It was one of my first jobs. Tim Hardy had an estate about twenty-five miles away. He lived there with his sister. They had a bit of money of their own and he'd bought the place. Rubber was pretty good then and he wasn't doing at all badly. We rather cottoned on to one another. Of course it's a tossup with planters. Some of them are very good fellows, but they're not exactly . . ." He sought for a word or a phrase that did not sound snobbish. "Well, they're not the sort of people you'd be likely to meet at home. Tim and Olive were of one's own class, if you understand what I mean."

"Olive was the sister?"

"Yes. They'd had a rather unfortunate past. Their parents had separated when they were quite small, seven or eight, and the mother had taken Olive and the father had kept Tim. Tim went to Clifton; they were West Country people, and only came home for the holidays. His father was a retired naval man who lived at Fowey. But Olive went with her mother to Italy. She was educated in Florence; she spoke Italian perfectly and French too. For all these years Tim and Olive never saw one another once, but they used to write to one another regularly. They'd been very much attached when they were children. As far as I could understand, life when their people were living together had been rather stormy with all sorts of scenes and upsets —you know the sort of thing that happens when two people who are married don't get on together—and that had thrown them on their own resources. They were left a good deal to themselves. Then Mrs. Hardy died and Olive came home to England and went back to her father. She was eighteen then and Tim was seventeen. A year later the war broke out. Tim joined up and his father, who was over fifty, got some job at Portsmouth. I take it he had been a hard liver and a heavy drinker. He broke down before the end of the war and died after a lingering illness. They don't seem to have had any relations. They were the last of a rather old family; they had a fine old house in Dorsetshire that had belonged to them for a good many generations, but they had never been able to afford to live in it and it was always let. I remember seeing photographs of it. It was very much a gentleman's house, of gray stone and rather stately, with a coat of arms carved over the front door and mullioned windows. Their great ambition was to make enough money to be able to live in it. They used to talk about it a lot. They never spoke as though either or both of them would marry, but always as though it were a settled thing that they would remain together. It was rather funny considering how young they were."

"How old were they then?" I asked.

"Well, I suppose he was twenty-five or twenty-six and she was a year older. They were awfully kind to me when I first went up to Sibuku. They took a fancy to me at once. You see, we had more in common than most of the people there. I think they were glad of my company. They weren't particularly popular."

"Why not?" I asked.

"They were rather reserved and you couldn't help seeing that they liked their own society better than other people's. I don't know if you've noticed it, but that always seems to put people's backs up. They resent it somehow if they have a feeling that you can get along very well without them."

"It's tiresome, isn't it?" I said.

"It was rather a grievance to the other planters that Tim was his own master and had private means. They had to put up with an old Ford to get about in, but Tim had a real car. Tim and Olive were very nice when they came to the club and they played in the tennis tournaments and all that sort of thing, but you had an impression that they were always glad to get away again. They'd dine out with people and make themselves very pleasant, but you couldn't help seeing that they'd just as soon have stayed at home. If you had any sense you couldn't blame them. I don't know if you've been much to planters' houses. They're pretty dreary—a lot of gimcrack furniture and silver ornaments and tiger skins, and the food's uneatable. But the Hardys had made their bungalow charming. There was nothing very grand in it; it was just easy and homelike and comfortable. Their living room was like a drawing room in an English country house. You felt that their things meant something to them

and that they had had them a long time. It was a very jolly house
to stay at. The bungalow was right in the middle of the estate,
but it was on the brow of a little hill and you looked right over
the rubber trees to the sea in the distance. Olive took a lot of
trouble with her garden and it was really topping. I never saw
such a show of cannas. I used to go there for weekends. It was
only about half an hour's drive to the sea and we'd take our
lunch with us and bathe and sail. Tim kept a small boat there.
Those days were grand. I never knew one could enjoy oneself so
much. It's a beautiful bit of coast and it was really extraordinar-
ily romantic. Then in the evenings we'd play patience and chess
or turn on the gramophone. The cooking was damned good too.
It was a change from what one generally got. Olive had taught
their cook to make all sorts of Italian dishes and we used to
have great wallops of macaroni and *risotto* and *gnochi* and
things like that. I couldn't help envying them their life—it was
so jolly and peaceful—and when they talked of what they'd do
when they went back to England for good I used to tell them
they'd always regret what they'd left.

" 'We've been very happy here,' said Olive.

"She had a way of looking at Tim, with a slow, sidelong
glance from under her long eyelashes, that was like a caress.

"In their own house they were quite different from what they
were when they went out. They were so easy and cordial. Everybody admitted that and I'm bound to say that people enjoyed
going there. They often asked people over. They had the gift of
making you feel at home. It was a very happy house if you know
what I mean. Of course no one could help seeing how attached
they were to one another. And whatever people said about their
being stand-offish and self-centered they were bound to be
rather touched by the affection they had for one another. People
said they couldn't have been more united if they were married,
and when you saw how some couples got on you couldn't help
thinking they made most marriages look rather like a washout.
They seemed to think the same things at the same time. They
had little private jokes that made them laugh like children.
They were so charming with one another, so gay and happy,

that really to stay with them was, well, a spiritual refreshment. I don't know what else you could call it. When you left them, after a couple of days at the bungalow, you felt that you'd absorbed some of their peace and their sober gaiety. It was as though your soul had been sluiced with cool, clear water. You felt strangely purified."

It was singular to hear Featherstone talking in this exalted strain. He looked so spruce in his smart white coat, technically known as a bum-freezer, his mustache was so trim, his thick curly hair so carefully brushed, that his high-flown language made me a trifle uncomfortable. But I realized that he was trying to express in his clumsy way a very sincerely felt emotion.

"What was Olive Hardy like?" I asked.

"I'll show you. I've got quite a lot of snapshots."

He got up from his chair and going to a shelf brought me a large album. It was the usual thing, indifferent photographs of groups of people, and of single figures. They were in bathing costumes or in shorts or tennis things, generally with their faces all screwed up because the sun blinded them, or puckered by the distortion of laughter. I recognized Hardy, not much change after ten years, with his wisp of hair hanging across his forehead. I remembered him better now that I saw the snapshots. In them he looked nice and fresh and young. He had an alertness of expression which was attractive and which I certainly had not noticed when I saw him. In his eyes was a sort of eagerness for life which danced and sparkled through the fading print. I glanced at the photographs of his sister. Her bathing dress showed that she had a good figure, well-developed, but slender; and her legs were long and slim.

"They look rather alike," I said.

"Yes, although she was a year older they might have been twins, they were so much alike. They both had the same oval face and that pale skin without any color in the cheeks and they both had those soft brown eyes, very liquid and appealing, so that you felt whatever they did you could never be angry with them. And they both had a sort of careless elegance which made them look charming whatever they wore and however untidy

they were. He's lost that now, I suppose, but he certainly had it
when I first knew him. They always rather reminded me of the
brother and sister in Twelfth Night. You know who I mean."

"Viola and Sebastian."

"They never seemed to belong quite to the present. There
was something Elizabethan about them. I don't think it was only
because I was very young then that I couldn't help feeling they
were strangely romantic somehow. I could see them living in
Illyria."

I gave one of the snapshots another glance.

"The girl looks as though she had a good deal more character
than her brother," I remarked.

"She had. I don't know if you'd have called Olive beautiful,
but she was awfully attractive. There was something poetic in
her, a sort of lyrical quality as it were, that colored her movements, her acts and everything about her. It seemed to exalt her
above common cares. There was something so candid in her expression, so courageous and independent in her bearing, that—
oh, I don't know, it made mere beauty just flat and dull."

"You speak as if you'd been in love with her," I interrupted.

"Of course I was. I should have thought you'd guessed that at
once. I was frightfully in love with her."

"Was it love at first sight?" I smiled.

"Yes, I think it was, but I didn't know it for a month or so.
When it suddenly struck me that what I felt for her—I don't
know how to explain it, it was a sort of shattering turmoil that
affected my whole self—that that was love, I knew that I'd had it
all along. It was not only her looks, though they were awfully
alluring, the smoothness of her pale skin and the way her hair
fell over her forehead and the grave sweetness of her brown
eyes; it was more than that; you had a sensation of well-being
when you were with her, as though you could relax and be quite
natural and needn't pretend to be anything you weren't. There
was nothing sloppy about her; if you were she could be rather
caustic, but even when she was, you were conscious of her kindli-
ness. You felt that she was incapable of meanness. It was impossible to think of her as envious of other people or catty. She

seemed to have a natural generosity of soul. One could be silent
with her for an hour at a time and yet feel that one had had a
good time."

"A rare gift," I said.

"She was a wonderful companion. If you made a suggestion to
do something she was always glad to fall in with it. She was the
least exacting girl I ever knew. You could throw her over at the
last minute and, however disappointed or inconvenienced she
was, it made no difference. Next time you saw her she was just as
cordial and serene as ever."

"Why didn't you marry her?"

Featherstone's cheroot had gone out. He threw the stub away
and deliberately lit another. He did not answer for a while. It
may seem strange to persons who live in a highly civilized state
that he should confide these intimate things to a stranger; it did
not seem strange to me. I was used to it. People who live, so desperately alone, in the remote places of the earth find it a relief
to tell someone whom in all probability they will never meet
again the story that has burdened, perhaps for years, their waking thoughts and their dreams at night. And I have an inkling
that the fact of your being a writer attracts their confidence.
They feel that what they tell you will excite your interest in an
impersonal way that makes it easier for them to discharge their
souls. Besides, as we all know from our own experience, it is
never unpleasant to talk about oneself.

"Why didn't you marry her?" I had asked him.

"I wanted to badly enough," Featherstone answered at length.
"But I hesitated to ask her. Although she was always so nice to
me and so easy to get on with, and we were such good friends,
I always felt that there was something a little mysterious in her.
Although she was so simple, so frank and natural, you never
quite got over the feeling of an inner kernel of aloofness, as if
deep in her heart she guarded, not a secret, but a sort of privacy
of the soul that not a living person would ever be allowed to
know. I don't know if I make myself clear."

"Perfectly—to me."

"I put it down to the strange upbringing she'd had. They
never talked of their mother, but somehow I got the impression

that she was one of those neurotic, emotional women who wreck their own happiness and are a pest to everyone connected with them. I had a suspicion that she'd led rather a hectic life in Florence and it struck me that Olive owed her beautiful serenity to a disciplined effort of her own will and that her aloofness was a sort of citadel she'd built to protect herself from the knowledge of all sorts of shameful things. But of course that aloofness was awfully captivating. It was strangely exciting to think that if she loved you, and you were married to her, you would at last pierce right into the hidden heart of that mystery; and you felt that if you could share that with her it would be, as it were, a consummation of all you'd ever desired in your life. Heaven wouldn't be in it. You know, I felt about it just like Bluebeard's wife about the forbidden chamber in the castle. Every room was open to me, but I should never rest till I had gone into that last one that was locked against me."

My eye was caught by a chik-chak, a little brown house lizard with a large head, high up on the wall. It is a friendly little beast and it is good to see it in a house. It watched a fly. It was quite still. On a sudden it made a dart and then, as the fly flew away, fell back with a sort of jerk into a strange immobility.

"And there was another thing that made me hesitate. I couldn't bear the thought that if I proposed to her and she refused me she wouldn't let me come to the bungalow in the same old way. I should have hated that; I enjoyed going there so awfully. It made me so happy to be with her. But you know, sometimes one can't help oneself. I did ask her at last, but it was almost by accident. One evening, after dinner, when we were sitting on the veranda by ourselves, I took her hand. She withdrew it at once.

" 'Why did you do that?' I asked her.

" 'I don't very much like being touched,' she said. She turned her head a little and smiled. 'Are you hurt? You mustn't mind; it's just a funny feeling I have. I can't help it.'

" 'I wonder if it's ever occurred to you that I'm frightfully fond of you,' I said.

"I expect I was terribly awkward about it, but I'd never proposed to anyone before." Featherstone gave a little sound that was not quite a chuckle and not quite a sigh. "For the matter of that I've never proposed to anyone since. She didn't say anything for a minute. Then she said,

" 'I'm very glad, but I don't think I want you to be anything more than that.'

" 'Why not?' I asked.

" 'I could never leave Tim.'

" 'But supposing he marries?'

" 'He never will.'

"I'd gone so far then that I thought I'd better go on. But my throat was so dry that I could hardly speak. I was shaking with nervousness.

" 'I'm frightfully in love with you, Olive. I want to marry you more than anything in the world.'

"She put her hand very gently on my arm. It was like a flower falling to the ground.

" 'No, dear, I can't,' she said.

"I was silent. It was difficult for me to say what I wanted to. I'm naturally rather shy. She was a girl. I couldn't very well tell her that it wasn't quite the same thing living with a husband and living with a brother. She was normal and healthy; she must want to have babies; it wasn't reasonable to starve her natural instincts. It was such waste of her youth. But it was she who spoke first.

" 'Don't let's talk about this any more,' she said. 'D'you mind? It did strike me once or twice that perhaps you cared for me. Tim noticed it. I was sorry because I was afraid it would break up our friendship. I don't want it to do that, Mark. We do get on so well together, the three of us, and we have such jolly times. I don't know what we should do without you now.'

" 'I thought of that too,' I said.

" 'D'you think it need?' she asked me.

" 'My dear, I don't want it to,' I said. 'You must know how much I love coming here. I've never been so happy anywhere before.'

" 'You're not angry with me?'

" 'Why should I be? It's not your fault. It only means that

you're not in love with me. If you were, you wouldn't care a hang about Tim.'

" 'You are rather sweet,' she said.

"She put her arm round my neck and kissed me lightly on the cheek. I had a notion that in her mind it settled our relation. She adopted me as a second brother.

"A few weeks later Tim went back to England. The tenant of their house in Dorset was leaving and though there was another in the offing, he thought he ought to be on the spot to conduct negotiations. And he wanted some new machinery for the estate. He thought he'd get it at the same time. He didn't expect to be gone more than three months and Olive made up her mind not to go. She knew hardly anyone in England, it was practically a foreign country to her, she didn't mind being left alone, and she wanted to look after the estate. Of course they could have put a manager in charge, but that wasn't the same thing. Rubber was falling and in case of accidents it was just as well that one or the other of them should be there. I promised Tim I'd look after her and if she wanted me she could always call me up. My proposal hadn't changed anything. We carried on as though nothing had happened. I don't know whether she'd told Tim. He made no sign that he knew. Of course I loved her as much as ever, but I kept it to myself. I have a good deal of self-control, you know. I had a sort of feeling I hadn't a chance. I hoped eventually my love would change into something else and we could just be wonderful friends. It's funny; it never has, you know. I suppose I was hit too badly ever to get quite over it.

"She went down to Penang to see Tim off and when she came back I met her at the station and drove her home. I couldn't very well stay at the bungalow while Tim was away, but I went over every Sunday and had tiffin and we'd go down to the sea and bathe. People tried to be kind to her and asked her to stay with them, but she wouldn't. She seldom left the estate. She had plenty to do. She read a lot. She was never bored. She seemed quite happy in her own company and when she had visitors it was only from a sense of duty. She didn't want them to think her ungracious. But it was an effort and she told me she heaved a sigh of relief when she saw the last of them and could again enjoy without disturbance the peaceful loneliness of the bunga-low. She was a very curious girl. It was strange that at her age she should be so indifferent to parties and the other small gaie-ties the station afforded. Spiritually, if you know what I mean, she was entirely self-supporting. I don't know how people found out that I was in love with her, I thought I'd never given myself away in anything, but I had hints here and there that they knew. I gathered they thought Olive hadn't gone home with her brother on my account. One woman, a Mrs. Sergison, the police-man's wife, actually asked me when they were going to be able to congratulate me. Of course I pretended I didn't know what she was talking about, but it didn't go down very well. I couldn't help being amused. I meant so little to Olive in that way that I really believe she'd entirely forgotten that I'd asked her to marry me. I can't say she was unkind to me; I don't think she could have been unkind to anyone, but she treated me with just the casualness with which a sister might treat a younger brother. She was two or three years older than I. She was always terribly glad to see me, but it never occurred to her to put herself out for me; she was almost amazingly intimate with me, but uncon-sciously, you know, as you might be with a person you'd known so well all your life that you never thought of putting on frills with him. I might not have been a man at all, but an old coat that she wore all the time because it was easy and comfortable and she didn't mind what she did in it. I should have been crazy not to see that she was a thousand miles away from loving me.

"Then one day, three or four weeks before Tim was due back, when I went to the bungalow I saw she'd been crying. I was startled. She was always so composed. I'd never seen her upset over anything."

" 'Hullo, what's the matter?' I said.

" 'Nothing.'

" 'Come off it, darling,' I said. 'What have you been crying about?'

"She tried to smile.

" 'I wish you hadn't got such sharp eyes,' she said. 'I think I'm being silly. I've just had a cable from Tim to say he's postponed his sailing.'

" 'Oh, my dear, I am sorry,' I said. 'You must be awfully disappointed.'

" 'I've been counting the days. I want him back so badly.'

" 'Does he say why he's postponing?' I asked.

" 'No, he says he's writing. I'll show you the cable.'

"I saw that she was very nervous. Her slow quiet eyes were filled with apprehension and there was a little frown of anxiety between her brows. She went into her bedroom and in a moment came back with the cable. I felt that she was watching me anxiously as I read. So far as I remember it ran: Darling, I cannot sail on the seventh after all. Please forgive me. Am writing fully. Fondest love. Tim.

" 'Well, perhaps the machinery he wanted isn't ready and he can't bring himself to sail without it,' I said.

" 'What could it matter if it came by a later ship? Anyhow it'll be hung up at Penang.'

" 'It may be something about the house.'

" 'If it is, why doesn't he say so? He must know how frightfully anxious I am.'

" 'It wouldn't occur to him,' I said. 'After all when you're away you don't realize that the people you've left behind don't know something that you take as a matter of course.'

"She smiled again, but now more happily.

" 'I daresay you're right. In point of fact Tim is a little like that. He's always been rather slack and casual. I daresay I've been making a mountain out of a molehill. I must just wait patiently for his letter.'

"Olive was a girl with a lot of self-control and I saw her by an effort of will pull herself together. The little line between her eyebrows vanished and she was once more her serene, smiling and kindly self. She was always gentle: that day she had a mildness so heavenly that it was shattering. But for the rest of the time I could see that she kept her restlessness in check only by the deliberate exercise of her commonsense. It was as though she had a foreboding of ill. I was with her the day before the mail was due. Her anxiety was all the more pitiful to see because

she took such pains to hide it. I was always busy on mail day,
but I promised to go up to the estate later on and hear the news.
I was just thinking of starting when Hardy's *seis* came along in
the car with a message from the amah asking me to go at once to
her mistress. The amah was a decent, elderly woman to whom I
had given a dollar or two and said that if anything went wrong
on the estate she was to let me know at once. I jumped into my
car. When I arrived I found the amah waiting for me on the
steps.

" 'A letter came this morning,' she said.

"I interrupetd her. I ran up the steps. The sitting room was
empty.

" 'Olive,' I called.

"I went into the passage and suddenly I heard a sound that
froze my heart. The amah had followed me and now she opened
the door of Olive's room. The sound I had heard was the sound
of Olive crying. I went in. She was lying on her bed, on her face,
and her sobs shook her from head to foot. I put my hand on her
shoulder.

" 'Olive, what is it?' I asked.

" 'Who's that?' she cried. She sprang to her feet suddenly, as
though she were scared out of her wits. And then: 'Oh, it's you,'
she said. She stood in front of me, with her head thrown back
and her eyes closed, and the tears streamed from them. It was
dreadful. 'Tim's married,' she gasped, and her face screwed up
in a sort of grimace of pain.

"I must admit that for one moment I had a thrill of exultation, it was like a little electric shock tingling through my heart;
it struck me that now I had a chance, she might be willing to
marry me; I know it was terribly selfish of me; you see, the news
had taken me by surprise; but it was only for a moment, after
that I was melted by her awful distress and the only thing I felt
was deep sorrow because she was unhappy. I put my arm round
her waist.

" 'Oh, my dear, I'm so sorry,' I said. 'Don't stay here. Come
into the sitting room and sit down and we'll talk about it. Let
me give you something to drink.'

"She let me lead her into the next room and we sat down on

the sofa. She was inert. I told the amah to fetch the whisky and siphon and I mixed her a good strong stengah and made her drink a little. I took her in my arms and rested her head on my shoulder. She let me do what I liked with her. The great tears streamed down her poor face.

" 'How could he?' she moaned. 'How could he?'

" 'My darling,' I said, 'it was bound to happen sooner or later. He's a young man. How could you expect him never to marry. It's only natural.'

" 'No, no, no,' she gasped.

"Tight-clenched in her hand I saw that she had a letter and I guessed that it was Tim's.

" 'What does he say?' I asked.

"She gave a frightened movement and clutched the letter to her heart as though she thought I would take it from her.

" 'He says he couldn't help himself. He says he had to. What does it mean?'

" 'Well, you know, in his way he's just as attractive as you are. He has so much charm. I suppose he just fell madly in love with some girl and she with him.'

" 'He's so weak,' she moaned.

" 'Are they coming out?' I asked.

" 'They sailed yesterday. He says it won't make any difference. He's insane. How can I stay here?'

"She began to cry hysterically. It was torture to see that girl, usually so calm, utterly shattered by her emotion. I had always felt that her lovely serenity masked a capacity for very deep feelings. But the abandon of her distress simply broke me up. I held her in my arms and kissed her, her eyes and her wet cheek and her hair. I don't think she knew what I was doing. I was hardly conscious of it myself. I was so deeply moved.

" 'What shall I do?' she wailed.

" 'Why won't you marry me?' I said.

"She tried to withdraw herself from me, but I would not let her go.

" 'After all, it would be a way out,' I said.

" 'How can I marry you?' she moaned. 'I'm years older than you are.'

" 'Oh, what nonsense, two or three. What do I care?'

" 'No, no.'

" 'Why not?' I said.

" 'I don't love you,' she said.

" 'What does that matter? I love you.'

"I don't know what I said. I told her that I'd try to make her happy. I said I'd never ask anything from her but what she was prepared to give me. I talked and talked. I tried to make her see reason. I felt that she didn't want to stay there, in the same place as Tim, and I told her that I'd be moved soon to some other district. I thought that might tempt her. She couldn't deny we'd always got on awfully well together. After a time she did seem to grow a little quieter. I had a feeling that she was listening to me. I had even a sort of feeling that she knew that she was lying in my arms and that it comforted her a little. I made her drink a drop more whisky. I gave her a cigarette. At last I thought I might be just mildly facetious.

" 'You know I'm not a bad sort really,' I said. 'You might do worse.'

" 'You don't know me,' she said. 'You know nothing whatever about me.'

" 'I'm capable of learning,' I said.

"She smiled a little.

" 'You're awfully kind, Mark,' she said.

" 'Say yes, Olive,' I begged.

"She gave a deep sigh. For a long time she stared at the ground. But she did not move and I felt the softness of her body in my arms. I waited. I was frightfully nervous and the minutes seemed endless.

" 'All right,' she said at last, as though she were not conscious that any time had passed between my prayer and her answer.

"I was so moved that I had nothing to say. But when I wanted to kiss her lips, she turned her face away, and would not let me. I wanted us to be married at once, but she was quite firm that she wouldn't. She insisted on waiting till Tim came back. You know how sometimes you see so clearly in people's thoughts that you're more certain of them than if they'd spoken them; I saw that she couldn't quite believe that what Tim had written was true and that she had a sort of miserable hope that it was all a mistake and he wasn't married after all. It gave me a pang, but I loved her so much, I just bore it. I was willing to bear anything. I adored her. She wouldn't even let me tell anyone that we were engaged. She made me promise not to say a word till Tim's return. She said she couldn't bear the thought of the congratulations and all that. She would not even let me make any announcement of Tim's marriage. She was obstinate about it. I had a notion that she felt that if the fact were spread about it gave it a certainty that she didn't want it to have.

"But the matter was taken out of her hands. News travels mysteriously in the East. I don't know what Olive had said in the amah's hearing when first she received the news of Tim's marriage; anyhow the Hardys' *seis* told the Sergisons' and Mrs. Sergison attacked me the next time I went into the club.

" 'I hear Tim Hardy's married,' she said.

" 'Oh?' I answered, unwilling to commit myself.

"She smiled at my blank face and told me that her amah having told her the rumor she had rung up Olive and asked her if it was true. Olive's answer had been rather odd. She had not exactly confirmed it, but said that she had received a letter from Tim telling her he was married.

" 'She's a strange girl,' said Mrs. Sergison. 'When I asked her for details she said she had none to give and when I said: Aren't you thrilled, she didn't answer.'

" 'Olive's devoted to Tim, Mrs. Sergison,' I said. 'His marriage has naturally been a shock to her. She knows nothing about Tim's wife. She's nervous about her.'

" 'And when are you two going to be married?' she asked me abruptly.

" 'What an embarrassing question!' I said, trying to laugh it off.

"She looked at me shrewdly.

" 'Will you give me your word of honor that you're not engaged to her?'

"I didn't like to tell her a deliberate lie, nor to ask her to mind her own business, and I'd promised Olive faithfully that I would say nothing till Tim got back. I hedged.

" 'Mrs. Sergison,' I said, 'when there's anything to tell I promise that you'll be the first person to hear it. All I can say to you now is that I do want to marry Olive more than anything in the world.'

" 'I'm very glad that Tim's married,' she answered. 'And I hope she'll marry you very soon. It was a morbid and unhealthy life that they led up there, those two; they kept far too much to themselves and they were far too much absorbed in one another.'

"I saw Olive practically every day. I felt that she didn't want me to make love to her, and I contented myself with kissing her when I came and when I went. She was very nice to me, kindly and thoughtful; I knew she was glad to see me and sorry when it was time for me to go. Ordinarily she was apt to fall into silence, but during this time she talked more than I had ever heard her talk before. But never of the future and never of Tim and his wife. She told me a lot about her life in Florence with her mother. She had led a strange lonely life, mostly with servants and governesses, while her mother, I suspected, engaged in one affair after another with vague Italian counts and Russian princes. I guessed that by the time she was fourteen there wasn't much she didn't know. I thought I saw why there was something mysterious about her. The thoughtful silence into which she sometimes fell and the aloofness that guarded her from intrusion were devices adopted, I suppose, half unconsciously by the child to escape from things she wished to ignore. It was natural for her to be quite unconventional: in the only world she knew till she was eighteen, conventions weren't mentioned because they didn't exist. Gradually Olive seemed to regain her serenity and I should have thought that she was beginning to accustom herself to the thought of Tim's marriage if it hadn't been that I couldn't but notice how pale and tired she looked. I made up my mind that the moment he arrived I'd press her to marry me at once. I could get short leave whenever I asked for it, and by the time that was up I thought I could manage a transfer to some other post. What she wanted was change of air and fresh scenes.

"We knew of course within a day when Tim's ship would

reach Penang, but it was a question whether she'd get in soon enough for him to catch the train and I wrote to the P & O agent asking him to telegraph as soon as he had definite news. When I got the wire and took it up to Olive I found that she'd just received one from Tim. The ship had docked early and he was arriving next day. The train was supposed to get in at eight o'clock in the morning, but it was liable to be anything from one to six hours late and I bore with me an invitation from Mrs. Sergison asking Olive to come back with me to stay the night with her so that she would be on the spot and need not go to the station till the news came through that the train was coming.

"I was immensely relieved. I thought that when the blow at last fell Olive wouldn't feel it so much. She had worked herself up into such a state that I couldn't help thinking that she must have a reaction now. She might take a fancy to her sister-in-law. There was no reason why they should not all three get on very well together. To my surprise Olive said she wasn't coming down to the station to meet them.

" 'They'll be awfully disappointed,' I said.

" 'I'd rather wait here,' she answered. She smiled a little. 'Don't argue with me, Mark, I've quite made up my mind.'

" 'I've ordered breakfast in my house,' I said.

" 'That's all right. You meet them and take them to your house and give them breakfast, and then they can come along here afterwards. Of course I'll send the car down.'

" 'I don't suppose they'll want to breakfast if you're not there,' I said.

" 'Oh, I'm sure they will. If the train gets in on time they wouldn't have thought of breakfasting before it arrived and they'll be hungry. They won't want to take this long drive without anything to eat.'

"I was puzzled. She had been looking forward so intensely to Tim's coming, it seemed strange that she should want to wait all by herself while the rest of us were having a jolly breakfast. I supposed she was nervous and wanted to delay as long as possible meeting the strange woman who had come to take her place. It seemed unreasonable; I couldn't see that an hour sooner or an hour later could make any difference, but I knew women were funny, and anyhow I felt Olive wasn't in the mood for me to press it.

" 'Telephone when you're starting so that I shall know when to expect you,' she said.

" 'All right,' I said, 'but you know I shan't be able to come with them. It's my day for going to Lahad.'

"This was a town that I had to go to once a week to take cases. It was a good way off and one had to ferry across a river, which took some time, so that I never got back till late. There were a few Europeans there and a club. I generally had to go on there for a bit to be sociable and see that things were getting along all right.

" 'Besides,' I added, 'with Tim bringing his wife home for the first time I don't suppose he'll want me about. But if you'd like to ask me to dinner I'll be glad to come to that.'

"Olive smiled.

" 'I don't think it'll be my place to issue any more invitations, will it?' she said. 'You must ask the bride.'

"She said this so lightly that my heart leaped. I had a feeling that at last she had made up her mind to accept the altered circumstances and, what was more, was accepting them with cheerfulness. She asked me to stay to dinner. Generally I left about eight and dined at home. She was very sweet, almost tender, and I was happier than I'd been for weeks. I had never been more desperately in love with her. I had a couple of gin *pahits* and I think I was in rather good form at dinner. I know I made her laugh. I felt that at last she was casting away the load of misery that had oppressed her. That was why I didn't let myself be very much disturbed by what happened at the end.

" 'Don't you think it's about time you were leaving a presumably maiden lady?' she said.

"She spoke in a manner that was so quietly gay that I answered without hesitation.

" 'Oh, my dear, if you think you've got a shred of reputation left you deceive yourself. You're surely not under the impres-

sion that the ladies of Sibuku don't know that I've been coming
to see you every day for a month. The general feeling is that if
we're not married it's high time we were. Don't you think it
would be just as well if I broke it to them that we're engaged?'

" 'Oh, Mark, you mustn't take our engagement very seriously,' she said.

"I laughed.

" 'How else do you expect me to take it? It is serious.'

"She shook her head a little.

" 'No. I was upset and hysterical that day. You were being
very sweet to me. I said yes because I was too miserable to say
no. But now I've had time to collect myself. Don't think me
unkind. I made a mistake. I've been very much to blame. You
must forgive me.'

" 'Oh, darling, you're talking nonsense. You've got nothing
against me.'

"She looked at me steadily. She was quite calm. She had even
a little smile at the back of her eyes.

" 'I can't marry you. I can't marry anyone. It was absurd of
me ever to think I could.'

"I did not answer at once. She was in a queer state and I
thought it better not to insist.

" 'I suppose I can't drag you to the altar by main force,' I
said.

"I held out my hand and she gave me hers. I put my arm
round her and she made no attempt to withdraw. She suffered me to kiss her as usual on her cheek.

"Next morning I met the train. For once in a way it was
punctual. Tim waved to me as his carriage passed the place
where I was standing and by the time I had walked up he had
already jumped out and was handing down his wife. He
grasped my hand warmly.

" 'Where's Olive?' he said, with a glance along the platform.
'This is Sally.'

"I shook hands with her and at the same time explained
why Olive was not there.

" 'It was frightfully early, wasn't it?' said Mrs. Hardy.

"I told them that the plan was for them to come and have a bit of breakfast at my house and then drive home.

" 'I'd love a bath,' said Mrs. Hardy.

" 'You shall have one,' I said.

"She was really an extremely pretty little thing, very fair, with enormous blue eyes and a lovely little straight nose. Her skin, all milk and roses, was exquisite. A little of the chorus girl type, of course, and you may happen to think that rather namby-pamby, but in that style she was enchanting. We drove to my house; they both had a bath and Tim a shave; I had just had two minutes alone with him. He asked me how Olive had taken his marriage. I told him she had been upset.

" 'I was afraid so,' he said, frowning a little. He gave a short sigh. 'I couldn't do anything else.'

"I did not understand what he meant. At that moment Mrs. Hardy joined us and slipped her arm through her husband's. He took her hand in his and gently pressed it. He gave her a look that had in it something pleased and humorously affectionate, as though he did not take her quite seriously but enjoyed his sense of proprietorship and was gratified by her very delicate beauty. She was not at all shy; she asked me to call her Sally before we'd known one another ten minutes. Of course just then she was excited at arriving. She'd never been East and everything thrilled her. It was quite obvious that she was head over heels in love with Tim. Her eyes never left him and she hung on his words. We had a jolly breakfast and then we parted. They got into their car to go home and I into mine to go to Lahad. I promised to go straight to the estate from there and in point of fact it was out of my way to pass by my house. I took a change with me. I didn't see why Olive shouldn't like Sally very much; she was frank and gay and ingenuous; she was extremely young, she couldn't have been more than nineteen, and her wonderful prettiness couldn't fail to appeal to Olive. I was just as glad to have had a reasonable excuse to leave the three of them by themselves for the day, but as I started out from Lahad I had a notion that by the time I arrived they would all be pleased to see me. I drove up to the

bungalow and blew my horn two or three times, expecting
someone to appear. Not a soul. The place was in total darkness.
I was surprised. It was absolutely silent. I couldn't make it out.
They must be in. Very odd, I thought. I waited a moment, then
got out of the car, and walked up the steps. At the top of them
I stumbled over something. I swore and bent down to see
what it was; it had felt like a body. There was a cry and I saw it
was the amah. She shrank back cowering as I touched her and
broke into loud wails.

"'What the hell's the matter?' I cried and then I felt a hand
on my arm and I heard a voice: 'Tuan, Tuan.' I turned and in
the darkness recognized Tim's head boy. He began to speak in
little frightened gasps. I listened to him with horror. What he
told me was unspeakable. I pushed him aside and rushed into
the house. The sitting room was dark. I turned on the light.
The first thing I saw was Sally huddled up in an armchair. She
was startled by my sudden appearance and cried out. I could
hardly speak. I asked her if it was true. When she told me it was
I felt the room suddenly going round and round me. I had to sit
down. As the car that bore Tim and Sally drove up the
road that led to the house and Tim sounded the claxon to announce their arrival and the boys and the amah ran out to greet
them there was the sound of a shot. They ran to Olive's room
and found her lying in front of the looking-glass in a pool of
blood. She had shot herself with Tim's revolver.

"'Is she dead?' I said.

"'No, they sent for the doctor and he took her to the
hospital.'

"I hardly knew what I was doing. I didn't even trouble to tell
Sally where I was going. I got up and staggered to the door. I
got into the car and told my *seis* to drive like hell to the hospital.
I rushed in. I asked where she was. They tried to bar my way,
but I pushed them aside. I knew where the private rooms were.
Someone clung to my arm, but I shook him off. I vaguely understood that the doctor had given instructions that no one was
to go into the room. I didn't care about that. There was an
orderly at the door, he put out his arm to prevent me from

passing. I swore at him and told him to get out of my way. I suppose I made a row; I was beside myself. The door was opened and the doctor came out.

" 'Who's making all this noise?' he said. 'Oh, it's you. What do you want?'

" 'Is she dead?' I asked.

" 'No. But she's unconscious. She never regained consciousness. It's only a matter of an hour or two.'

" 'I want to see her.'

" 'You can't.'

" 'I'm engaged to her.'

" 'You?' he cried, and even at that moment I was aware that he looked at me strangely. 'That's all the more reason.'

"I didn't know what he meant. I was stupid with horror.

" 'Surely you can do something to save her,' I cried.

"He shook his head.

" 'If you saw her you wouldn't wish it,' he said.

"I stared at him aghast. In the silence I heard a man's convulsive sobbing.

" 'Who's that?' I asked.

" 'Her brother.'

"Then I felt a hand on my arm. I looked round and saw it was Mrs. Sergison.

" 'My poor boy,' she said, 'I'm so sorry for you.'

" 'What on earth made her do it?' I groaned.

" 'Come away, my dear,' said Mrs. Sergison. 'You can do no good here.'

" 'No, I must stay,' I said.

" 'Well, go and sit in my room,' said the doctor.

" 'I was so broken that I let Mrs. Sergison take me by the arm and lead me into the doctor's private room. She made me sit down. I couldn't bring myself to realize that it was true. I thought it was a horrible nightmare from which I must awake. I don't know how long we sat there. Three hours. Four hours. At last the doctor came in.

" 'It's all over,' he said.

"Then I couldn't help myself, I began to cry. I didn't care what they thought of me. I was so frightfully unhappy.

"We buried her next day.

"Mrs. Sergison came back to my house and sat with me for a while. She wanted me to go to the club with her. I hadn't the heart. She was very kind, but I was glad when she left me by myself. I tried to read, but the words meant nothing to me. I felt dead inside. My headboy came in and turned on the lights. My head was aching like mad. Then he came back and said that a lady wished to see me. I asked him who it was. He wasn't quite sure, but he thought it must be the new wife of the tuan at Putatan. I couldn't imagine what she wanted. I got up and went to the door. He was right. It was Sally. I asked her to come in. I noticed that she was deathly white. I felt sorry for her. It was a frightful experience for a girl of that age, and for a bride a miserable homecoming. She sat down. She was very nervous. I tried to put her at her ease by saying conventional things. She made me very uncomfortable, because she stared at me with those enormous blue eyes of hers and they were simply ghastly with horror. She interrupted me suddenly.

" 'You're the only person here I know,' she said. 'I had to come to you. I want you to get me away from here.'

"I was dumbfounded.

" 'What do you mean?' I said.

" 'I don't want you to ask me any questions. I just want you to get me away. At once. I want to go back to England!'

" 'But you can't leave Tim like that just now,' I said. 'My dear, you must pull yourself together. I know it's been awful for you. But think of Tim. I mean, he'll be miserable. If you have any love for him the least you can do is to try and make him a little less unhappy.'

" 'Oh, you don't know,' she cried. 'I can't tell you. It's too horrible. I beseech you to help me. If there's a train tonight let me get on it. If I can only get to Penang I can get a ship. I can't stay in this place another night. I shall go mad.'

"I was absolutely bewildered.

" 'Does Tim know?' I asked her.

" 'I haven't seen Tim since last night; I'll never see him again. I'd rather die.'

"I wanted to gain a little time.

" 'But how can you go without your things? Have you got any luggage?'

" 'What does that matter?' she cried impatiently. 'I've got what I want for the journey.'

" 'Have you any money?'

" 'Enough. Is there a train tonight?'

" 'Yes,' I said. 'It's due just after midnight.'

" 'Thank God. Will you arrange everything. Can I stay here till then?'

" 'You're putting me in a frightful position,' I said. 'I don't know what to do for the best. You know, it's an awfully serious step you're taking.'

" 'If you knew everything you'd know it was the only possible thing to do.'

" 'It'll create an awful scandal here. I don't know what people'll say. Have you thought of the effect on Tim?' I was worried and unhappy. 'God knows I don't want to interfere in what isn't my business. But if you want me to help you I ought to know enough to feel justified in doing so. You must tell me what's happened.'

" 'I can't. I can only tell you that I know everything.'

"She hid her face with her hands and shuddered. Then she gave herself a shake as though she were recoiling from some frightful sight.

" 'He had no right to marry me. It was monstrous.'

"And as she spoke her voice rose shrill and piercing. I was afraid she was going to have an attack of hysterics. Her pretty, doll-like face was terrified and her eyes stared as though she could never close them again.

" 'Don't you love him any more?' I asked.

" 'After that?'

" 'What will you do if I refuse to help you?' I said.

" 'I suppose there's a clergyman here or a doctor. You can't refuse to take me to one of them.'

" 'How did you get here?'

" 'The headboy drove me. He got a car from somewhere.'

" 'Does Tim know you've gone?'

" 'I left a letter for him.'

" 'He'll know you're here.'

" 'He won't try to stop me. I promise you that. He daren't. For God's sake, don't you try either. I tell you I shall go mad if I stay here another night.'

"I sighed. After all she was of an age to decide for herself."

I, the writer of this, hadn't spoken for a long time.

"Did you know what she meant?" I asked Featherstone.

He gave me a long, haggard look.

"There was only one thing she could mean. It was unspeakable. I suppose it was unreasonable of me; at that moment I only felt a horror of that little, pretty fair-haired thing with her terrified eyes. I hated her. I didn't say anything for a while. Then I told her I'd do as she wished. She didn't even say thank you. I think she knew what I felt about her. When it was dinnertime I made her eat something and then she asked me if there was a room she could go and lie down in till it was time to go to the station. I showed her into my spare room and left her. I sat in the sitting room and waited. My God, I don't think the time has ever passed so slowly for me. I thought twelve would never strike. I rang up the station and was told the train wouldn't be in till nearly two. At midnight she came back to the sitting room and we sat there for an hour and a half. We had nothing to say to one another and we didn't speak. Then I took her to the station and put her on the train."

"Was there an awful scandal?"

Featherstone frowned.

"I don't know. I applied for short leave. After that I was moved to another post. I heard that Tim had sold his estate and bought another. But I didn't know where. It was a shock to me at first when I found him here."

Featherstone, getting up, went over to a table and mixed himself a whisky and soda. In the silence that fell now I heard the monotonous insistent chorus of the croaking frogs. And suddenly the bird that is known as the fever bird, perched in a tree close to the house, began to call. First three notes in a descending chromatic scale, then five, then four. The varying notes of the scale succeeded one another with maddening persistence. One was compelled to listen and to count them and, because one did not know how many there would be, it tortured one's nerves.

"Blast that bird," said Featherstone. "That means no sleep for me tonight."

Nathaniel Hawthorne

ALICE DOANE'S APPEAL

NATHANIEL HAWTHORNE, American, (1804 to 1864) was a major figure in nineteenth century literature in the United States. Called "the most distinguished craftsman of the New England school of letters," his works include *The Scarlet Letter, The Marble Faun,* and numerous short stories and lesser known novels. He was deeply concerned with the moral heritage upon which the youthful United States was founded, and he constantly questioned this morality and ethic. As he had focused attention on adultery in the longer work, *The Scarlet Letter,* so he examined incest in this shorter story, *Alice Doane's Appeal.* "He was the romancer of a grim Puritan past," wrote Vernon Parrington, "that both fascinated and repelled him." Lloyd Morris entitled his study of Hawthorne: *The Rebellious Puritan.*

On a pleasant afternoon of June, it was my good fortune to be the companion of two young ladies in a walk. The direction of our course being left to me, I led them neither to Legge's Hill, nor to the Cold Spring, nor to the rude shores and old batteries of the Neck, nor yet to Paradise; though if the latter place were rightly named, my fair friends would have been at home there. We reached the outskirts of the town and, turning aside from a street of tanners and curriers, began to ascend a hill, which at a distance, by its dark slope and the even line of its summit, resembled a green rampart along the road. It was less steep than its aspect threatened. The eminence formed part of an extensive tract of pasture land, and was traversed by cowpaths in various directions; but, strange to tell, though the whole slope and summit were of a peculiarly deep green, scarce a blade of grass was visible from the base upward. This deceitful verdure was occasioned by a plentiful crop of woodwax, which wears the same dark and glossy green throughout the summer, except at one short period, when it puts forth a profusion of yellow blossoms. At that season, to a distant spectator, the hill appears absolutely overlaid with gold, or covered with a glory of sunshine, even beneath a clouded sky. But the curious wanderer on the hill will perceive that all the grass, and everything that should nourish man or beast, has been destroyed by this vile and ineradicable weed: its tufted roots make the soil their own, and permit nothing else to vegetate among them, so that a physical curse may be said to have blasted the spot where guilt and frenzy consummated the most execrable scene that our history blushes to record. For this was the field where Superstition won her darkest triumph; the high place where our fathers set up their shame, to the mournful gaze of generations far remote. The dust of martyrs was beneath our feet. We stood on Gallows Hill.

For my own part, I have often courted the historic influence of the spot. But it is singular how few come on pilgrimage to this famous hill; how many spend their lives almost at its base, and never once obey the summons of the shadowy past, as it beckons them to the summit. Till a year or two since, this portion of our history had been very imperfectly written, and, as we are not a people of legend or tradition, it was not every citizen of our ancient town that could tell, within half a century, so much as the date of the witchcraft delusion. Recently, indeed, a historian has treated the subject in a manner that will keep his name alive, in the only desirable connection with the errors of our ancestry, by converting the hill of their disgrace into an honorable monument of his own antiquarian lore, and of that better wisdom, which draws the moral while it tells the tale. But we are a people of the present, and have no heartfelt interest in the olden time. Every fifth of November, in commemoration of they know not what, or rather without an idea beyond the momentary blaze, the young men scare the town with bonfires on this haunted height, but never dream of paying funeral honors to those who died so wrongfully and, without a coffin or a prayer, were buried here.

Though, with feminine susceptibility, my companions caught all the melancholy associations of the scene, yet these could but imperfectly overcome the gayety of girlish spirits.

Their emotions came and went with quick vicissitude, and
sometimes combined to form a peculiar and delicious excitement, the mirth brightening the gloom into a sunny shower of
feeling, and a rainbow in the mind. My own more somber
mood was tinged by theirs. With now a merry word and next a
sad one, we trod among the tangled weeds, and almost hoped
that our feet would sink into the hollow of a witch's grave. Such
vestiges were to be found within the memory of man, but have
vanished now and with them, I believe, all traces of the precise
spot of the executions. On the long and broad ridge of the
eminence, there is no very decided elevation of any one point,
nor other prominent marks, except the decayed stumps of two
trees, standing near each other, and here and there the rocky
substance of the hill, peeping just above the woodwax.

There are few such prospects of town and village, woodland
and cultivated field, steeples and country seats, as we beheld
from this unhappy spot. No blight had fallen on old Essex; all
was prosperity and riches, healthfully distributed. Before us lay
our native town, extending from the foot of the hill to the harbor, level as a chessboard, embraced by two arms of the sea, and
filling the whole peninsula with a close assemblage of wooden
roofs, overtopped by many a spire, and intermixed with frequent heaps of verdure, where trees threw up their shade from
unseen trunks. Beyond was the bay and its islands, almost the
only objects, in a country unmarked by strong natural features,
on which time and human toil had produced no change. Retain-
ing these portions of the scene, and also the peaceful glory and
tender gloom of the declining sun, we threw, in imagination,
a veil of deep forest over the land, and pictured a few scattered
villages, and this old town itself a village, as when the prince
of hell bore sway there. The idea thus gained of its former aspect, its quaint edifices standing far apart, with peaked roofs
and projecting stories, and its single meetinghouse pointing
up a tall spire in the midst; the vision, in short, of the town in
1692, served to introduce a wondrous tale of those old times.

I had brought the manuscript in my pocket. It was one of a
series written years ago, when my pen, now sluggish and
perhaps feeble because I have not much to hope or fear, was

driven by stronger external motives and a more passionate impulse within that I am fated to feel again. Three or four of these tales had appeared in the Token, after a long time and various adventures, but had encumbered me with no troublesome notoriety, even in my birthplace. One great heap had met a brighter destiny: they had fed the flames; thoughts meant to delight the world and endure for ages had perished in a moment, and stirred not a single heart but mine. The story now to be introduced, and another, chanced to be in kinder custody at the time, and thus, by no conspicuous merits of their own, escaped destruction.

The ladies, in consideration that I had never before intruded my performances on them by any but the legitimate medium— through the press, consented to hear me read. I made them sit down on a moss-grown rock, close by the spot where we chose to believe that the death tree had stood. After a little hesitation on my part, caused by a dread of renewing my acquaintance with fantasies that had lost their charm in the ceaseless flux of mind, I began the tale, which opened darkly with the discovery of a murder.

A hundred years, and nearly half that time, have elapsed since the body of a murdered man was found, at about the distance of three miles, on the old road to Boston. He lay in a solitary spot, on the bank of a small lake, which the severe frost of December had covered with a sheet of ice. Beneath this, it seemed to have been the intention of the murderer to conceal his victim in a chill and watery grave, the ice being deeply hacked, perhaps with the weapon that had slain him, though its solidity was too stubborn for the patience of a man with blood upon his hand. The corpse therefore reclined on the earth, but was separated from the road by a thick growth of dwarf pines. There had been a slight fall of snow during the night and, as if Nature were shocked at the deed and strove to hide it with her frozen tears, a little drifted heap had partly buried the body and lay deepest over the pale, dead face. An early traveler, whose dog had led him to the spot, ventured to uncover the features but was affrighted by their expression.

A look of evil and scornful triumph had hardened on them, and made death so lifelike and so terrible that the beholder at once took flight, as swiftly as if the stiffened corpse would rise up and follow.

I read on, and identified the body as that of a young man, a stranger in the country, but resident during several preceding months in the town which lay at our feet. The story described, at some length, the excitement caused by the murder, the unavailing quest after the perpetrator, the funeral ceremonies, and other commonplace matters, in the course of which I brought forward the personages who were to move among the succeeding events. They were but three: a young man and his sister, the former characterized by a diseased imagination and morbid feelings, the latter, beautiful and virtuous, and instilling something of her own excellence into the wild heart of her brother but not enough to cure the deep taint of his nature. The third person was a wizard, a small, gray, withered man with fiendish ingenuity in devising evil and superhuman power to execute it but senseless as an idiot and feebler than a child to all better purposes. The central scene of the story was an interview between this wretch and Leonard Doane, in the wizard's hut, situated beneath a range of rocks at some distance from the town. They sat beside a smoldering fire, while a tempest of wintry rain was beating on the roof. The young man spoke of the closeness of the tie which united him and Alice, the consecrated fervor of their affection from childhood upwards, their sense of lonely sufficiency to each other, because they only of their race had escaped death in a night attack by the Indians. He related his discovery or suspicion of a secret sympathy between his sister and Walter Brome, and told how a distempered jealousy had maddened him. In the following passage, I threw a glimmering light on the mystery of the tale.

"Searching," continued Leonard, "into the breast of Walter Brome, I at length found a cause why Alice must inevitably love him. For he was my very counterpart! I compared his mind by each individual portion, and as a whole, with mine. There was a resemblance from which I shrank with sickness and loathing and horror as if my own features had come and stared upon

me in a solitary place, or had met me in struggling through a
crowd. Nay! the very same thoughts would often express themselves in the same words from our lips, proving a hateful sympathy in our secret souls. His education, indeed, in the cities of
the old world, and mine in this rude wilderness, had wrought a
superficial difference. The evil of his character, also, had been
strengthened and rendered prominent by a reckless and un-
governed life, while mine had been softened and purified by
the gentle and holy nature of Alice. But my soul had been
conscious of the germ of all the fierce and deep passions, and of
all the many varieties of wickedness, which accident had
brought to their full maturity in him. Nor will I deny that, in
the accursed one, I could see the withered blossom of every virtue which, by a happier culture, had been made to bring forth
fruit in me. Now, here was a man whom Alice might love with
all the strength of sisterly affection, added to that impure passion which alone engrosses all the heart. The stranger would
have more than the love which had been gathered to me from
the many graves of our household—and I be desolate!"

Leonard Doane went on to describe the insane hatred that
had kindled his heart into a volume of hellish flame. It
appeared, indeed, that his jealousy had grounds, as far as that
Walter Brome had actually sought the love of Alice, who also
had betrayed an undefinable but powerful interest in the unknown youth. The latter, in spite of his passion for Alice,
seemed to return the loathful antipathy of her brother; the
similarity of their dispositions made them like joint possessors
of an individual nature, which could not become wholly the
property of one, unless by the extinction of the other. At last,
with the same devil in each bosom, they chanced to meet, they
two, on a lonely road. While Leonard spoke, the wizard had
sat listening to what he already knew, yet with tokens of pleas-
urable interest, manifested by flashes of expression across his
vacant features, by grisly smiles, and by a word here and there,
mysteriously filling up some void in the narrative. But when
the young man told how Walter Brome had taunted him with
indubitable proofs of the shame of Alice and, before the trium-

phant sneer could vanish from his face, had died by her brother's hand, the wizard laughed aloud. Leonard started, but just then a gust of wind came down the chimney, forming itself into a close resemblance of the slow, unvaried laughter, by which he had been interrupted. "I was deceived," thought he; and thus pursued his fearful story.

"I trod out his accursed soul, and knew that he was dead; for my spirit bounded as if a chain had fallen from it and left me free. But the burst of exulting certainty soon fled, and was succeeded by a torpor over my brain and a dimness before my eyes, with the sensation of one who struggles through a dream. So I bent down over the body of Walter Brome, gazing into his face, and striving to make my soul glad with the thought that he, in very truth, lay dead before me. I know not what space of time I had thus stood, nor how the vision came. But it seemed to me that the irrevocable years since childhood had rolled back, and a scene, that had long been confused and broken in my memory, arrayed itself with all its first distinctness. I thought I stood a weeping infant by my father's hearth,—by the cold and blood-stained hearth where he lay dead. I heard the childish wail of Alice, and my own cry arose with hers, as we beheld the features of our parent, fierce with the strife and distorted with the pain in which his spirit had passed away. As I gazed, a cold wind whistled by and waved my father's hair. Immediately I stood again in the lonesome road, no more a sinless child, but a man of blood, whose tears were falling fast over the face of his dead enemy. But the delusion was not wholly gone; that face still wore a likeness of my father; and because my soul shrank from the fixed glare of the eyes, I bore the body to the lake, and would have buried it there. But before his icy sepulchre was hewn I heard the voices of two travelers, and fled."

Such was the dreadful confession of Leonard Doane. And now tortured by the idea of his sister's guilt, yet sometimes yielding to a conviction of her purity; stung with remorse for the death of Walter Brome, and shuddering with a deeper sense of some unutterable crime, perpetrated, as he imagined, in

madness or a dream; moved also by dark impulses, as if a fiend
were whispering to him to meditate violence against the life of
Alice, he had sought this interview with the wizard, who, on
certain conditions, had no power to withhold his aid in unravel-
ing the mystery. The tale drew near its close.

The moon was bright on high; the blue firmament appeared
to glow with an inherent brightness; the greater stars were
burning in their spheres; the northern lights threw their mysterious glare far over the horizon; the few small clouds aloft
were burdened with radiance; but the sky, with all its variety
of light, was scarcely so brilliant as the earth. The rain of the
preceding night had frozen as it fell and, by that simple magic,
had wrought wonders. The trees were hung with diamonds
and many-colored gems; the houses were overlaid with silver,
and the streets paved with slippery brightness; a frigid glory
was flung over all familiar things, from the cottage chimney to
the steeple of the meetinghouse, that gleamed upward to the
sky. This living world, where we sit by our firesides, or go forth
to meet beings like ourselves, seemed rather the creation of
wizard power, with so much of resemblance to known objects
that a man might shudder at the ghostly shape of his old
beloved dwelling, and the shadow of a ghostly tree before his
door. One looked to behold inhabitants suited to such a town,
glittering in icy garments, with motionless features, cold, sparkling eyes, and just sensation enough in their frozen hearts to
shiver at each other's presence.

By this fantastic piece of description, and more in the same
style, I intended to throw a ghostly glimmer round the reader,
so that his imagination might view the town through a medium
that should take off its everyday aspect, and make it a proper
theatre for so wild a scene as the final one. Amid this unearthly
show, the wretched brother and sister were represented as setting forth at midnight through the gleaming streets, and directing their steps to a graveyard, where all the dead had been
laid, from the first corpse in that ancient town to the murdered
man who had been buried three days before. As they went, they

seemed to see the wizard gliding by their sides, or walking dimly on the path before them. But here I paused, and gazed into the faces of my two fair auditors, to judge whether, even on the hill where so many had been brought to death by wilder tales than this, I might venture to proceed. Their bright eyes were fixed on me; their lips apart. I took courage, and led the fated pair to a new-made grave, where for a few moments, in the bright and silent midnight, they stood alone. But suddenly there was a multitude of people among the graves.

Each family tomb had given up its inhabitants who, one by one, through distant years, had been borne to its dark chamber, but now came forth and stood in a pale group together. There was the gray ancestor, the aged mother, and all their descendants, some withered and full of years, like themselves, and others in their prime; there, too, were the children who had gone prattling to the tomb, and there the maiden who yielded her early beauty to death's embrace, before passion had polluted it. Husbands and wives arose, who had lain many years side by side, and young mothers who had forgotten to kiss their first babes, though pillowed so long on their bosoms. Many had been buried in the habiliments of life, and still wore their ancient garb; some were old defenders of the infant colony, and gleamed forth in their steel caps and bright breastplates, as if starting up at an Indian war cry; other venerable shapes had been pastors of the church, famous among the New England clergy, and now leaned with hands clasped over their gravestones, ready to call the congregation to prayer. There stood the early settlers, those old illustrious ones, the heroes of tradition and fireside legends, the men of history whose features had been so long beneath the sod that few alive could have remembered them. There, too, were faces of former townspeople, dimly recollected from childhood, and others, whom Leonard and Alice had mourned in later years, but who now were most terrible of all, by their ghastly smile of recognition. All, in short, were there; the dead of other generations, whose moss-grown names could scarcely be read upon their tombstones, and their successors, whose graves were not yet green; all whom black fu-

nerals had followed slowly thither now reappeared where the
mourners left them. Yet none but souls accursed were there,
and fiends counterfeiting the likeness of departed saints.

The countenances of those venerable men, whose very features had been hallowed by lives of piety, were contorted now
by intolerable pain or hellish passion, and now by an unearthly
and derisive merriment. Had the pastors prayed, all saintlike as
they seemed, it had been blasphemy. The chaste matrons, too,
and the maidens with untasted lips, who had slept in their
virgin graves apart from all other dust, now wore a look from
which the two trembling mortals shrank, as if the unimaginable
sin of twenty worlds were collected there. The faces of fond
lovers, even of such as had pined into the tomb, because there
their treasure was, were bent on one another with glances of
hatred and smiles of bitter scorn, passions that are to devils
what love is to the blest. At times, the features of those who had
passed from a holy life to heaven would vary to and fro between
their assumed aspect and the fiendish lineaments whence they
had been transformed. The whole miserable multitude, both
sinful souls and false specters of good men, groaned horribly
and gnashed their teeth as they looked upward to the calm
loveliness of the midnight sky and beheld those homes of bliss
where they must never dwell. Such was the apparition, though
too shadowy for language to portray; for here would be the
moonbeams on the ice, glittering through a warrior's breast-
plate, and there the letters of a tombstone, on the form that
stood before it; and whenever a breeze went by, it swept the
old men's hoary heads, the women's fearful beauty, and all the
unreal throng into one indistinguishable cloud together.

I dare not give the remainder of the scene, except in a very
brief epitome. This company of devils and condemned
souls had come on a holiday, to revel in the discovery of a complicated crime, as foul a one as ever was imagined in their
dreadful abode. In the course of the tale, the reader had been
permitted to discover that all the incidents were results of the
machinations of the wizard, who had cunningly devised that
Walter Brome should tempt his unknown sister to guilt and

shame, and himself perish by the hand of his twin brother. I
described the glee of the fiends at this hideous conception, and
their eagerness to know if it were consummated. The story concluded with the Appeal of Alice to the specter of Walter
Brome; his reply, absolving her from every stain; and the
trembling awe with which ghost and devil fled, as from the
sinless presence of an angel.

The sun had gone down. While I held my page of wonders in
the fading light, and read how Alice and her brother were left
alone among the graves, my voice mingled with the sigh of a
summer wind, which passed over the hilltop, with the broad
and hollow sound as of the flight of unseen spirits. Not a word
was spoken till I added that the wizard's grave was close beside
us, and that the woodwax had sprouted originally from his un-
hallowed bones. The ladies started; perhaps their cheeks might
have grown pale had not the crimson west been blushing on
them; but after a moment they began to laugh, while the breeze
took a livelier motion, as if responsive to their mirth. I kept an
awful solemnity of visage, being, indeed, a little piqued that a
narrative which had good authority in our ancient superstitions,
and would have brought even a church deacon to Gallows Hill,
in old witch times, should now be considered too grotesque
and extravagant for timid maids to tremble at. Though it was
past supper time, I detained them a while longer on the hill,
and made a trial whether truth were more powerful than fiction.

We looked again toward the town, no longer arrayed in that
icy splendor of earth, tree, and edifice, beneath the glow of a
wintry midnight, which shining afar through the gloom of a
century had made it appear the very home of visions in visionary streets. An indistinctness had begun to creep over the mass
of buildings and blend them with the intermingled treetops,
except where the roof of a statelier mansion, and the steeples
and brick towers of churches, caught the brightness of some
cloud that yet floated in the sunshine. Twilight over the land-
scape was congenial to the obscurity of time. With such eloquence as my share of feeling and fancy could supply, I called
back hoar antiquity, and bade my companions imagine an

ancient multitude of people, congregated on the hillside, spreading far below, clustering on the steep old roofs, and climbing the adjacent heights, wherever a glimpse of this spot might be obtained. I strove to realize and faintly communicate the deep, unutterable loathing and horror, the indignation, the affrighted wonder, that wrinkled on every brow, and filled the universal heart. See! the whole crowd turns pale and shrinks within itself, as the virtuous emerge from yonder street. Keeping pace with that devoted company, I described them one by one; here tottered a woman in her dotage, knowing neither the crime imputed her, nor its punishment; there another, distracted by the universal madness, till feverish dreams were remembered as realities, and she almost believed her guilt. One, a proud man once, was so broken down by the intolerable hatred heaped upon him, that he seemed to hasten his steps, eager to hide himself in the grave hastily dug at the foot of the gallows. As they went slowly on, a mother looked behind, and beheld her peaceful dwelling; she cast her eyes elsewhere, and groaned inwardly yet with bitterest anguish, for there was her little son among the accusers. I watched the face of an ordained pastor, who walked onward to the same death; his lips moved in prayer; no narrow petition for himself alone, but embracing all his fellow sufferers and the frenzied multitude; he looked to Heaven and trod lightly up the hill.

Behind their victims came the afflicted, a guilty and miserable band; villains who had thus avenged themselves on their enemies, and viler wretches, whose cowardice had destroyed their friends; lunatics, whose ravings had chimed in with the madness of the land; and children, who had played a game that the imps of darkness might have envied them, since it disgraced an age, and dipped a people's hands in blood. In the rear of the procession rode a figure on horseback, so darkly conspicuous, so sternly triumphant, that my hearers mistook him for the visible presence of the fiends himself; but it was only his good friend, Cotton Mather, proud of his well-won dignity, as the representative of all the hateful features of his time; the one blood-thirsty man, in whom were concentrated those vices of spirit and errors of opinion that sufficed to madden the whole surrounding multitude. And thus I marshaled them onward, the innocent who were to die, and the guilty who were to grow old in long remorse—tracing their every step, by rock, and shrub, and broken track, till their shadowy visages had circled round the hilltop, where we stood. I plunged into my imagination for a blacker horror, and a deeper woe, and pictured the scaffold.

But here my companions seized an arm on each side; their nerves were trembling; and, sweeter victory still, I had reached the seldom-trodden places of their hearts, and found the wellspring of their tears. And now the past had done all it could. We slowly descended, watching the lights as they twinkled gradually through the town, and listening to the distant mirth of boys at play, and to the voice of a young girl warbling somewhere in the dusk, a pleasant sound to wanderers from old witch-times. Yet, ere we left the hill, we could not but regret that there is nothing on its barren summit, no relic of old, nor lettered stone of later days, to assist the imagination in appealing to the heart. We build the memorial column on the height which our fathers made sacred with their blood, poured out in a holy cause. And here, in dark, funereal stone, should rise another monument, sadly commemorative of the errors of an earlier race, and not to be cast down, while the human heart has one infirmity that may result in crime.

Marguerite de Navarre
A TALE OF INCEST

MARGARET OF NAVARRE, or Marguerite d'Angouleme, (1492-
1549) as she is more properly called, lived a stormy political and literary
life in France and for a time was queen of Navarre. Her best-known work
is *The Heptameron*, published posthumously, constructed somewhat along
the lines of the more famous *Decameron* of Boccaccio. Critics today are
of the opinion that the *Heptameron* was not the sole work of Margaret;
nevertheless, it is attributed to her and has been widely published and
read. The brief story, *A Tale of Incest*, was published in English in a
recent anthology, *The Palace of Pleasure*, from which this translation is
taken.

When Louis XII was king, the legate at Avignon being then a
lord of the house of Amboise, nephew to the legate of France,
whose name was George, there was a lady in Languedoc who
had an income of more than four thousand ducats. Her name
I will not mention, for sake of her relations. She was still very
young when her husband died, leaving her but one son; and
whether from regret for her husband, or love of her son, she
resolved never to marry again.

To avoid all occasion for doing so, she frequented only the
society of the devout, thinking that opportunity makes sin, and
not knowing that sin forges opportunity. She gave herself up
wholly to the divine service, shunning all parties of pleasure,
and everything worldly, insomuch that she made it a matter of
conscience to be present at a wedding, or to hear the organ
played in church. When her son was seven years old, she chose
a man of holy life as his preceptor, to bring him up in piety
and sanctity.

But when he was between fourteen and fifteen, nature, who
is a very mysterious schoolmaster, finding him well grown and

idle, taught him a very different lesson from any he had learned
from his preceptor; for under that new instruction he began to
look upon and desire such things as seemed to him fair; and
among others a demoiselle who slept in his mother's room.
No one had the least suspicion of this, for he was regarded as a
child, and nothing was ever heard in the house but Godly
discourse.

The young gallant having begun secretly to solicit this girl,
she went and told her mistress. The mother loved her son so
much that she believed this to be a story told to get him into
disgrace; but the girl repeated her complaints so often that her
mistress at last said she would find out the truth of the matter:
if it was as the girl stated, she would punish her son severely,
but if not, the accuser should pay the penalty. In order, then, to
come at the truth, she ordered the demoiselle to make an ap-
pointment with the young gentleman that he should come to
her at midnight, to the bed in which she lay alone near the
door in his mother's chamber.

The demoiselle obeyed her orders, and that night the mother
lay down in the demoiselle's bed, resolving that if her son came
thither she would chastise him in such a manner that he should
never lie with a woman without remembering it. Such were
her angry thoughts when her son actually entered the bed in
which she lay; but unable still to bring herself to believe that
he had any unchaste intention, she waited for some plainer evidence of his bad purpose before she would speak to him.

But she waited so long, and nature is so frail, that her anger
ended in an abominable pleasure, and she forgot that she was a
mother. As water retained by force is more impetuous when let
loose, so was it with this unfortunate woman, who made her
whole pride consist in the violence she did her body. When she
began to descend the first step from her chastity she found herself at once at the bottom, and became pregnant that night by
him whom she wished to hinder from getting another with
child.

No sooner was the sin committed than she was seized with
the most poignant remorse, and her repentance lasted as long
as her life. So keen was her anguish on rising from beside her

son, who never discovered his mistake, that entering a closet, and calling to mind the firm resolution she had formed and which she had so badly executed, she passed the whole night alone in an agony of tears. But instead of humbling herself and owning that of ourselves alone, and without the aid of God, we can do nothing but sin, she thought by her own efforts and by her tears to repair the past and prevent future mischief, always imputing her sin to the occasion, and not to wickedness, for which there is no remedy but the grace of God. As if there was but one sort of sin which could bring damnation, she applied her whole mind to avoid that one; but pride, which the sense of extreme sinfulness should destroy, was too strongly rooted in her heart, and grew in such a manner, that, to avoid one evil, she committed several others.

Early next morning she sent for her son's governor, and said to him, "My son is coming to maturity, and it is time that he should be removed from the house. One of my relations, who is beyond the mountains with the Grand Master of Chaumont, will be glad to have him. Take him away, then, forthwith; and to spare me the pain of parting, do not let him come to bid me farewell." Without more ado she gave him money for the journey, and he set out the next day with his pupil, who was very glad of it, and having had what he wanted of his mistress, desired nothing better than to go to the wars.

The lady was long plunged in extreme grief, and but for the fear of God she could have wished that the unhappy fruit of her womb should perish. To conceal her fault she pretended to be ill; and having a bastard brother in whom she confided above all men, and for whom she had done many favors, she sent for him, informed him of the misfortune that had happened to her, but not of her son's share in it, and begged him to save her honor by his help, which he did.

Some days before she expected to be confined, he advised her to try change of air and to move to his house, where she would be more likely to recover than at home. She went thither with hardly any attendants and found there a midwife, who had been sent for as if to attend her brother's wife, and who, without knowing the lying-in woman, delivered her by night of a fine little girl. The gentleman put the infant out to nurse as his own; and the lady, after a month's stay, returned home, where she lived more austerely than ever.

Her son being grown up, and Italy being at peace, he sent to beg his mother's permission to return to her. But as she was afraid of relapsing into the same crime, she put him off from time to time as well as she could; but he pressed her so much that at last she gave him leave to come home, having no plausible reason to allege for persisting longer in her refusal. She sent him word, however, not to appear before her until he was married; to choose a wife whom he loved passionately; and not to let his choice be determined by wealth, for if he chose a comely wife that was enough.

During this time the daughter, who had been left with the bastard brother, having grown up into a very handsome girl, her guardian thought of removing her to some place where she should not be known. He consulted the mother on the subject, and it was her wish that she should be given to the Queen of Navarre, named Catherine. The girl was so handsome and well-bred at twelve or thirteen, that the Queen of Navarre had a great regard for her, and wished much to marry her well; but the girl being poor, many lovers presented themselves, but no husband.

The unknown father, returning from Italy, visited the court of the Queen of Navarre, and no sooner saw his daughter than he fell in love with her. As he had his mother's permission to marry any woman he liked, he only asked was she of noble lineage, and being told that she was, he demanded her in marriage of the Queen of Navarre, who very gladly bestowed her upon him, knowing well that the cavalier was as wealthy as he was well-bred and handsome.

The marriage having been consummated, the gentleman wrote to his mother, saying she could no longer close her doors against him, since he brought with him a wife as handsome and as perfect as she could wish for. His mother made inquiries as to the wife he had taken, and found that it was their own daughter, which caused her such excessive affliction that she was near dying suddenly, seeing that the means she employed to put a stop to the course of her misfortune only served to make it greater.

Finding no remedy for what had occurred, she went to the legate of Avignon, confessed the enormity of her crime, and asked his advice. The legate, to satisfy her conscience, summoned several theologians, to whom he submitted the affair without naming the person concerned. The decision of this council of conscience was that the lady was never to reveal the secret to her children, who had not sinned, inasmuch as they had known nothing; but that, as for herself, she was to do penance all her life.

So the poor lady returned home, where soon after arrived her son and her daughter-in-law, who loved each other so much that never was there a fonder couple, or one more like each other, for she was his daughter, sister and wife; and he her father, brother, and husband. Their love continued unabated to the last, while their profoundly penitent mother never saw them caress but she withdrew to weep.

Giambattista Basile

THE PENTAMERON [*Selections*]

Translated by Sir Richard Burton

GIAMBATTISTA BASILE (1575-1632), a Neapolitan, collected his stories mainly from the oral tradition. His time was, by our present-day standards, a bawdy and unrestrained one; and perhaps the best evidence for this is the fact that the *Pentameron*—dealing not only with incest, but with bestiality, adultery and other sexual activities nowadays proscribed—was intended as a book for children.

Benedetto Croce once described the volume from which these selections are taken as "the most remarkable book of the Baroque period." That may seem to the reader an over-valuation; but the tales are undeniably charming even today—and even in a translation (Burton's) that probably leaves much to be desired.

Sir Richard Burton's translation first appeared in 1893, several years after the famed explorer-author's death. Burton translated the *Pentameron* shortly after completing his monumental edition of the *Thousand Nights and A Night,* and the style developed in the earlier work was carried over into the later. This was not altogether inappropriate, since so many of the tales set down by Basile are obviously of Eastern origin.

Penta the Handless

Penta scorneth to wed her brother, and cutting off her hands, sendeth them to him as a present. He commandeth that she be put within a chest and thrown into the sea. The tide casteth her upon a seashore. A sailor findeth her, and leadeth her to his home, but his wife thrusts her again into the same chest and into the sea. She is found by a king, and he taketh her to wife; but by the wickedness of the same woman, Penta is expelled from that kingdom. After sore troubles and travail she is recovered by her husband and her brother.

Having heard Zeza's story, the company were of the mind that Cannetella deserved what befell her and more, because she sought for a hair within an egg: yet they felt pleased when they beheld her saved from so much sorrow, and there was matter for reflection in that, knowing how all men were dirt for her, she was reduced to the pass of humbling herself and bowing down before a locksmith, so that he might save her from so much travail. But the prince signed to Cecca to begin her story, and she did not delay in speaking, proceeding thus:

Virtue is tried in the crucible of troubles, and the candle of goodness shineth the more where it is darkest, and fatigue begetteth merit. Who sitteth idle triumpheth not, but whoso turneth the ladle, as did the daughter of the King of Preta-secca, with sweat of blood and danger of death, buildeth for himself the house of contentment, like unto the fortunes I am going to relate.

The King of Preta-secca having been bereft of his wife, the evil one entered his head, and suggested that he should take his sister Penta to wife. For this reason, sending for her one day, he met her alone, and said, " 'Tis not a matter, O my sister, to be done by a man with sound judgment, to let the good which he hath in his own house depart; and besides one knoweth not how it will be, when one alloweth strange people to put their feet in one's house; therefore having well digested this business, I came to the resolution, and I purpose to take thee to wife, because thou art made of mine own breath, and I know thy nature. Be thou content therefore to be tied in this knot, to be set in this setting, to join this partnership, to enter into this *uniantur acta,* this mixture, *et fiat patio,* and let it be done, as both of us will do a good day's work."

Penta, hearing this thrust in filth, stood nearly out of her mind, and her color came and went, and she could scarce believe her own ears, thinking it impossible that her brother could jump to this height and try to sell her a pair of rotten eggs when he needed a hundred fresh ones. Remaining silent for a while, thinking how she should answer to such an impertinent question, and out of purpose, at last, unloading the fardel of patience, she said, "If thou hast lost thy wits, I will not lose my

shame. I am in a transport of surprise at thee, that thou allow-
est such words to escape thy mouth, which if said in joke befit
an ass, and if in earnest stink of lecherousness. I report that,
if thou hast tongue to speak such outrageous language, I
have not ears to hearken thereto. I thy wife? Yes 'tis done for
thee: oh, smell thy fill: since when dost thou these foul tricks?
this *olla podrida?* these mixtures? and where are we? in the ice?
His sister, O baked-cheese! Ask thy priest to correct thee, and
never allow such words to escape thy lips, or else I will do incredible things, and whilst thou esteem me not as a sister, I will
not hold thee for what thou art to me." And thus saying, she
departed, and entering a chamber, locked and bolted the door,
and saw not the face of her brother for more than a month,
leaving the wretched king, who had listened with a hardened
brow, to tire out the shot, scorned as a child who hath broken
the juglet, and confounded as a cook-maid when the cat hath
stolen the meat.

After some days were past, the king again gave vent to his
licentious desires, and she desiring to know what had caused
her brother such great longing, and what was in her person
that should put such a thought in his head, came forth out of
her chamber, and went to him, and said, "O my brother, I have
admired myself and looked at myself in the mirror, and I cannot find anything in my face which could deserve and inspire
such love as thine, as I am not such a sweet morsel to cause folk
to pant and long for me." And answered the king, "Penta mine,
thou art beauteous and accomplished from head to foot, but
thine hand is the thing which above all other causeth me to
faint with excessive desire: that hand is the fork which extract-
eth from the pot of this breast my heart and entrails: that hand
is the hook, which lifteth from the cistern of my life the pail of
my soul: that hand is the pincers, wherein is held my spirit
whilst love is filling it. O hand, O beauteous hand, spoon, which
administereth the soup of sweetness: nippers, which nip my
longing and desire: shovel, which casteth dust within my heart!"
And he would have said more, but Penta replied, "Thou mayest go, I have heard thee; we will meet again"; and entering her
chamber, she sent for a witless slave, and giving him a large

knife and a handful of coins, said to him, "Ali mine, cut off mine hands, I wish to make them beautiful in secret, and whiter." The slave, believing he was doing her pleasure, with two blows cut them off. Then she had them laid in a faenza basin and sent them covered with a silken napkin to her brother, with a message that she hoped he would enjoy what he coveted most, and desiring him good health and twins, she saluted him.

The king, beholding such a deed, was wroth with exceeding wrath, and he waxed furious, and ordered that a chest should be made straightway, well tarred outside, and commanded that his sister should be put therein, and cast into the sea. And this was done, and the chest sailed on, battered by the waves until the tide projected it upon a seashore, where, found by some sailors who had been casting their nets, it was opened, and therein they beheld Penta, far more beautiful than the moon when it riseth after having spent its Lenten time at Taranto. Masiello, who was the chief and the most courageous of those folk, carried her home, bidding Nuccia his wife to entreat her with kindness. But no sooner had her husband gone forth, than she, who was the mother of suspicion and jealousy, put Penta again within the chest, and cast her once more into the sea, where beaten by the waves, and buffeted here and there, it was at last met by a large vessel, on board of which was the King of Terra-Verde. Perceiving this chest floating about, the king in-structed the sailors to strike sail and lay to, and ordering the small boat to be lowered, sent some of the sailors to pick up the chest. When they brought it on board they opened it and discovered therein the unhappy damsel, and the king, behold-ing this beauty alive within a coffin for the dead, believed that he had found a great treasure, although his heart wept because the casket of so many gems of love was found without handles. Taking her to his realm, the king gave her as maid of honor to the queen; and she did all possible services to the queen, as sew, thread the needle, starch the collars, and comb the queen's hair, with her feet, for which reason, no less than for her good-ness, youth and beauty, she was held dear as the queen's own daughter.

Now after a month or so was past, the queen was called to

appear before the judgment seat of destiny to pay the debt to
nature, and she asked the king to her bed-side, and said to him,
"But a short while can my soul remain till she looseth the matrimonial knot between herself and the body; therefore hearten
thy heart, O my husband, and strengthen thy soul. But if thou
lovest me, and desirest that I should go content and consoled
and comforted into the next world, thou must grant me a
boon." "Command, O mine heart," said the king, "that if I cannot give thee proof whilst in life of my great love, I may give
thee a sign of the affection I bear thee even after death." Replied the queen, "Now listen, as thou has promised. As soon as
mine eyes will be closed in the dust, thou must marry Penta,
although we know not who she is, nor whence she came: yet by
good breeding and fine bearing is known a steed of good race."
Answered the king, "Live thou a hundred years; but even if
thou shouldst say goodnight to give me the evil day, I swear to
thee that I shall take her to wife, and I care not that she is
without hands and short of weight, for of the bad ones one must
always take the least." But these last words were uttered in an
undertone so that his wife should not hear them. And as soon
as the candle of the queen's days was put out, he took Penta to
wife; and the first night that he lay with her she conceived. But
after a time the king was obliged to sail for the kingdom of
Antoscuoglio, and farewelling Penta, he weighed anchor.

The nine months being over, Penta brought to the light a
beauteous man-child, and all the city was illumined and tables
spread in honor of the new-born babe, and the ministers and
counsellors quickly dispatched a felucca to advise the king of
what had taken place. Now the ship met stormy weather on the
way, so that one moment it seemed as if she would meet the
stars, and another moment that she would plunge into the very
bottom of the ocean. At last, by the grace of Heaven, she
went ashore in the same place where Penta had been found,
and had met with kindness and compassion from the chief of
the sailors, and had been cast again into the sea by a woman's
cruelty. As ill fortune would have it, the same Nuccia was washing the linen of her child at the seashore, and curious to know
the business of other people, as 'tis the nature of women, en-

quired of the felucca's master whence he came, and whither
he was bound, and who had sent him. And the master answered,
"I come from Terra-Verde, and am going to Antoscuoglio to
find the king of that country, to give him a letter, and for this I
have been sent on purpose. I believe 'tis his wife that hath
written to him. But I could not tell thee clearly what is the
message." Replied Nuccia, "And who is the wife of this king?"
and the master rejoined, "From what I have heard said, she is a
beauteous young dame, and she is called Penta the Handless,
as she hath lost both her hands. And I have heard them saying
that she was found within a chest in the midst of the sea, and
by her good fortune and destiny she hath become the king's
wife, and I know not why she is writing to him in such haste
that I needs must run against time and tide to reach him
quickly." Hearing these words, that jewess of a Nuccia invited
the master to come and drink a glass in her house, and she plied
him with liquor till he was dead drunk, and then taking the
letter out of his pocket, she called a scribe and bade him read it.
All the time the man read, she was dying with envy, and every
syllable made her sigh deeply, and at the last she bade the
same scribe to falsify the writing, and write to the king that
the queen had given birth to a dog, and they awaited his orders
to know what they should do with it. After it was written they
sealed it, and she put it in the sailor's pocket, and when he
awakened and beheld the weather changed, he weighed anchor,
and tacked the ship, and fared with a light wind for Antoscuoglio. Arriving thereto, he presented the letter to the king, who,
after reading it, answered that they should keep the queen in
cheerful spirits, so that she should not be troubled at all, for
these things came through Heaven's commandments, and a
good man should not rebel against the stars' decree.

And the master departed, and in a few days arrived at the
same place, where Nuccia met him, and entreating him with exceeding great kindness, and giving him wine of extra good
vintage, he fell to the ground intoxicated once more. And he
slept heavily, and Nuccia putting her hand in his pocket found
the answer; and calling the scribe bade him read it, and again
bade him falsify a reply for the ministers and counselors of

Terra-Verde, which was that they should burn at once mother
and son. When the master got over his drinking bout, he departed; and arriving at Terra-Verde, presented the letter to
the counselors, and they opened it. When they had mastered
its contents, there was a murmuring and whispering among
those old sages; and they conversed at length about this matter,
and concluded at last that either the king must be going mad,
or that some one had cast a spell upon him, for when he had
such a pearl of a wife and a gem of an heir, he ordered to make
powder of them for death's teeth. So they took the middle
course, and decided to send the queen and her son away from
the city, where no news could ever be heard of them: and so,
giving her some money so as to keep body and soul together,
they sent out of the house a treasure, and from the city a great
light, and from the husband the two props uplifting his hopes.

The unhappy Penta, perceiving that they had expelled her,
although she was not a dishonest woman, nor related to bandits,
nor a fastidious student, taking the child in her arms, whom
she watered with her tears, and fed with her milk, departed,
and fared toward Lago-truvolo where dwelt a magician, and
he beholding this beautiful maimed damsel who moved the
hearts to compassion, this beauty who made more war with her
maimed arms than Briareus with his hundred hands, asked her
to relate to him the whole history of her misadventures. And
she related to him how her brother, because she would not
satisfy his lust of her flesh, sent her to be food for the fishes, and
she continued her story up to the day in which she had set her
foot in his kingdom. The magician, hearing this sad tale, wept
with ceaseless weeping; and the compassion which entered
through the ear-holes issued in sighs from the mouth; at last
comforting her with kind words, he said, "Keep a good heart, O
my daughter, for no matter how rotten is the soul's home, it can
be supported with the props of hope; and therefore let not thy
spirit go forth, as Heaven sometimes sendeth great trouble
and travail, so as to make appear all the greater the marvelous
coming of success. Doubt not, therefore, thou hast found father and mother here, and I will help thee with my own
blood." The sadhearted Penta thanked him gratefully, and said,

"I care not now for aught. Let Heaven rain misfortunes upon my head, and let a storm of ruin come, now that I am under thy shelter I fear naught as thou wilt protect me with thy grace as thou canst and wilt; and I feel like under the spell of childhood." And after a thousand words of kindness on one side and thanks on the other, the magician allotted her a splendid apartment in his palace, and bade that she should be entreated as his own daughter.

The next morning he sent for the crier and commanded that a ban should be published, that whosoever would come and relate at his court the greatest misfortune, he would present them with a crown and sceptre of gold, of the worth of a kingdom. And the news of his edict flew to all parts of Europe, and to that court came folk more than broccoli to gain such great riches, and one related that he had served at court all the days of his life, and had found that he had lost the water and the soap, his youth and health, and had been paid with a form of cheese. And another, that he had met with injustice from a superior, which he could not resent; and that he had been obliged to swallow the pill, and could not give vent to his anger. One lamented that he had put all his substance within a vessel, and owing to contrary winds had lost the cooked and the raw. Another complained that he had spent all his years in the exercise of his pen and had had so little fortune that never had it brought him any gain, and he despaired himself, seeing that matters of pen and ink were so fortunate in the world, whilst his only failed. Such was their case.

In the meanwhile the King of Terra-Verde had returned to his kingdom; and finding this fine sirup at home, he became frantic, and acted as a mad unchained lion, and would have slain all the ministers and counselors, if they had not shown him his own letter, and perceiving that it had been counterfeited, he sent for the ship's master, and bade him relate to him what had occurred in the voyage. And the king keenly divined that Masiello's wife must have worked him this evil; and arming and equipping a galley, he departed and sailed for that coast, and arriving there he sought and found the woman, and with kindly words he drew out from her the whole intrigue, and thus ascertaining that envy and jealousy had been the cause of this great misfortune, he commanded that the woman should be punished: and they well anointed her with wax and tallow, and put her among a heap of wood, setting fire thereto. And the king stood and watched till he beheld that the fire with its red tongues had licked up that wretched woman. He then ordered the sailors to weigh anchor and depart. And whilst sailing amid the sea, his craft was met by a large vessel, and on enquiry being made he found that on board of it was the King of Preta-secca. They exchanged a thousand ceremonious compliments, and the King of Preta-secca informed the King of Terra-Verde that he was sailing towards Lago-truvolo, as the king of that kingdom had published a certain ban, and he was going to tempt his fortune, as he did not yield to any in misfortune, being the most sorrow-stricken man in all the world. Answered the King of Terra-Verde, "If 'tis for such case thou goest, I can surpass thee, or at least equal thee, and I can give fifteen for a dozen, and excel the most unfortunate, whoever he be, and where the others measure their cark and care with a small lantern, I can measure it even to the grave. Therefore I will also come with thee, and let us act as gentlemen, each one of us, and whoso shall win of us two shall divide the winnings with the other, even to a fennel." "I agree to it," answered the King of Preta-secca, and plighting their word between them, they sailed together for Lago-truvolo, where they disembarked, and fared to the royal palace, and presented themselves before the magician. And when he knew who they were, he entreated them with honor as due to kings, and bade them be seated under the dais, and said, "Well come, and a thousand times welcome!" And hearing that they also had come to the trial of wretchedness and unhappiness of men, the magician enquired of what great sorrow had subjected them to the south wind of sighs. And the King of Preta-secca first began to tell of his love, and the wrong done to his own flesh and blood, and the honorable deed of a virtuous woman done by his sister, and his own dog-heartedness in shutting her up into the chest, and casting her into the sea. And he grieved with exceeding grief as his conscience reproached him of his own error, and his sorrow was great, passing all distress, for the loss of his sister. In one way he was tormented by shame, in the other by the great loss: so that all the cark and care of the most great affliction in others was in him like hell compared to a lantern, and the quintessence of sorrow was as naught, compared with the anguish which gnawed at his heart. Having ended his say, the King of Terra-Verde began to relate, saying, "Alas! thy sorrow and trouble are like small lumps of sugar, and cakes, and sweetmeats compared with mine because that very Penta the Handless of whom thou hast spoken, and whom I found in that chest, like a Venice wax torch to burn at my funeral, I took to wife. And she conceived, and bare me a son of passing beauty, and by the envy and malignity of a hideous witch, both had nearly been slain. But, O sore nail to my heart, O anguish and sore affliction, I can never find peace and rest in this world! They were both expelled from my kingdom: and I have taste for naught, and I know not how under the heavy load of such cark and care, doth not fall the ass of this weary life."

The magician, having heard both their say, understood at once from the points of their noses that one of them was the brother, and the other the husband of Penta, and sending for Nufriello the son, said to him, "Go and kiss thy sire and lord's feet"; and the child obeyed the magician, and the father seeing the good breeding and beauty and grace of the little child threw a gold chain round his neck. And this done, the magician said again to the child: "Go and kiss thy uncle's hand, O beauteous boy mine," and the child obeyed at once. The uncle marveling with exceeding marvel at the wit and spirit of the little one, presented him with a valuable gem, and enquired of the magician if he were his son, and he answered that they must enquire of his mother. Penta, who had been hid behind a curtain, and had heard the whole business, now came forth, and like a little dog who, having been lost, and after some days finding his master again, barks, and wags its tail, and bounds, and licks his hand, and gives a thousand signs of its delight: thus it was with her, now going to the brother, and then to her husband, now clasped by the love of the one, and then drawn by the blood's instinct of the other, she embraced first one and

then the other, and their delight, and joy, and happiness knew
no bounds. Ye must suppose that it was a concert in three of
broken words and interrupted sighs; but having ended this music, they then returned to caress the child, first the father
and then the uncle clasped him, and kissed him, and embraced
him. After that from both sides all was said and done, the magician concluded with these words, "Heaven knoweth how this
heart fluttereth with joy in beholding the happiness of all, and
the lady Penta comforted, who for her own good deeds deserveth
to be held in the palm of the hand, and by this scheme I tried to
draw to this kingdom her husband and her brother, and to
one and the other I submit myself their slave; but as man bind-
eth himself with words, and the ox is bound by the horns, and
the promise of a worthy man is his bond, judging that the King
of Terra-Verde was in sooth the one most likely to burst with
grief, I will maintain my promise to him, and therefore I give
him not only the crown and sceptre as hath been published by
the ban, but my kingdom also. And as I have neither chick nor
child, by your good grace I desire to take as my adopted children this handsome couple, husband and wife, and ye will be
dear unto me as the eye-ball of mine eyes; and because there
should be naught left for Penta to desire, let her put her maimed
limbs between her legs, and she will withdraw them with a
pair of hands more beauteous than she had before." And this
being done, and all happening as the magician had said, the joy
was great: they were out of mind with delight. The husband esteemed this the greater good fortune, more than the other kingdom given to him by the magician; and for a few days there
were great joyances and feasting, and then the King of Preta-
secca returned to his kingdom, and the King of Terra-Verde
sent his brother-in-law to his realm, bidding his younger brother
take his place, and he and his wife remained with the magician, forgetting in joy and delight the past travail, and taking
the world to witness, that

> "There is naught sweet and dear
> Unless one hath been first tried by the bitter."

The She-Bear

The King of Rocc' Aspra desireth to take his own daughter to wife. The princess, by the cunning of an old woman, changeth her shape, and becometh a she-bear, and escapeth from her father's palace. She is taken home by a prince, who once beholdeth her in her own shape in the garden, where she is dressing her hair, and falleth deeply in love with her. After many adventures she discovereth herself, and taketh her own shape once more, and becometh the prince's wife.

All enjoyed heartily Popa's story, but when she spake of women's craft and flattery, which were sufficient to outwit a fox, they laughed till they fell backwards; and truly women are cunning, and their craftiness is threaded like beads in every hair of their head. Fraud is their mother; falsehood their nurse; allurement their teacher; dissimulation their adviser; deceit their companion: and thus they can turn man round and round according to their liking. But let us return to Antonella who was eager to begin her story. She stood a little while as one in deep thought, and at last thus began her say:

Spake well the sage who said that to a command mixed with gall cannot be rendered obedience sweet as sugar. Man must require matters justly ordered and rightly measured, if it be his desire to meet with justly weighed obedience. From undue commands are born resistance, and rebellion, and evils which cannot easily be remedied: as happened to the King of Rocc' Aspra, who sought from his daughter an undue thing, thus causing her flight at the risk of her life and honor.

Now it is said that once upon a time there lived a king of Rocc' Aspra, who had a wife who for beauty, and grace, and comeliness exceeded all other women. Truly she was the mother of beauty, but this beauteous being, at the full time of her life, fell from the steed of health, and brake the threads of life. But before the candle of life was finally put out, she called her husband and said, "I know well that thou hast loved me with excessive love, therefore show unto me a proof of thy love and give me a promise that thou wilt never marry, unless thou meetest one beauteous as I have been; and if thou wilt not do so, I will leave thee a curse, and I will hate thee even in the other world." The king, who loved her above all things, hearing this her last will, began to weep and lament, and for a while could not find a word to say: but after his grief subdued, he replied, "If I ever think of taking a wife, may the gout seize me, and may I become as gaunt as an asparagus; O my love, forget it, believe not in dreams, or that I can ever put my affection upon another woman. Thou wilt take with thee all my joyance and desire." And whilst he spake thus, the poor lady, who was at her last, turned up her eyes and stretched her feet.

When the king saw that her soul had taken flight, his eyes became fountains of tears, and he cried with loud cries, and buffeted his face, and wept, and wailed, so that all the courtiers ran to his side, and he continually called upon the name of that good soul, and cursed his fate, which had deprived him of her, and tore his hair, and pulled out his beard, and accused the stars of having sent to him this great misfortune. But he did as others do; pain of elbow and of wife acheth much but doth not last. Two, one in the grave, and other on the knee. Night had not yet come forth in the place of Heaven to look about her for the bats, when he began to make counts with his fingers, saying "My wife is dead, and I am a widower, and sad-hearted without hope of any kind but my only daughter, since she left me. Therefore it will be necessary to find another wife that will bear me a son. But where can I find one? Where can I meet a woman dowered with my wife's beauty, when all other damsels seem witches in my sight? There is the rub! Where shall I find another like unto her? Where am I to seek her with the bell, if nature moulded Nardella (whose soul rest in glory), and then brake the mould? Alas! in what labyrinth am I! What a mistake was the promise I made her! But what? I have not seen the wolf yet, and am going to fly: let us seek, let us see, and let us understand. Is it possible, that no other she-ass will be found to stable in Nardella's place? Is it possible that the world will be lost for me? Will there be such a misfortune, that no damsel will shoot, or will the seed be lost?" And thus saying, he commanded the public crier to publish a ban that all the beautiful women in the world should come and undergo the comparison of beauty, that he would take to wife the handsomest of all, and make her a queen of his realm. And this news spread in all parts of the world, and not one of the women in the whole universe failed to come and try this venture, and not even flayed hags stayed behind, they came by the dozen, because, when the point of beauty is touched, there is none who will yield, there is no sea-monster who will give herself up as hideous; each and every boasteth of uncommon beauty; and if an ass speaketh the truth, the mirror is blamed, which reflecteth not the form as it is naturally; 'tis the fault of the quicksilver at the back. And now the land was full of women, and the king ordered that they should all stand in file, and he began to walk up and down, like a sultan when he entereth his harem to choose the best Genoa stone to sharpen his blade damascene. He came and went, up and down, like a monkey who is never still, looking and staring at this one and that one. And one had a crooked brow, another had a long nose, one had a large mouth, and another had thick lips, this one was too tall and gaunt, that other was short and badly formed, this one was too much dressed, another was too slightly robed; the Spaniard pleased him not because of the hue of her skin; the Neapolitan was not to his taste because of the way in which she walked; the German seemed to him too cold and frozen; the French woman too light of brains; the Venetian a spinning wheel full of flax; and at the last, for one reason and for another, he sent them all about their business with one hand in front and another behind. And seeing so many beautiful heads of celery turned to hard roots, having resolved to have his will, he turned to his own daughter, saying, "What am I seeking about these Marys of Ravenna, if my daughter Preziosa is made of the same mould like unto her mother? I have this beauteous face at home, and shall I go to the end of the world seeking it?" And he explained to

his daughter his desire, and was severely reproved and cen-
sured by her, as Heaven knoweth. The king waxed wroth at her
censure, and said to her, "Speak not so loud, and put thy tongue
behind thee, and make up thy mind this evening to be tied
in this matrimonial knot, otherwise the least thing that I will do
to thee is that I will have thine ears cut off." Preziosa, hearing
this resolve, retired within her chamber, and wept and lamented her evil fate. And whilst she lay in this plight with such
a sorrowful face, an old woman, who used to bring her un-
guents, and pomade, and cosmetics, and salve to anoint herself,
came to her, and finding her in such a plight, looking one
more ready for the other world than for this, enquired the cause
of her distress, and when the old woman mastered it, she said,
"Be of good cheer, O my daughter, and despair not, as every evil
hath a remedy: death alone hath no cure. Now hearken to me:
when thy sire this evening cometh into thee, and being an
ass, would like to act the stallion, put thou this piece of wood
in thy mouth, when at once thou wilt become a she-bear and
then thou canst fly; as he being afraid of thee will let thee go.
And fare thou straight to the forest, where 'twas written in the
book of fate, the day that thou wert born, that thou shouldst
meet thy fortune: and when 'tis thy desire to appear a woman
as thou art and wilt ever be, take out of thy mouth the bit of
wood, and thou wilt return to thy pristine form." Preziosa embraced and thanked the old woman, and bidding the servants
give her an apron-full of flour and some slices of ham, sent her
away. And the sun beginning to change his quarters like a
bankrupt strumpet, the king sent for his minister, and bade
him issue invitations to all the lords and grandees to come to
the marriage-feast. And they all crowded thither. And after
spending five or six hours in high revel, and eating out of
measure, the king made his way to the bed-chamber, and
called to the bride to come and fulfill his desire. But instantly
putting the bit of wood in her mouth, she took the shape of a
she-bear, terrible of aspect, and stood before him. And he,
frightened at the sudden change, rolled himself up amongst the
mattresses, and did not put forth a finger or an eye until the
morning.

Meanwhile Preziosa came forth and fared towards the forest, where the shadows met concocting together how they could annoy the sun, and there she lay in unison and in good fellowship with the other animals. When the day dawned, it was decreed by the Decreer that there should come to that forest the son of the King of Acqua-corrente, and he, sighting the she-bear, was frightened with excessive fear; but the beast came forward, and wagging her tail, walked round him, and put her head under his hand for him to caress her. At this sight, which seemed passing strange to him, he heartened his heart, smoothed its head as he would have done to a dog, and said to it, "Lie down, down, quiet, quiet, ti ti, good beast"; and seeing the beast was very tame, he took her home with him, commanding his servants to put her in the garden by the side of the royal palace, and there to attend to and feed her well, and treat her as they would his own person, and to take her to such a spot that he might see her from the windows of his palace whenever he had a mind to.

Now it so chanced, one day of the days, that all his people had gone forth on some errand, and the prince being left alone, bethought himself of the bear, and looked out of the window to see her, and at that very moment Preziosa, believing she was utterly alone, had taken out the bit of wood from her mouth, and stood combing her golden hair. The prince, beholding this damsel of passing beauty, marveled with excessive marvel, and descending the stairs ran to the garden. But Preziosa, perceiving the ambush, at once put the bit of wood in her mouth and became a she-bear once more. The prince looked about him, and could not discern what he had seen from above, and not finding what he came to seek, remained sorely disappointed, and was melancholy and sadhearted, and in a few days was taken with grievous sickness. And he kept repeating, "O my bear, my bear." His mother, hearing this continual cry, imagined that perhaps the bear had bit him or done him some evil, and therefore ordered the servants to slay her. But all the servants loved the beast because it was so very tame, even the stones in the roadway could not help liking her, and they had compassion of and could not endure to slay her: therefore they led her to the forest, and returning to the queen, told her that she was dead. When this deed came to the prince's ears, he acted as a madman, and leaving his bed, ill as he was, was about to make mincemeat of the servants; but when they told him the truth of the affair, he mounted his steed, and searched, and turned backward and forwards till at length he came to a cave and found the bear. Then he took her, and carried her home with him, and putting her in a chamber, said, "O thou beauteous morsel fit for kings, why dost thou hide thy passing beauty in a bear's hide? O light of love, why art thou closed in such a hairy lantern? Why hast thou acted thus toward me, is it so that thou mayest see me die a slow death? I am dying of despair, charmed by thy beauteous form, and thou canst see the witness of my words in my failing health and sickening form. I am become skin and bone, and the fever burneth my very marrows, and consumeth me with heart-sore pain: therefore lift thou the veil of that stinking hide, and let me behold once more thy grace and beauty; lift up the leaves from this basket's mouth, and let me take a view of the splendid fruit within; lift thou the tapestry, and allow mine eyes to feast upon the luxury of thy charms. Who hath enclosed in a dreary prison such a glorious work? Who hath enclosed in a leathern casket such a priceless treasure? Let me behold thy passing grace, and take thou in payment all my desires; O my love, only this bear's grease can cure the nervous disease of which I suffer." But perceiving that his words had no effect, and that all was time lost, he took to his bed, and his illness daily increased, till the doctors despaired of his life. The queen his mother, who had no other love in the world, seated herself at the bedside, and said to him, "O my son, wherefrom cometh all thy heart-sickness? What is the cause of all this sadness? Thou art young, thou art rich, thou art beloved, thou art great; what does thou want, O my son, speak, for only a shameful beggar carrieth an empty pocket. Dost thou desire to take a wife, choose thou, and I will bid; take thou, and I will pay; canst thou not see that thy sickness is my sickness? that thy pulse beats in unison with my heart? if thou burnest with fever in thy blood, I burn with fever on the brain. I have no other support for my old age but thou. Therefore, O my son, be cheerful, and cheer my heart, and do not darken this realm, and raze to the ground this house, and bereave thy mother." The prince hearing these words, said, "Nothing can cheer me, if I may not see the bear; therefore, if thou desirest to see me in good health again, let her stay in this room, and I do not wish that any other serve me, and make my bed, and cook my meals, if it be not herself, and if what I desire be done, I am sure that I shall be well in a few days." To the queen it seemed folly for her son to ask that a bear should act as cook and housemaid, and she believed that the prince must be delirious; nevertheless, to please his fancy, she went for the bear, and when the beast came to the prince's bedside she lifted her paw and felt the invalid's pulse, and the queen smiled at the sight, thinking that by and by the bear would scratch the prince's nose. But the prince spake to the bear, and said, "O mischievous mine, wilt thou not cook for me, and feed me, and serve me?" And the bear signed yes with her head, showing that she would accept the charge. Then the queen sent for some chickens, and had a fire lit in the fireplace in the same chamber, and had a kettle with boiling water put on the fire. The bear, taking hold of a chicken and scalding it, dexterously plucked off its feathers, and cleaning it, put half of it on the spit, and stewed the other half, and when it was ready, the prince, who could not before eat even sugar, ate it all and licked his fingers. When he had ended his meal, the bear brought him some drink, and handed it so gracefully that the queen kissed her on the head. After this the prince arose, and went to the salon to receive the doctors, and stood under the touchstone of their judgment. And the bear at once made the bed, and ran to the garden and gathered a handful of roses and orange blossoms, and came and strewed them upon it, and she delivered herself so well of her divers duties that the queen said in her mind, "This bear is worth a treasure, and my son is quite right in being fond of the beast." And when the prince returned to his chambers, seeing how well the bear had acquitted herself of her duties, it seemed like adding fuel to the fire, and if he consumed himself in a slow fire before, he burned with intense heat now; and he said to the queen, "O my lady mother, if I give not a kiss to this bear, I shall give up the ghost." The queen, seeing her son nearly fainting, said to the bear, "Kiss him, kiss him, O my beauteous bear, leave not this my poor son to die in despair." Then the bear obediently neared the prince, who taking her cheeks between his fingers, could not leave off kissing her on the lips. Whilst thus engaged, I know not how, the bit of wood fell from Preziosa's mouth, and she remained in the prince's embrace, the most beauteous and ravishing being in the world; and he strained her to his bosom with tightly clasped arms, and said, "Thou are caught at last, and thou shalt not escape so easily without a reason." Preziosa, reddening with the lovely tint of modesty and of shame, the most beautiful of natural beauties, answered, "I am in thine hands, I recommend to thy loyalty mine honor, and do otherwise as thou wilt." And the queen enquired who was this charming damsel, and what had caused her to live such a wild life; and she related to them all her misfortunes, and the queen praised her as a good and honored child, and said to her son that she was well satisfied that he should marry the princess. And the prince, who desired for naught else, plighted his troth at once to her, and both kneeling before the queen received her blessing, and with great feasting the marriage took place: and Preziosa thus measured the truth of human judgment that

"He who doeth good may good expect."

Pierre Louys

THE CONFESSION OF A YOUNG WOMAN

PIERRE LOUYS, well-known French poet and novelist, (1870-1925) was prominent among the aesthetes as well as the lyricists, and his work concerns itself with sensuality and love. His best-known work is *Aphrodite,* which depicts the moral values of lovers in classic Alexandria. *The Confession of a Young Woman* is one of a group of short stories that appeared in *Sanguines.* The new translation is by D. W. Cory.

Father Couezy did not like to be asked certain questions, even in the most sincere manner, about his experiences in the confessional. Nevertheless, hardly a day passed when someone did not pose such questions to him.

It could be said of the Father that he was a man of high society, provided that this description implied nothing derogatory about his character, for he was seen almost as frequently in the church as in drawing rooms; and, if he could be reproached at all, one should stop and recall that a mass is a briefer ceremony than a visit or a dinner. Father Couezy was deeply religious.

The dominant trait of his plump yet delicate physiognomy was, first of all, his intelligence and, more specifically, his perspicacity. When he gazed upon a newcomer, his small eyes traveled slowly, exploring the entire person in front of him; then his eyelids closed with a peculiar flutter, like lips that murmured: "All right, that will do, I understand just what you are."

He was the confessor for all of Paris. The ladies by the thousands chose him as adviser of their consciences, which were constantly, and for good reason, in a state of anxiety. They knew him to be enough of a man of the world not to dispatch a penitent to Rome merely because she had relapsed peace-

fully into an affair of adultery which might be causing no great
alarm; and yet his indulgence was limited in that, in throwing
herself on his mercy, no penitent, even though she might have
committed only the slightest infraction, had any absolute certainty in advance of being pardoned. When the ladies consent
to sin, one would be ill-advised to tell them that their vice does
not exist.

Well, when the Father, on a visit, left the drawing room
sofa for the smoking room armchair, in order to slip deliberately into the conversations of men, his presence immediately
transformed the tone of a discussion without altering its character, save for a new reticence which was introduced. He was
willingly accepted as one well informed, although he indignantly
refused to play the role of a carrier of information. The skillful
men would attempt to obtain his confidences by discreetly leading the conversation from the general to the particular, and
might get him started with such a sentence as this:

"Father, you know our age better than anyone; what do
you think of our morals?"

"What sort of a question are you asking me?" he cried out.
"Why, I have nothing to say! Nothing at all to say! We should
derive from each confession only the experience necessary to
understand the confessions that follow, and in this way acquire
a just spirit, or rather a more judicious spirit, to guide us in
handling the difficult cases. But if we are forbidden to reveal
a confession, even an anonymous one, for a still stronger reason
we should not publicly summarize all the confessions we hear,
drawing from them the quintessence of their meanings and
offering this to the curious under the pretext of a philosophy."

The day that I heard him pronounce this sentence, someone took him up on the final word:

"What if this philosophy were salutary?"

"It can only be nefarious, sir, as all morality must be that
relies on a description of the evil to be avoided. Man is completely demoralized only in the countries which suffer from
an overabundance of moralists. To state that a vice is wide-
spread so as to inspire horror of it is, first of all, to forget that

the listener retains a recollection of the example given him, which will serve him as an excuse if he falls into the same error. Therefore, I will carefully guard myself against telling you what I know of the morals of my times, for your own would only get worse, and I would be more distressed as a result of this than you."

We were convinced, most modestly, of the admirable sentiments expressed by the Father. However, the same voice as had spoken before insisted:

"The whole world does not have your reserve, dear Father. I recently met a priest who for two years was vicar near here, at Sainte Clotilde. He was astonished by what he heard during his two years of confession in that section. Astonished. He did not conceal it. Adulterers everywhere, seduction of young girls, abortions, infanticides, poisoning of fathers and husbands— frightening things take place right in the midst of families, and no one knows of it, outside of the confessional. Every potential scandal is crushed before it is permitted to germinate. Others are admitted, welcomed, even imposed upon us, if this is necessary. Everywhere one sees, like a plague, one vice that was formerly unknown among the upper classes. You know which one, Reverend Father?"

"Oh, there are so many," the priest replied softly. "I would not be able to say which one you are referring to."

"Incest—yes, plain incest. Who among us ever heard anyone speak of incest twenty years ago? In my youth, it was known to us only through the Bible. A man who had misled his sister or his daughter would have been adjudged insane and locked up, since the penal code did not foresee such a case. And now, today, it is the most fashionable of vices. That's all you hear at confessionals, if my information is correct. The first lover is the brother. We are returning to the era of the Ptolemies. The brother initiates, teaches, perverts, seduces, and is loved. If by chance there are only girls in the children's room, their crime becomes complicated or simplified, depending on how you look at it."

The Father maintained his silence.

"Come now, give us your opinion," repeated the interlocutor. "Am I correctly informed? You who have confessed the entire area of Varennes, do you find that I have blackened the picture of the morals of our times? On the subject of incest specifically, have I vilified the young girls? Do they confess it, pray tell, do they?"

Father Couezy leaned his elbow on the armchair, and with a very faint smile, hardly visible around his eyes, and which seemed to be directed inward to himself, he whispered:

"Yes, but they are boasting."

When he raised his eyelids, the priest realized that he had not been understood. We all betrayed the expression of those who, after awaiting a serious announcement, are presented with a mere jest. Somewhat hurt, he proceeded to elaborate:

"If I were speaking here in front of confessors, I should have no need to say more. By this time, they would have understood my thought; but it is natural that you should not realize what intuition we must have in order to discern truth from falsehood, taking into consideration the reticence people have on facts they wish to conceal and at the same time the exaggerations they make with regard to vices they reveal."

"Exaggerations?"

"Very frequent. Just look at this situation: the confessional is a mysterious and awe-inspiring place only for the parishioners who remain away from it. The faithful who come there every Saturday, to kneel on a little bench, end up by acquiring a familiarity with it which you would never suspect. We reassure them: this is indispensable; without our encouragement, we would never know anything; but it often happens that our affability defeats its own purpose, and you are going to find out how."

The Father lowered his voice:

"At the age of eleven, the young girls start coming to us. First they confess their small sins: anger, selfishness, or laziness, for example; then suddenly, toward thirteen or fourteen, they arrive at the age of a new sin, the confession of which brings forth in them an extreme shame. Some of them can never resolve this shame to the point of speaking to us about it. Well, on the one hand, there is no indication that any of them correct this situation before marriage; on the other, they quickly come to understand that an undeserved absolution puts them in a state of impenitence more serious than simple impenitence itself; they struggle for a year or two, and then they desert the confessional and are lost to the church.

"On the other hand, we see girls who harden themselves with an ease that astonishes us. At the beginning, it is not a matter of immodesty on their part—not at all: it is piety, humility, submission, mortification. But all that goes through a metamorphosis. Strangely enough, the confession for them also becomes a pleasant habit. For it is true that in many instances the sin has its accomplices, so that the girl can use the occasion to narrate an adventure. If a friend, a cousin, a dancer is brought into it, then the confession becomes endless, and the more we repeat, 'My dear child, please, no more details,' the more we are told: 'My Father, I must explain everything, for unless I do you would not understand.' "

We looked at one another in utter silence.

"Well—and this is what I have been coming to—some girls who are excessively high-strung accuse themselves without moderation. They tell us things when there is nothing to tell. Perhaps unconsciously they look upon the sins of the soul as equally real as those that exist only in their minds. They attribute to themselves all sorts of vices that they would not dare commit. They depict for us a scene on a parlor sofa, something which may actually have begun there, but which terminated only in their imaginations. And that is what must be avoided by a newly initiated confessor, lest he judge the customs of his times more severely than is justified. Among the stories that are narrated, the most vicious are fictional. Again, let me emphasize, the confessional is not an extraterrestrial spot: there, as elsewhere, people boast about everything—even the evil that has not been committed."

The reverend changed his position on the armchair, assuming the air of a man who has just resolved a dispute.

However, we remained unconvinced. And the same opponent who had spoken before now spoke up again:

"I do not doubt, my dear Father, that you are a most expert

psychologist, and more skilled than any in penetrating into the
innermost secrets of man. People who are able to look beyond
the surface possess a gift as inestimable as it is rare, but nonetheless such a gift has its limitations, even among those who
possess it to the highest degree. On what do you base yourself
in unmasking the lie? On your judgment alone. There is neither proof nor witness in the confessional. Can you be positive
that, among these serious confessions in which you have no
faith, your judgment is not colored by a preconceived optimism? Do you imagine that a certain scene is apocryphal because it is so unlikely? Doctors who are preoccupied with psy-
chopathology accept as axiomatic that everything is possible.
You do not seem to be of this opinion."

The clergyman made a vague gesture while shaking his
head, as if to indicate: "That is not the question." Then, after
a calculated silence, he simply replied:

"I have my proof."

All of us asked him, by our expressions, for his proof. With a
sudden movement that indicated that he had arrived at a moment of decision, he crossed his legs and began:

"As a matter of fact, I think I can talk. A moment ago, I was
taking refuge in the inviolability of the secret confessional. But
once I had a confession from a woman that I can reveal without
sin. You will understand why presently."

He raised his head and leaned it against the top of the chair,
and with a circular but almost imperceptibly vain smile, which
seemed to be taking stock of the aroused curiosity, he finally
began his story:

"At a time that I shall not specify with precision, I was the
priest in a Parisian parish that I shall not further describe: it will
be sufficient for you to know that my church was very far from
St. Thomas and that my parishioners were very poor. As I
waited, one day, in front of the confessional, for the time when
my penitents were due to arrive, I saw a very elegant woman
approaching me, but with a fine elegance that made me certain
that she was not a parishioner of mine. Certain hats, for instance, are only worn in other sections of Paris. She had the
face and the general appearance of a woman of, let us say,

twenty-eight; other than that, there is no point for me to describe her to you. On my invitation, she knelt down, and here is
what I learned from her, after a preliminary warning that her
confession would be serious:

"Since the age of twelve she had not attended communion. At
seventeen, traveling alone with her father in the interior of
Italy, she arrived one day at a hotel in Pisa, which was so crowded
that the two of them were forced to accept a single room with
two beds: a fatal circumstance which led to their downfall.
From that point on, for the remainder of the trip, they no
longer registered as Mr. and Miss, but as Mr. and Mrs., so as to
preserve a freedom of movement for themselves. Up to this
point, there is nothing extraordinary in this story, is there?"

There were several exclamations.

"Upon their return," the reverend continued imperturba-
bly, "the situation continued, more secretive no doubt, for the
girl's mother was still alive, but the affair was uninterrupted.
Under the pretext of long walks taken side by side, the guilty
pair went to hide their errant ways in a rented apartment. I am
of course passing over the details, but the penitent did not
spare me anything.

"Suddenly, however, the father died. For two years following
his death, the moral health of the girl steadily deteriorated.
Her senses, awakened to the extreme, were but poorly contained within the limits of maternal surveillance. Several projected marriages failed to materialize. Nervous disorders in-
tervened, accompanied and followed by great suffering.

"One night, no longer able to resist the temptation of sin, she
arose, went into the bedroom of her younger brother (he was
then fourteen years old) and, without ruse or pretext, silent
and maddened with desire, she possessed him in his bed.

"She narrated this to me with the violence of the act still in
her voice, telling everything—struggles, refusals, prayers, and
the Christian refusal of the child, which could not win out in
the battle to govern his body, and finally his surrender.

"For two weeks she kept him with her; although less hostile,
he was nonetheless more and more tortured by guilt; and
finally the first confession of the little one tore him from her once

and for all. The more she begged him, the more he resisted her, locking himself in his room, and threatening to divulge everything.

"Well, gentlemen, she finally poisoned him. She took her instructions from a process that she found in a popular work, and obtained a slow poison that left no trace or pain, and which kills little by little. She watched her victim deteriorate and expire under her unpardoning eyes. Each day she mentally allowed him to make a choice between the crime and the tomb, without unmasking the hand which was holding the stone and which would finally let it fall upon him."

The eyes of the priest watched us with a tragic gleam, and remained for a time lit up with horror; and then, looking us straight in the face, took on a smile of open gaiety.

As for us, we had been listening to this story and had forgotten until the very last moment that it concerned a confession that was suspect. The tone of the narrator was so formally affirmative that we had lost sight of the occasion and the objective of the recital.

"What was truthful in the whole story?" someone asked.

"Not a word. Nothing, but nothing, not one scene, not one detail, not one person, not one fact, nothing, literally nothing, exactly what we mean when we say nothing. Six months after having received this confession, I changed my parish; the mother of the young girl became my penitent and I was invited to her home. There are such coincidences, aren't there? I learned successively that the daughter had never traveled in Italy; that her father had died when she was two years old; that she was an only child; and finally that her moral reputation was beyond reproach. Thus, not only was the story false, but it was physically impossible for it to have been true in either of its two parts, since both accomplices had not existed. Thus the narration that you have just heard—the first incest, the second, the hotel in Pisa, the apartment in Paris, the mourning, the violent scene, the confession of the young boy, the struggle, the poison—all that, and the thousand other details that I have not told you—all that, I repeat, had been born in the mind of a

Christian virgin who would not even go to a dance because she fled from any such temptation."

Father Couezy arose and, ending his long visit with a little Latin and a little malice, said:

"*Lasciva pagina vita proba.* With these four words, so clear and lucid, one can draw a moral portrait of a young girl."

Dylan Thomas
THE BURNING BABY

DYLAN THOMAS (1914-1953), born in Wales, has gained recognition as one of the greatest lyric poets and prose stylists of his time. His work consists of poetry, some of which he read for recordings, from which his voice emerges with incomparable power and beauty; plays, short stories, and other literary work that defies usual classification. Among his works, in addition to *Collected Poems*, are *Under Milk Wood*, *Portrait of the Artist as a Young Dog*, and *A Child's Christmas in Wales*. The short story, *The Burning Baby*, appeared in his collection entitled *Adventures in the Skin Trade*.

They said that Rhys was burning his baby when a gorse bush broke into fire on the summit of the hill. The bush, burning merrily, assumed to them the sad white features and the rickety limbs of the vicar's burning baby. What the wind had not blown away of the baby's ashes, Rhys Rhys had sealed in a stone jar. With his own dust lay the baby's dust, and near him the dust of his daughter in a coffin of white wood.

They heard his son howl in the wind. They saw him walking over the hill, holding a dead animal up to the light of the stars. They saw him in the valley shadows as he moved, with the motion of a man cutting wheat, over the brows of the fields. In a sanatorium he coughed his lung into a basin, stirring his fingers delightedly in the blood. What moved with invisible scythe through the valley was a shadow and a handful of shadows cast by the grave sun.

The brush burned out, and the face of the baby fell away with the smoking leaves.

It was, they said, on a fine sabbath morning in the middle of the summer that Rhys Rhys fell in love with his daughter. The gorse that morning had burst into flames. Rhys Rhys, in clerical

black, had seen the flames shoot up to the sky, and the bush on
the edge of the hill burn red as God among the paler burning
of the grass. He took his daughter's hand as she lay in the garden hammock, and told her that he loved her. He told her that
she was more beautiful than her dead mother. Her hair smelled
of mice, her teeth came over her lip, and the lids of her eyes
were red and wet. He saw her beauty come out of her like a
stream of sap. The folds of her dress could not hide from him
the shabby nakedness of her body. It was not her bone, nor her
flesh, nor her hair that he found suddenly beautiful. The poor
soil shudders under the sun, he said. He moved his hand up
and down her arm. Only the awkward and the ugly, only the
barren bring forth fruit. The flesh of her arm was red with
the smoothing of his hand. He touched her breast. From the
touch of her breast he knew each inch of flesh upon her. Why
do you touch me there? she said.

In the church that morning he spoke of the beauty of the
harvest, of the promise of the standing corn and the promise in
the sharp edge of the scythe as it brings the corn low and whis-
tles through the air before it cuts into the ripeness. Through the
open windows at the end of the aisles, he saw the yellow fields
upon the hillside and the smudge of heather on the meadow
borders. The world was ripe.

The world is ripe for the second coming of the son of man,
he said aloud.

But it was not the ripeness of God that glistened from the
hill. It was the promise and the ripeness of the flesh, the good
flesh, the mean flesh, flesh of his daughter, flesh, flesh, the flesh
of the voice of thunder howling before the death of man.

That night he preached of the sins of the flesh. O God in
the image of our flesh, he prayed.

His daughter sat in the front pew, and stroked her arm. She
would have touched her breast where he had touched it, but
the eyes of the congregation were upon her.

Flesh, flesh, flesh, said the vicar.

His son, scouting in the fields for a mole's hill or the signs of
a red fox, whistling to the birds and patting the calves as they
stood at their mother's sides, came upon a dead rabbit sprawl-

ing on a stone. The rabbit's head was riddled with pellets, the dogs had torn open its belly, and the marks of a ferret's teeth were upon its throat. He lifted it gently up, tickling it behind the ears. The blood from its head dropped on his hand. Through the rip in the belly, its intestines had dropped out and coiled on the stone. He held the little body close to his jacket, and ran home through the fields, the rabbit dancing against his waistcoat. As he reached the gate of the vicarage, the worshipers dribbled out of church. They shook hands and raised their hats, smiling at the poor boy with his long green hair, his ass's ears, and death buttoned under his jacket. He was always the poor boy to them.

Rhys Rhys sat in his study, the stem of his pipe stuck between his flybuttons, the Bible unopened upon his knees. The day of God was over, and the sun, like another sabbath, went down behind the hills. He lit the lamp, but his own oil burned brighter. He drew the curtains, shutting out the unwelcome night. But he opened his own heart up, and the bald pulse that beat there was a welcome stranger. He had not felt love like this since the woman who scratched him, seeing the woman witch in his male eyes, had fallen into his arms and kissed him, and whispered Welsh words as he took her. She had been the mother of his daughter and had died in her pains, stealing, when she was dead, the son of his second love, and leaving the green-haired changeling in its place. Merry with desire, Rhys Rhys cast the Bible on the floor. He reached for another book, and read, in the lamplit darkness, of the old woman who had deceived the devil. The devil is poor flesh, said Rhys Rhys.

His son came in, bearing the rabbit in his arms. The lank, red-coated boy was a flesh out of the past. The skin of the unburied death patched to his bones, the smile of the changeling on his mouth, and the hair of the sea rising from his scalp, he stood before Rhys Rhys. A ghost of his mother, he held the rabbit gently to his breast, rocking it to and fro. Cunningly, from under half-closed lids, he saw his father shrink away from the vision of death. Be off with you, said Rhys Rhys. Who was this green stranger to carry in death and rock it, like a baby un-

der a warm shawl of fur, before him? For a minute the flesh of
the world lay still; the old terror set in; the waters of the
breast dried up; the nipples grew through the sand. Then he
drew his hand over his eyes, and only the rabbit remained, a
little sack of flesh, half empty, swaying in the arms of his son.
Be off, he said. The boy held the rabbit close, and rocked it,
and tickled it again.

Changeling, said Rhys Rhys. He is mine, said the boy, I'll
peel him and keep the skull. His room in the attic was crowded
with skulls and dried pelts, and little bones in bottles.

Give it to me.

He is mine.

Rhys Rhys tore the rabbit away, and stuffed it deep in the
pockets of his smoking coat. When his daughter came in, dressed
and ready for bed, with a candle in her hand, Rhys Rhys had
death in his pocket.

She was timid, for his touch still ached on her arm and
breast but she bent unblushing over him. Saying goodnight, she
kissed him, and he blew her candle out. She was smiling as he
lowered the wick of the lamp.

Step out of your shift, said he. Shiftless, she stepped toward
his arms.

I want the little skull, said a voice in the dark.

From his room at the top of the house, through the webs
on the windows, and over the furs and the bottles, the boy saw a
mile of green hill running away into the darkness of the first
dawn. Summer storm in the heat of the rain, flooring the grassy
mile, had left some new morning brightness, out of the dead
night, in each reaching root.

Death took hold of his sister's legs as she walked through the
calf-deep heather up the hill. He saw the high grass at her
thighs. And the blades of the upgrowing wind, out of the four
windsmells of the manuring dead, might drive through the
soles of her feet, up the veins of the legs and stomach, into
her womb and her pulsing heart. He watched her climb. She
stood, gasping for breath, on a hill of the wider hill, tapping
the wall of her bladder, fondling her matted chest (for the

hair grew on her as on a grown man), feeling the heart in
her wrist, loving her coveted thinness. She was to him as ugly
as the sowfaced woman of Llareggub who had taught him the
terrors of the flesh. He remembered the advances of that unlovely woman. She blew out his candle as he stepped toward her on the night the great hail had fallen and he had hidden in her rotting house from the cruelty of the weather. Now,
half a mile off, his sister stood in the morning, and the vermin
of the hill might spring upon her as she stood, uncaring, round-
ing the angles of her ugliness. He smiled at the thought of the
devouring rats, and looked around the room for a bottle to hold
her heart. Her skull, fixed by a socket to the nail above his bed,
would be a smiling welcome to the first pains of waking.

But he saw Rhys Rhys stride up the hill, and the bowl of his
sister's head, fixed invisibly above his sheets, crumbled away.
Standing straight by the side of a dewy tree, his sister beckoned. Up went Rhys Rhys through the calf-deep heather, the
death in the grass, over the boulders and up through the reaching ferns to where she stood. He took her hand. The two
shadows linked hands, and climbed together to the top of the
hill. The boy saw them go, and turned his face to the wall as they
vanished, in one dull shadow, over the edge, and down to the
dingle at the west foot of the lovers' alley.

Later, he remembered the rabbit. He ran downstairs and
found it in the pocket of the smoking coat. He held death
against him, tasting a cough of blood upon his tongue as he
climbed, contented, back to the bright bottles and the wall of
heads.

In the first dew of light he saw his father clamber for her
white hand. She who was his sister walked with a swollen belly
over the hill. She touched him between the legs, and he
sighed and sprang at her. But the nerves of her face mixed
with the quiver in his thighs, and she shot from him. Rhys
Rhys, over the bouldered rim, led her to terror. He sighed
and sprang at her. She mixed with him in the fourth and the
fifth terrors of the flesh. Said Rhys Rhys, Your mother's eyes. It

was not her eyes that saw him proud before her, nor the eyes in
her thumb. The lashes of her fingers lifted. He saw the ball
under the nail.

It was, they said, on a fine sabbath morning in the early
spring that she bore him a male child. Brought to bed of her
father, she screamed for an anaesthetic as the knocking head
burst through. In her gown of blood she slept until twilight,
and a star burst bloody through each ear. With a scissors and
rag, Rhys Rhys attended her, and, gazing on the shriveled features and the hands like the hands of a mole, he gently took
the child away, and his daughter's breast cried out and ran
into the mouth of the surrounding shadows. The shadow
pouted for the milk and the binding cottons. The child spat
in his arms, the noise of the running air was blind in its ears,
and the deaf light died from its eyes.

Rhys Rhys, with the dead child held against him, stepped
into the night, hearing the mother moan in her sleep and the
deadly shadow, filled sick with milk, flowing around the
house. He turned his face toward the hills. A shadow walked
close to him and, silent in the shadow of a full tree, the
changeling waited. He made an image for the moon, and the
flesh of the moon fell away, leaving a star-eyed skull. Then
with a smile he ran back over the lawns and into the crying
house. Halfway up the stairs, he heard his sister die. Rhys
Rhys climbed on.

On the top of the hill he laid the baby down, and propped it
against the heather. Death propped the dark flowers. The
baby stiffened in the rigor of the moon. Poor flesh, said Rhys
Rhys as he pulled at the dead heather and furze. Poor angle, he
said to the listening mouth of the baby. The fruit of the
flesh falls with the worm from the tree. Conceiving the worm,
the bark crumbles. There lay the poor star of flesh that had
dropped, like the bead of a woman's milk, through the nipples
of a wormy tree.

He stacked the torn heathers in a circle. On the head of the
purple stack, he piled the dead grass. A stack of death, the

heather grew as tall as he, and loomed at last over his windy hair.

Behind a boulder moved the accompanying shadow, and the shadow of the boy was printed under the fiery flank of a tree. The shadow marked the boy, and the boy marked the bones of the naked baby under their chilly cover, and how the grass scraped on the bald skull, and where his father picked out a path in the cancerous growths of the silent circle. He saw Rhys Rhys pick up the baby and place it on the top of the stack, saw the head of a burning match, and heard the crackle of the bush, breaking like a baby's arm.

The stack burst into flame. Rhys Rhys, before the red eye of the creeping fire, stretched out his arms and beckoned the shadow from the stones. Surrounded by shadows, he prayed before the flaming stack, and the sparks of the heather blew past his smile. Burn, child, poor flesh, mean flesh, flesh, flesh, sick sorry flesh, flesh of the foul womb, burn back to dust, he prayed.

And the baby caught fire. The flames curled round its mouth and blew upon the shrinking gums. Flames round its red cord lapped its little belly till the raw flesh fell upon the heather.

A flame touched its tongue. Eeeeeh, cried the burning baby, and the illuminated hill replied.

Maxim Gorky

THE HERMIT

MAXIM GORKY (1868-1936), born in Russia, was the best-known intellectual and writer of the Russian Revolution. Gorky was a pen name for Alexey Maximovich Peshkov, but under the name of Gorky he established a world-wide reputation as dramatist, short story writer, and novelist. He joined the Russian revolutionary movement in his youth, and became a friend of Lenin during the exile period between the revolutions of 1905 and 1917. Among his works for which Gorky is still well known are *Mother, Childhood,* and *The Lower Depths.* His works are deeply concerned with poverty and with those difficulties of life which he felt were imposed upon man by an outmoded social system. *The Hermit* appears in various collections of the short stories of Gorky.

The forest ravine slopes gently down to the yellow waters of the Oka; a brook rushes along its bottom, hiding in the grass; above the ravine, unnoticed by day and tremulous by night, flows the blue river of the sky—the stars play in it like golden minnows. Rank, tangled underbrush grows on the southeastern bank of the ravine. Under the steep side of it, in the thicket, a cave is dug out, closed by a door made of branches, ingeniously tied together; before the door is an earthen platform about seven feet square, buttressed by cobbles. From it, heavy boulders descend in a stairway toward the brook. Three young trees grow in front of the cave: a lime, a birch, and a maple.

Everything around the cave is made sturdily and with care, as though it were fashioned to last a lifetime. The interior has the same air of sturdiness: the sides and the vault are covered with mats made of willow withies; the mats are plastered with clay mixed with the silt of the brook; a small stove rises to the left of the entrance; in the corner is an altar, covered by heavy matting which does for brocade; on the altar, in an iron sconce, is an oil burner; its bluish flame flickers in the dusk and is hardly visible.

Three black icons stand behind the altar; bundles of new bast shoes hang on the walls; strips of bast lie about on the floor. The cave is permeated with the sweet smell of dry herbs.

The owner of this abode is an old man of middle height, thickset, but crumpled and misshapen. His face, red as a brick, is hideous. A deep scar runs across the left cheek from ear to chin, giving a twist to his mouth and lending it an expression of painful scorn. The dark eyes are ravaged by trachoma; they are without lashes and have red scars instead of lids; the hair on the head has fallen out in tufts and there are two bald patches on the bumpy skull, a small one on the crown, and another which has laid bare the left ear. In spite of all this the old man is spry and nimble as a polecat; his naked, disfigured eyes have a kindly look; when he laughs, the blemishes of his face almost vanish in the soft abundance of his wrinkles. He wears a good shirt of unbleached linen, blue calico trousers, and slippers made of cord. His legs are wrapped in hareskins instead of leggings.

I came to him on a bright May day and we made friends at once. He had me stay the night, and on my second visit told me the story of his life.

"I was a sawyer," he said, lying under an elder-bush, having pulled off his shirt to warm his chest, muscular as a youngster's, in the sun. "For seventeen years I sawed logs; see the mess a saw made of my face! That's what they called me, Savel the Saw-yer. Sawing is no light job, my friend—you stand there, waving your hands about in the sky, a net over your face, logs over your head and the sawdust so thick you can't see, ugh! I was a gay lad, a playful one, and I lived like a tumbler. There is, you know, a certain type of pigeon: they soar as high up as they can into the sky, into the utmost depth and there they fold their wings, tuck their heads under them—and bang! down they come! Some get killed that way, hitting the roofs, or the ground. Well, that's what I was like. Gay and harmless, a blessed one; women, girls were as fond of me as of sugar, 'pon my word! What a life it was! It does one good to remember it. . . ."

And rolling from side to side he laughed the clear laughter of youth, except for a slight rattle in the throat, and the brook echoed his laugh. The wind breathed warmly; golden reflections glided on the velvety surface of the spring foliage.

"Well, let's have a go at it, friend," Savel suggested. "Bring it on!"

I went to the brook, where a bottle of vodka had been put to cool and we each had a glass, following it up with pretzels and fish. The old man chuckled with rapture.

"A fine invention that, drink!" And passing his tongue over his gray, tousled mustache: "A fine thing! Can't do with a lot of it, but in small quantities it's great! They say the devil was first to make vodka. Well, I'll say thanks even to the devil for a good thing."

He half-closed his eyes, remained silent for a moment and then exclaimed, indignantly:

"Yes, they did hurt me to the core, all the same, they did. Ah, friend, how people have grown into the habit of hurting one another, it's a shame! Conscience lives among us like a homeless pup, it does! It isn't welcome anywhere. Well, never mind, I'll go on with my story. I married and all was as it should be; the wife was called Natalia, a beautiful, soft creature. I got on with her all right; she was a bit of a philanderer, but I'm not all too virtuous myself, not exactly a stay-at-home, and when there is a nicer, kinder woman about, to her I go. That is all only too human, there's no running away from it, and in one's lusty years, what better can one do? At times when I returned home bringing some money or other goods with me, people would laugh! 'Savel, you should tie your wife's skirts before you leave your house!' Jeering, they were. Well, for decency's sake, I'd beat her a bit and then give her a present to make up for it and just scold her gently: 'You fool,' I'd say, 'why do you make people laugh at me? Am I not your pal, instead of your enemy?' She'd cry, of course, and say they were lying. I know, too, that people are fond of lies, but you can't fool me, all the same: the night gives away the truth about a woman—you can feel it, at night, if she's been in another man's arms or not."

Something rustled in the bushes behind him.

"Ps-sh!" the old man shook a branch of the elder. "A hedge-hog lives right here, I pricked my foot on it the other day as I went to wash in the brook; I did not see it in the grass and the needle went straight into my toe."

He smiled as he looked at the bush and then, straightening himself out, went on.

"Yes, friend. So I was saying how deeply they had hurt me, yes, how deeply. I had a daughter, Tasha, Tatyana. I may say in a word, without boasting, she was a joy to the whole world, that daughter. A star. I used to dress her up in fine clothes—a heavenly beauty she was when she came out on a holiday. Her gait, her bearing, her eyes . . . Our teacher Kuzmin—Trunk was his nickname, for he was a clumsy-looking chap—called her by some whimsical name, and when he got drunk he would weep and beg me to take care of her. So I did. But luck had always favored me—and that never makes one popular with other men; it just breeds envy. So the rumor was spread, that Tasha and I . . ."

He fidgeted uneasily on the grass, took his shirt from the bush, put it on and carefully buttoned up the collar. His face twitched nervously, he pressed his lips together, and the sparse bristles of his gray brows descended on the naked eyes.

Twilight was setting in. There was a freshness in the air. A quail was crying shrilly close by: "Pit-pit . . . wet my lip . . ." The old man was peering down into the ravine.

"Well, so that set the ball rolling. Kuzmin, the priest, the clerk, some of the men and most of the women began wagging their tongues, hissing and hooting, and hauling a man over the coals. It is always a treat for us to bait a man; we love it. Tasha sat weeping, unable to leave the house, for fear of the jeering of street urchins—everybody was having the time of their lives. so I said to Tasha, 'Come, let us leave.' "

"And your wife?"

"The wife?" the old man repeated with astonishment. "But

she was dead by then. She just gave a sigh and died one night. Yes—yes. That was long before all this happened. Tasha was only twelve. . . . She was my enemy, a bad woman, unfaithful."

"But you were praising her a moment ago," I reminded him. This did not embarrass him at all.

He scratched his neck, lifted his beard with his palm and gazing at it, said calmly, "Well, what if I did praise her? No one remains bad all his life, and even a bad person is often worthy of praise. A human being is not a stone and even a stone changes with time. Do not, however, get any wrong ideas into your head—she died a natural death, all right. It must have been her heart; her heart played tricks on her. Sometimes at night we would be having a bit of fun and she would suddenly go off in a dead faint. Quite terrible it was!"

His soft husky voice had a melodious sound; it mingled tirelessly and intimately in the warm evening air with the smell of grass, the sighs of the wind, the rustle of leaves, the soft patter of the brook on the pebbles. Had he kept still, the night would not have been so complete, so beautiful, so sweet to the soul.

Savel spoke with a remarkable ease, showing no effort in finding the right words, dressing up his thoughts lovingly, as a little girl does her dolls. I had listened to many a Russian talker, men who, intoxicated with flowery words, often, almost always, lose the fine thread of truth in the intricate web of speech. This one spun his yarn with such convincing simplicity, with such limpid sincerity, that I feared to interrupt him with questions. Watching the play of his words, I realized that the old man was the possessor of living gems, able to conceal all filthy and criminal lies with their bewitching power; I realized all that and nevertheless yielded to the magic of his speech.

"The whole dirty business began then, my friend: a doctor was summoned; he examined Tasha thoroughly with his shameless eyes, and he had another fop with him, a baldish man with gold buttons—an investigator, I suppose—asking questions as to who and when? She just kept silent; she was so ashamed. They arrested me and took me to the district prison.

There I sat. The bald one says to me, 'Confess and you'll get off lightly!

"So I reply obligingly, 'Let me go to Kiev, Your Honor, to the holy relics, and pray for the forgiveness of my sins!'

" 'Ah,' he said, 'now you've confessed all right!' Believing he'd caught me, the bald cat! I hadn't confessed anything, of course, just dropped the words from sheer boredom. I was very bored in jail, uncomfortable, too, what with the thieves and murderers and other foul people around; besides, I couldn't help wondering what they were doing to Tasha. The whole blasted business lasted over a year before the trial came. And then, behold, Tasha appeared at it, with gloves and smart little boots and all —very unusual! A blue frock like a cloud—her soul shining through it. All the jury staring at her and the crowd and all of it just like a dream, my friend. At Tanya's side—Madame Antzyferova, our lady of the manor, a woman sharp as a pike, sly as a fox. Hm, I thought to myself—this one will put me to the rack and worry me to death."

He laughed with great good humor.

"She had a son, Matvey Alexevich—I always believed him to be a bit wrong in the head—a dull youth. Not a drop of blood in his face, a pair of spectacles on his nose, hair down to his shoulders, no beard to speak of, and all he ever did was to write down songs and fairy tales in a little book. A heart of gold—he'd give you anything you asked for. The peasants around all made use of it: one would ask for a scythe, the other for some timber, the third for bread, taking anything going whether they wanted it or not. I would say to him: 'Why do you give everything away, Alexevich? Your fathers and grandfathers piled it all up, grew rich, stripped people to the skin regardless of sin, and you give it all away without rhyme or reason. Aren't you wasting human labor?'

" 'I feel I must do it!' he said. Not a very clever lad, but gentle-natured, anyway. Later on, the Deputy Governor packed him off to China—he was rude to the Governor, so to China he had to go.

"Well—then came the trial. My counsel spoke for two hours, waving his hands about. Tasha stuck up for me, too."

"But was there ever actually anything between you two?"

He thought for a moment as though trying to remember, then said, unconcernedly watching the flight of a hawk with his naked eyes, "That happens sometimes—between fathers and daughters. There was even a saint once who lived with two of them, and the prophets Abraham and Isaac were born to them. I will not say I did so myself. I played about with her, that is true, in the long, dreary, winter nights. Dreary they are indeed, all the more so for one who is used to tramping around the world —going here and there and everywhere, as was my case. I used to make up stories for her—I know hundreds of fairy tales. Well, you know, a tale is a thing of fancy. And it warms up the blood. And Tasha . . ." He shut his eyes and sighed, shaking his head.

"An extraordinary beauty she was! And I was extraordinary with women, mad about them, I was."

The old man became excited and went on with pride and rapture, choking over his words, "See friend: I'm now a man of sixty-seven and still I can get all the pleasure I want out of any woman, that's the truth! About five years after all this happened how many a wench would beg me, 'Savel, dear, do let me go, I'm quite played out.' I'd take pity on her and do so and she would come back again in a few days. 'Well, so here you are again, are you?' I would say. A female, my friend, is a great thing, the whole world raves about her—the beast and the bird and the tiny moth—all just live for her alone. What else is there to live for?"

"What, anyway, did your daughter say at the trial?"

"Tasha? She made up a story—or perhaps it was the Antzyferova woman who suggested it to her (I'd once done her a service of sorts)—that she had brought the injury upon herself and that I was not to blame. Well, I was let off. It's all a put-up job with them, a thing of no account, just to show what a watch they keep on the laws. It's all a fraud, all these laws, orders and papers; it's all unnecessary. Let everyone live as he pleases, that would be cheaper and pleasanter. Here am I, living and not getting into anyone's way and not pushing forward."

"And what about murderers?"

"They should be killed," Savel decided. "The man who kills should be done away with on the spot with no nonsense about it! A man is not a mosquito or a fly; he is no worse than you, you scum. . . ."

"And—thieves?"

"That's an odd idea! Why should there be any thieves, if there is nothing to steal? Now, what would you take from me? I haven't any too much, so there is no envy, no greed. Why should there be any thieves? There are thieves where there is a surplus of things; when he sees plenty he just grabs a bit. . . ."

It was dark by now; night had poured into the ravine. An owl hooted three times. The old man hearkened to its eerie cries and said with a smile:

"It lives close by in a hollow tree. Sometimes it gets caught by the sun, can't hide in time, and just stays out in the light. I pass by and stick out my tongue at it. It can't see a thing, just sits quite still. Lucky if the smaller birds don't catch sight of it."

I asked how he had come to be a hermit.

"Just like that: wandered and wandered around and then stopped short. All because of Tasha. The Antzyferova woman played me a trick there—did not let me see Tasha after the trial. 'I know the whole truth,' she said, 'and you should be grateful to me for escaping hard labor, but I won't give you back your daughter.' A fool she was, of course. I hovered around for a time, but no, there was nothing doing! So off I went—to Kiev and Siberia, earned a lot of money there and came home. The Antzyferova woman had been run over and killed by a train, and as for Tasha, she had been married off to a surgeon's assistant in Kursk. To Kursk I went, but the surgeon's assistant had left for Persia, for Uzun. I pushed on to Tzaritzyn, from there by ship to Uzun—but Tasha had died. I saw the man— a red-haired, red-nosed, cheerful lad. A drunkard, he turned out to be.

" 'Are you her father, maybe?' he asked.

" 'No,' I said, 'nothing like that, but I'd seen her father in Siberia.' I did not wish to confide in a stranger. Well, so then I went to New Mt. Athos, almost stayed there—a fine place! But after a while—I decided I did not like it. The sea roars and rolls the stones about; the Abkhazians come and go; the ground is uneven, mountains all around; and the nights, as black as though you'd been drowned in pitch. And the heat! So I came here, and here I've been for nine years and they haven't been wasted. I've built all this, planted a birch the first year, after three years a maple, then a lime—see them? And I'm a great consoler to the people round here, my friend—you come and watch me on Sunday!"

He hardly ever mentioned God's name—while as a rule it is always on the lips of people of his kind. I asked whether he prayed a lot.

"No, not too much," he said thoughtfully, shutting his naked eyes. "I did so at first, a lot; for hours would I kneel down and keep on crossing myself. My arms were used to a saw, and so they didn't get tired, or my back either. I can bow down a thousand times without a murmur, but the bones in my knees can't stand it: they ache. And then I thought to myself: what am I praying for, and why? I've got all I want, people respect me— why bother God? He's got His own job to do, why trouble Him? Human rubbish should be kept away from Him. He takes care of us and do we take care of Him? No. And also: He is there for people of importance; where will He get time for small fry like me? So now I just come out of the cave on sleepless nights, sit down somewhere or other and, gazing into God's heaven, wonder to myself: 'And how is He getting along, up there?' This, friend, is a pleasant occupation; I can't tell you how fine; it's like dreaming awake. And one doesn't grow weary as at prayer. I don't ask Him for anything and I never advise others to do so, but when I see they need it, I tell them: 'Have pity on God!' You come along and see how helpful I can be to Him and to people. . . ."

He did not boast, but spoke with the calm assurance of a craftsman confident of his skill. His naked eyes smiled gaily, toning down the ugliness of his disfigured face.

"How I live in winter? It's all right, my cave is warm even in winter. It's only that in wintertime people find it hard to come

because of the snow; sometimes for two or three days I have
to go without bread. Once it so happened that I hadn't had a
crumb in my mouth for over eight days. I felt so weak that
even my memory went. Then a young girl came and helped me
out. She was a novice in a convent, but she has got married to a
teacher since. It was I who advised her to do so; I said: 'What
are you fooling about like this for, Lenka? What good is it to
you?'

" 'I'm an orphan,' she said.

" 'Well, go and get married and that will be the end of the
orphan.' And to the teacher, Pevtzov, a good, kind man, I said:
'Have a good look at that girl, Misha.' Yes. So very soon they got
together. And they're getting along fine. Well, in wintertime,
I also go to the Sarov or Optina or the Diveyev monastery—
there are many of them hereabouts. But the monks don't like me,
they all urge me to take the hood—it would be a profit for them,
of course, and serve as bait to people, but I have no wish for
that. I'm alive; it does not suit me. As though I were a saint! I'm
just a quiet man, friend."

Laughing and rubbing his thighs with his hands, he said with
exultation, "But with nuns, I'm always welcome. They just love
me, they certainly do! That is no boast; it's the truth. I know
women through and through, friend, any sort, whether a lady or
a merchant's wife, and as for a peasant woman, she's as clear to
me as my own soul. I just look into her eyes and I know everything, all that troubles her. I could tell you such tales about
them. . . ."

And again he invited persuasively: "Come and see how I
talk to them. And now, let's have another little go."

He drank. Closing his eyes tightly and shaking his head, he
said with fresh rapture, "It does one good, that drink!"

The short spring night was visibly melting away; the air
grew cool. I suggested that we light a fire.

"No, what for? Are you cold? I, an old man, don't feel the
cold, and you do? That's too bad. Go to the cave, then, and lie
down there. You see, friend, if we light a fire, all sorts of small
living things will come flying here and will get burnt in the
flames. And I don't like that. Fire to them is like a trap, leading

them to their death. The sun—the father to all fire, kills no one, but why should we, for the sake of our bones, burn up these little folk? No, no. . . ."

I agreed with him, and went into the cave, while he remained outside fussing about for some time; he went off somewhere, splashed about in the brook, and I could hear his gentle voice:

"Phuit . . . don't be afraid, you little fool. . . . Phueeet . . ."

Then he broke into a soft tremulous song, as though lulling someone to sleep.

When I woke up and walked out of the cave, Savel, crouching on the ground, was deftly weaving a bast shoe and saying to a chaffinch singing vehemently in the bushes:

"That's it, go on, buzz on, the day is yours! Slept well, friend? Go and have a wash, I've put the kettle to boil for tea and I'm waiting for you."

"Haven't you had any sleep yourself?"

"I'll have time to sleep when I die, friend."

A blue May sky shone over the ravine.

I came to see him again about three weeks later, on a Saturday evening, and was welcomed as an old, close friend.

"I'd been thinking already: why, the man has forgotten all about me! Ah, and you've brought some of that good drink as well. Thanks, many thanks! And some wheat bread? So fresh, too. What a kind lad indeed! People must surely like you; they love kind folk; they know what's good for them! Sausage? No, I have no liking for that, that's dog's food, you can keep it for yourself if you wish; but fish I love. This fish, it's a sweet fish, comes from the Caspian Sea, I know all about it. Why, you must have brought food for more than a ruble, you queer fellow! Well, never mind, many thanks!"

He seemed to me still more alive, more cordially radiant—all burdens seemed to fall away from me; I felt lighthearted and gay, and I thought to myself, "Devil take it, I believe I actually am in the presence of a happy man!"

Nimble and gentle, he performed little domestic duties, storing away my gifts, while he scattered like sparks those endearing, bewitching Russian words, which act like wine on the soul.

The movements of his sturdy body, swift as the movements of an adder, harmonized beautifully with the precision of his speech. In spite of the mutilated face, the eyes without lashes —torn apart as though on purpose to enable him to see more widely and more boldly—he seemed almost handsome, with the beauty of a life whose confusion was multi-colored and intricate. And his outward disfigurement gave a particular emphasis to that beauty.

Again, almost the whole night through, his gray little beard fluttered and the meager mustache bristled as he burst into uncontrollable laughter, opening wide the crooked mouth, in which gleamed the sharp white teeth of a polecat. At the bottom of the ravine it was still; the wind was stirring above; the tops of the pine trees rocked; the harsh foliage of the oaks rustled; the blue river of the skies seemed violently disturbed —covered by a gray foam of clouds.

"Sh . . ." he exclaimed, softly raising his hand in warning. I hearkened—all was quiet.

"A fox is prowling about—it has a hole here. Many hunting people have asked me: is there a fox near by, grandfather? And I lie to them! Foxes? What should foxes be doing here? I have no liking for hunters, to the dickens with them!"

I had noticed by then that the old man often wanted to break out into real foul language, but realizing that it was out of character for him to do so, he resorted to milder expressions.

After a glass of cowslip vodka, he said, half-closing his lacerated eyes, "What tasty fish this is—thank you kindly for it—I do love everything tasty. . . ."

His attitude toward God was not very clear to me and cautiously I tried to broach the subject. At first he answered with the hackneyed words of pilgrims, cloister habitues, and professional holy men, but I felt that this manner was in fact irksome to him, and I was not mistaken. Drawing closer to me and lowering his voice, he suddenly began to talk with more animation, "I'll tell you this, friend, about a little Frenchie, a French priest—a little man, black as a starling, with a spot shaved bare on his head, golden spectacles on his nose, tiny little hands, like a little girl's, and all of him like a toy of God's. I met him at the Pochaev monastery; that is a long way off, over there!"

He waved his hand toward the East, in the direction of India, stretched out his legs more comfortably, and continued, propping his back against some stones:

"Polish people living all around—a foreign soil, not our own. I was palavering with a monk one day, who thought people should get punished more often; so I just smiled and said that if one was to begin punishing rightly, all men would have to go through it, and then there would be time for nothing else, no other work done but just flaying one another. The monk got quite angry with me, called me a fool, and walked away. Then the little priest, who had been sitting in the corner, nestled up to me and started telling me, oh, great things. I tell you, friend, he seemed to me like a kind of John the Baptist. He wasn't quite easy in his speech, for not all our words can be put into a foreign tongue, but his big soul shone through all right.

" 'I see you do not agree with that monk,' he said, so polite-like, 'and you are right. God is not a fiend; He is a dear friend to people; but this is what has happened, owing to His kindness; He's melted in our tearful life like sugar in water, and the water is filthy and full of dregs, so that we do not feel Him any more; we do not get the taste of Him in our lives. Nevertheless, He is spread over the whole world and lives in every soul as the purest spark; we should seek Him in man, collect Him into a single ball, and when the divine spark of all these living souls is gathered into this powerful whole—the devil will come and say to the Lord: 'Thou art great, my God, and Thy might is measureless—I didn't know this before, so pray forgive me! I won't struggle with Thee any more now—please take me into Thy service.' "

The old man spoke with emphasis, and his dilated pupils gleamed strangely in his dark face.

"And then the end will come to all evil and wickedness and human strife, and people will return to their God, like rivers flowing into the ocean."

He choked over his words, slapped his knees, and continued joyfully, with a hoarse little laugh, "All this came as such balm to my heart; it struck a light in my soul—I didn't know how to say it to the Frenchie. 'Might I be allowed to embrace you, you image of Christ?' I said. So we embraced one another and started crying, both of us. And how we cried! Like small children, finding their parents after a long parting. We were both quite old, you know; the bristle round his shaven spot was gray, too. So I told him then and there: 'You're like John the Baptist to me, Christ's image.' Christ's image is what I called him; funny, isn't it, when I told you he resembled a starling! The monk, Vitaly, kept abusing him and saying: 'A nail, that's what you are.' And true it was indeed, he was like a nail, as sharp as one. Of course, friend, you do not understand this sweet joy of mine; you can read and write; you know all about everything; but I, at that time, went about as one blind—I was able to see all right, but just couldn't make out: where is God? And all of a sudden this man comes and reveals it all to me—just think, what that meant to me! I told you only a little of what he said to me—we talked until dawn; he went on and on; but I can recall only the kernel of it, I've lost all the shell. . . ."

He stopped speaking and sniffed the air like an animal, "Guess it's going to rain, eh?"

He sniffed again, and then decided contentedly, "No, it won't rain, it's just the night's dampness. I'll tell you, friend, all these Frenchmen and inhabitants of other lands, they are people of high intelligence. In the province of Kharkov—or was it Poltava —an Englishman, who managed the estate of a great lord, kept watching me; then he called me into the room one day and said: 'Here's a secret parcel, old man; will you take it to such and such a place, and hand it over to such and such a person— can you do it?' Well—why not? It did not matter to me where I went, and it was about sixty miles to the place indicated. I took the parcel, tied it up with a string, thrust it in my bosom and off I went. On getting to the place, I begged to be allowed to see the landowner. Of course, they gave it to me in the neck— they beat me up and chased me away. 'Curse you,' I thought to myself, 'may you blow up and burst!' Well, the wrapping of the

parcel must have got damp from my sweat, and it came apart—
and what do you think I saw peeping through it—money! Big
money! Maybe three hundred rubles. I got scared; someone
might notice it and steal it at night. What was I to do? There I
was, sitting in the field, on the road, under a tree—when a carriage comes up with a gentleman sitting in it. Maybe that's the
man I want—I thought. So I stood on the road waving my staff.
The coachman lashed out at me with the whip, but the gentleman told him to stop and even scolded him a bit. Yes, he was
the right man. 'Here is a secret parcel for you,' I said.

" 'Right,' he replied. 'Sit down next to me and we'll drive
back.' He brought me into a luxurious room and asked whether
I knew the contents of the parcel. So I told him I thought it
was money, as I'd seen it peep through the sweaty paper. 'And
who gave it to you?' he asked. I couldn't tell; that would have
been against orders. He started shouting and threatening to
send me to prison.

" 'Well,' I said, 'do so, if you think you must.' He went on
threatening, but it did not work. I would not be frightened.
Suddenly the door opened—and there on the threshold stood
the Englishman roaring with laughter! Now, what did that
mean? He'd arrived by rail earlier in the day and had sat waiting: would I come or would I not? They both knew all along
when I arrived and saw the servants chase me away; they'd
given them the orders to do so, not to beat me, but just to
throw me out. It was a joke, don't you see, to test whether I
would deliver the money or not. Well—they seemed pleased
that I'd brought it, told me to go and wash, gave me clean clothes
and asked me to come and eat with them. . . . Yes, friend . . .
I must say, we did have a meal! The wine too—you just take a
sip of it and you can't close your mouth afterwards. It burns all
your insides—and has such a flavor, too. They gave me so much
of it that I parted with it. The next day again I ate with
them, and I told them things that surprised them very much.
The Englishman got tight, and tried to prove that the Russian
people were the most remarkable in the world and that nobody
knew what they'd be up to next. He banged his fist on the table,

so excited he got. That money they just handed over to me
and I took it, although I've never been greedy for money—it has
no interest for me, that's all. But I'm fond of buying things, it's
true. One day, for instance, I bought a doll. I was walking along
a street and saw a doll in the window: just like a live child,
even rolling its eyes, it was. So I bought it. Dragged it about
with me for four days—would sit down on the road somewhere,
take it out of my sack and look at it. Later on I gave it to a little
girl in the village. Her father asked: 'Did you steal it?' 'Yes,' I
said—I was ashamed to own I'd bought it. . . ."

"Well, and what about the Englishman?"

"They just let me go, that's all. Shook me by the hand and
said they were sorry about the joke, and so on. . . .

"I must go and sleep now, friend, I've got a hard day before
me tomorrow. . . ."

Settling down to sleep, he said, "An odd bird I was. . . .
Suddenly joy would seize me, it would flood my innards, my
whole heart—I would be ready to dance. And I would dance—
much to everybody's amusement. Well—why not? I've got no
children—nobody to be ashamed of me. . . .

"That means the soul is at play, friend"—he went on
thoughtfully and softly. "A capricious thing, the soul, one never
knows what might attract it all of a sudden, something quite
funny at times, and just make you cling to it. For instance—
just like that doll—one day a little girl bewitched me. I once
came across a little girl in a country house. There she was, a
child about nine years of age, sitting beside a pond, stirring
the water with a twig and shedding tears—her little muzzle
bathed in them, like a flower in dew, tears dropping down her
breast like pearls. I sat by her side, of course, and asked why
she was crying like that on a merry day? An angry little thing
she turned out to be, tried to send me away.

"But I was stubborn, made her speak; so she said to me: 'Don't
you come wandering around here; my daddy has a dreadful
temper; and so has mammy and also my little brother!' I
laughed to myself, but pretended I was really frightened, taking her at her word. Then she buried her little muzzle in

my shoulder and just sobbed and sobbed, fairly shook with sobs. Her sorrow proved to be not a very heavy one: her parents had gone to a party nearby and had punished her by not taking her, as she'd been naughty and had refused to wear the right frock. I played up to her, of course, and soothed her, and said what bad people these parents were. So she begged me to take her away from them; she didn't want to live with them any longer. Take her away with me? Why, of course I would, no trouble about that! So off we went. And I took her to where her parents were having a party—she had a little friend there, Kolya, a curly-headed little sprig—that was the real reason for her sorrow. Well, they all laughed at her, of course, and she stood there blushing worse than a poppy. Her father gave me half a ruble, and I went off. And what do you think, friend? My soul had clung to that little girl, I couldn't tear myself away from the place. I hovered around for a week, waiting to see her, to talk to her; funny, isn't it? I just couldn't help it. She had been taken away to the seaside; she had a weak chest; and there I was roaming about like a lost dog. That's how things happen at times. Yes . . . the soul is a capricious bird—who knows where it may go when it takes its flight?"

The old man paused and yawned as he spoke, as though he were half asleep, or in a trance; then suddenly he brightened up again as though splashed by a cold rain.

"Last autumn a lady from town came to me. She was not very comely, rather weedy and dried-up, I'd say, but when I glanced into her eyes—God Almighty, if only I could have her, if only for one night, I said to myself. After that—cut me to pieces, let horses tear me asunder—I don't care, I'll take any death. So I told her straight away: 'Go. Please go, or I may hurt you, go! I can't talk to you, d'you hear? I beg of you, go!' I don't know if she guessed, or what, but she hurried away, anyhow. How many nights did I not lay awake thinking of her, seeing those eyes in front of me—a real torture. And me an old man, too. . . . Old, yes . . . The soul knows no laws, it takes no account of years. . . ."

He stretched himself out on the ground, twitched the red, scar-like eyelids, then said, smacking his lips:

"Well, I'm off to sleep now. . . ." And wrapping his head in his cloak he remained still.

He awakened at dawn, looked into the cloudy sky, and hastily ran to the brook where he stripped himself naked, grunting, washed his strong brown body from head to toe, and shouted out to me:

"Hi, friend, hand me over my shirt and trousers; they're in the cave."

Pulling on a long shirt that reached to his knees, and blue trousers, he combed out his wet hair with a wooden comb and, almost handsome, faintly reminding one of an icon, he said:

"I always wash with particular care before receiving people."

While we had our tea he refused vodka:

"No, none of that today. I won't eat anything either, just have a little tea. Nothing should go to one's head; one should keep it light. One needs great lightness of soul in this business. . . ."

People started coming after midday; until then the old man remained silent and dull. His merry, lively eyes had a concentrated look; a grave poise marked all his movements. He looked frequently at the sky and hearkened to the light rustle of the wind. His face was drawn, it seemed more disfigured, and the twitching of the mouth more poignant.

"Someone is coming," he said softly.

I heard nothing.

"Yes. Women. Look here, friend, don't speak to anyone and keep out of the way—or you'll scare them. Sit quietly somewhere nearby."

Two women crawled noiselessly out of the bushes: one, plump, middle-aged, with the meek eyes of a horse; the other, a young woman with a gray, consumptive face; they both stared at me in fear.

I walked away along the slope of the ravine, and heard the old man saying:

"He does not matter; he's not in our way. He's a bit touched in the head; he does not care, does not bother about us. . . ."

The younger woman started to speak in a cracked voice, in hurried and hurt tones, coughing and wheezing, her compan-

ion interrupting her speech with short, low, deep notes, while
Savel, in a voice that sounded like a stranger's, exclaimed, full of
sympathy:

"So—so—so! What people, eh?"

The woman began to whimper plaintively—then the old
man drawled melodiously:

"Dear—wait a bit; stop that; listen . . ."

It seemed to me that his voice had lost its hoarseness, sounded
more clear and high; and the melody of his words reminded
me curiously of the artless song of a goldfinch. I could see,
through the net of branches, that he was bending toward the
woman, speaking straight into her face; while she, sitting awk-
wardly at his side, opened her eyes wide and pressed her
hands to her breast. Her friend, holding her head on one side,
rocked it to and fro.

"They've hurt you; that means they've hurt God!" the old
man said loudly and the brisk, almost cheerful sound of his
words was strikingly out of keeping with their meaning. "God
—where is He? In your soul, behind your breasts, lives the
Holy Ghost; and these witless brothers of yours have injured
Him by their foolishness. You should take pity on the fools—
they've done the wrong. To hurt God is like hurting a small
child of yours. . . ."

And once more he drawled:

"Dee-ear . . ."

I started: never before had I heard this familiar, trivial little word spoken with such triumphant tenderness. Now the
old man was talking in a quick whisper; his hand on the
woman's shoulder, he pushed her gently, and the woman
rocked as though half-asleep. The older woman sat down on
the stones at the old man's feet, methodically spreading the
hem of her blue skirt around her.

"A pig, a dog, a horse—every beast trusts in human reason;
and your brothers are human beings, remember this! And tell
the elder one to come to me on Sunday."

"He won't," said the big woman.

"He will!" the old man exclaimed confidently.

Somebody else was descending into the ravine; clots of earth were rolling down; the branches of the bushes rustled.

"He will come," repeated Savel. "Now, go with God's blessing. All will be well."

The consumptive woman rose silently and bowed low to the old man. He raised her head with the palm of his hand and said:

"Remember, you carry God in your soul."

She bowed again and handed him a small bundle.

"May Christ keep you . . ."

"Thanks, friend. . . . And now, go." And he made the sign of the cross over her.

Out of the bushes came a broad-shouldered, black-bearded peasant, in a new pink shirt, that had not yet been washed; it bulged out in stiff folds, protruding from the belt. He was hatless; his disheveled shock of grayish hair stuck out on all sides in unruly locks; his small, bearlike eyes peered sullenly from under frowning brows.

Making way for the women, he followed them with a glance, coughed loudly, and scratched his chest.

"How do, Olesha," said the old man with a smile. "What is it?"

"Here I am," said Olesha dully; "want to sit awhile with you."

"Good, let's do so."

They sat for a moment in silence, earnestly gazing at each other, then started talking simultaneously.

"Working?"

"Father, I'm fed up . . ."

"You're a big peasant, Olesha."

"If only I had your kind heart. . . ."

"You're a strong man."

"What good is my strength to me? It's your soul I want. . . ."

"Well, when your house burned down, another, like an ass, would have lost courage."

"And I?"

"You—no! You've started all over again. . . ."

"My heart is bitter," the man said loudly, and cursed his heart in foul language.

Savel went on with quiet assurance, "Your heart's just a common, human, anxious heart; it does not want trouble; it longs for peace. . . ."

"It's true, father. . . ."

They went on like that for about half an hour—the peasant telling of a fierce wicked man, whose life was burdened by many failures; while Savel spoke of another man, a strong one, who worked stubbornly, a man who would let nothing slip away from him, nothing escape him, a man with a fine soul.

With a broad smile on his face, the peasant said, "I've made it up with Peter."

"So I've heard."

"Yes. Made it up. We had a drink together. I said to him, 'What are you up to, you devil? . . .' And he said: 'Well, what about you?' Yes. A fine man, damn his soul. . . ."

"You're both the children of one God."

"A fine man. And clever, too. Father—what about my getting married?"

"Of course. She's the one for you to marry."

"Anfisa?"

"Why, yes. She's a good housewife. What a beauty she is, too, and what strength she has. She's a widow; her first husband was an old man, and she had a bad time with him; but you two will get on well together, take my word for it. . . ."

"I will get married . . . really."

"So you should."

Then the peasant proceeded to relate something unintelligible about a dog, about letting cider out of a barrel; he went on with his stories, guffawing like a woodsprite. His sullen, brigand's scowl had become completely transformed, and he now had the silly, good-natured look of a domesticated animal.

"Well, Olesha, move on, here's someone else coming."

"More sufferers? All right . . ."

Olesha descended to the brook, drank some water out of the palm of his hand, then sat down for a few moments motionless as a stone, threw himself back on the ground, folded his arms under his head and apparently went to sleep at once. Then there came a crippled girl, in a motley frock, a thick brown plait down her back, and with big blue eyes. Her face was striking and like a picture; but her skirt was annoyingly vivid, covered with green and yellow spots, and there were scarlet spots, the color of blood, on her white blouse.

The old man welcomed her with joy, and tenderly bade her sit down. Then a tall, black old woman, looking like a nun, appeared, and with her a large-headed, tow-haired lad with a congealed smile on his fat face.

Savel hastily led the girl away into the cave, and concealing her there, closed the door—I could hear the wooden hinges screech.

He sat on a stone between the old woman and the boy, his head bent down, and listened to her murmur in silence for a long time.

"Enough!" he suddenly pronounced, sternly and loudly. "So he does not listen to you, you say?"

"No, he doesn't. I tell him this and that . . ."

"Wait. So you don't do as she tells you, lad?"

The lad remained silent, smiling vacantly.

"Well, that's right, don't listen to her.—Understand? And you, woman, you've started a bad job. I tell you frankly; it's against the law. And there couldn't be anything worse than that. Go, there's nothing for us to talk about.—She's out to do you in, lad. . . ."

The lad, with a sneer, said in a high falsetto:

"Oh, I know that, I do-o. . . ."

"Well, go," Savel said, with a disgusted gesture of dismissal. "Go! You will have no success, woman. None!"

Downcast, they bowed to him in silence and went upwards through the thicket, along a hidden path; I could see that having walked up about a hundred feet, they both started talking, standing close together, facing one another; then they sat down at the foot of a pine, waving their arms about, and a quarrelsome drone reached one's ears. Meanwhile from the cave came pouring out an indescribably moving exclamation:

"Dee-ear . . ."

God alone knows how that disfigured old man contrived to put into this word so much enchanting tenderness, so much exultant love.

"It's too early for you to think of it," he said, as though he were uttering an incantation, leading the lame girl out of the cave. He held her by the hand as though she were a child who still walked uncertainly. She staggered as she walked, pushing him with her shoulder, wiping the tears from her eyes, with the movements of a cat—her hands were small and white.

The old man made her sit on the stone by his side, talking uninterruptedly, clearly and melodiously—as though telling a fairy tale, "Don't you see you are a flower on earth? God nurtured you to give joy; you can give great happiness; the clear light of your eyes alone is a feast to the soul—dea-ear! . . ."

The capacity of this word was inexhaustible, and truly it seemed to me that it contained in its depth the key to all the mysteries of life, the solution of all the painful muddle of human relationships. Through its fascination it was able to bewitch not only peasant women, but all men, all living things. Savel uttered it in infinitely various ways—with emotion, with solemnity, with a kind of touching sadness. It sounded at times reproachful, at times tender, or else it poured out in a radiant music of joy; and I always felt, whatever the way in which it was said, that its source was a limitless, an inexhaustible love, a love which knows nothing but itself and marvels at itself, seeing in itself alone the meaning and aim of existence, all the beauty of life, capable of enveloping the world in its power.

At that time I had already taught myself to doubt; but in these hours, on this cloudy day, all my unbelief fled like shadows before the sun at the sound of the familiar word, worn threadbare by long usage.

The lame girl gasped happily as she went away, nodding her head to the old man:

"Thank you, grandfather, thank you, dear."

"That's all right. Go, friend, go. And remember—you're going toward joy, toward happiness, toward a great task—toward joy! Go!"

She retreated sideways, never tearing her eyes away from

Savel's radiant face. Black-haired Olesha, waking up, stood by
the brook, shaking his still more disheveled head, and watched
the girl with a smile. Suddenly he pushed two fingers into his
mouth and gave a shrill whistle. The girl staggered and dived
like a fish into the dense waves of the thicket.

"You're crazy, Olesha!" the old man reproved him.

Olesha, playing the buffoon, crouched on the ground, pulled
a bottle out of the brook, and brandishing it in the air, suggested:

"Shall we have a drink, father?"

"Have one if you like. I can't, not until tonight."

"Well, I'll wait till evening, too. . . . Ah, father—" and
strong curses followed like an avalanche of bricks—"a sorcerer,
that's what you are—but a saint, too, 'pon my word! You play
with the soul—the human soul, just as a child would. I lay here
and thought to myself . . ."

"Don't bawl, Olesha. . . ."

The old woman with the lad came back, and talked to Savel
in a low and contrite tone. He shook his head distrustfully,
and led them away into the cave, while Olesha, catching sight
of me in the thicket, clumsily made his way across to me, breaking the branches as he came.

"A town bird, are you?"

He was in a cheerful and talkative mood, gently quarrelsome,
and kept singing Savel's praises, "A great consoler, Savel. Take
me, for instance, I simply live on his soul; my own is overgrown
with malice, as with hair. I'm a desperate man, brother. . . ."

He painted himself for a long time in the most sinister
colors, but I did not believe him.

The old woman emerged from the cave, and, with a deep
bow to Savel, said, "Don't you be angry with me, father. . . ."

"Very well, friend . . ."

"You yourself know . . ."

"Yes, I know that everybody is afraid of poverty. A pauper
is never liked by anyone, I know. But all the same: one should
avoid offending God in oneself as well as in others. If we
were to keep God in mind always, there would be no poverty
in the world. So it is, friend. Now go, with God's blessing. . . ."

The lad kept sniveling, glancing fearfully at the old man, and hiding behind his stepmother. Then a beautiful woman arrived, a woman from the town, to judge by her appearance; she wore a lavender-colored frock and a blue kerchief, from under which gleamed two large gray-blue eyes angrily and suspiciously.

And again the enchanting word resounded: "Dee-ear . . ."

Olesha kept on talking, preventing me from hearing what the old man was saying, "He can melt every soul like tin. . . . A great help he is to me. If it were not for him, Hell alone knows what I'd have done by now. . . . Siberia . . ."

Savel's words rose from below, "Every man should be a source of happiness to you, my beauty, and here you are saying all these malicious things. Chase anger away, dear. It is goodness we glorify, isn't it, when we glorify our saints on feast days, not malice. What is it you mistrust? It's yourself you mistrust, your womanly power, your beauty—and what is it that is hidden in beauty? God's spirit, that's what it is . . . Dee-ear. . . ."

Deeply moved, I was on the verge of weeping for joy, so great is the magic force of a word vivified by love.

Before the ravine had filled with the dense darkness of a cloudy night, about thirty people had come to see Savel—dignified, old villagers carrying staffs, distressed people overcome with grief; more than half of the visitors were women. I did not listen any more to their uniform complaints; I only waited impatiently for *the* word to come from Savel. When night came, he allowed Olesha and me to build a bonfire on the stone platform. We got tea and food ready while he sat by the flames, chasing away with his cloak all the "living things" attracted by the fire.

"Another day gone in the service of the soul," he murmured, thoughtfully and wearily.

Olesha gave him some practical advice: "A pity you don't take money from people. . . ."

"It's not suitable for me. . . ."

"Well, you can take from one and give to another. Me, for instance. I'd buy a horse. . . ."

"You tell the children to come tomorrow, Olesha; I've got

some gifts for them. The women brought a lot of stuff today."

Olesha went over to the brook to wash his hands, and I said to Savel, "You speak to people so well, grandfather. . . ."

"Ye-es," he agreed calmly. "I told you I did! And people have respect for me. I tell them each the truth they need. That's what it is."

He smiled merrily and went on, with less weariness, "It's the women I talk best to, isn't it? It just so happens, friend, that when I see a woman, or a girl, who is at all beautiful—my soul soars up and seems to blossom out. I feel a kind of gratitude to them: at the sight of one, I recall all those I have ever known and they are numberless."

Olesha came back, saying, "Father Savel, will you stand surety for me in the matter of the sixty rubles I'm borrowing from Shakh? . . ."

"Very well."

"Tomorrow, eh?"

"Yes . . ."

"See?" Olesha turned to me triumphantly, stepping on my toe as he did so. "Shakh, my boy, is the kind of man who has only to look at you from a distance and your shirt crawls down of itself from your back, right into his hands. But if Father Savel comes to see him—Shakh squirms before him like a little pup. Look at all the timber he gave to the victims of the fire, for instance." Olesha fussed about noisily and did not allow the old man to relax. One could see that Savel was very tired. He sat wearily by the fire, all crumpled up, his arm waving over the flames, the skirt of his coat reminding one of a broken wing. But nothing could subdue Olesha; he had had two glasses of vodka and had become still more exuberantly cheerful.

The old man also had some vodka, ate a baked egg with bread after it; and suddenly he said, quite softly, "Now go home, Olesha!"

The great black beast rose, made the sign of the cross, and glanced into the black sky.

"Keep well, father, and many thanks!" he said. Then he pushed his hard, heavy paw into my hand and obediently crawled into the thicket, where a narrow path was concealed.

"A good man?" I asked.

"Yes, but he has to be watched carefully; his is a violent nature! He beat his wife so hard that she could not bear any children, kept having miscarriages, and went mad in the end. I would ask him: why do you beat her?—and he would say: I don't know, just want to, that's all. . . ."

He remained silent, let his arm drop, and sat motionless, peering into the flames of the bonfire, his gray eyebrows raised. His face, lit up by the fire, seemed red-hot and became terrible to look at: the dark pupils of the naked, lacerated eyes had changed their shape—it was hard to tell whether they were narrower or more dilated—the whites had grown larger and he seemed to have suddenly become blind.

He moved his lips; the scanty hair of his mustache stirred and bristled—as though he wanted to say something and could not. But when he started to speak again, he did so calmly, thoughtfully, in a peculiar manner, "It happens to many a man, this, friend; that you suddenly want to beat up a woman, without any fault of her own and—at what a moment, too! You've just been kissing her, marveling at her beauty; and suddenly, at that very moment, the desire overcomes you to beat her! Yes, yes, friend, it happens . . . I can tell you; I am a quiet, gentle man and did love women so much, sometimes to the point of wanting to get deep inside the woman, right to her very heart and hide in it, as a dove does in the sky—that's how wonderful it was. And then, suddenly, would come the desire to hit her, pinch her as hard as one could; and I would do so, yes! She would shriek and cry: what's the matter? And there is no answer—what answer could there be?"

I looked at him in amazement, unable, too, to say anything or ask any question—this strange confession astonished me. After a pause, he went on about Olesha.

"After his wife went mad, Olesha became still more ill-tempered—a fierce mood would come over him, he'd believe himself damned, and beat everyone up. A short while ago the peasants brought him to me tied up; they'd almost thrashed him to death. He was all swollen, covered with blood like bread with crust. 'Tame him, father Savel,' they said, 'or we'll

kill him, there's no living with the beast!' Yes, friend. I spent
about five days bringing him back to life. I can doctor a bit,
too, you know. . . . Yes, it isn't easy for people to live, friend, it
isn't. Not always is life sweet, my dear clear-eyed friend. . . .
So I try to console people, I do. . . ."

He gave a piteous smile, and his face grew more hideous and
terrible.

"Some of them I have to deceive a little; there are, you see,
some people who have no comfort left to them at all but deceit.
There are some like that, I tell you. . . ."

There were many questions I wanted to put to him, but he
had eaten nothing the whole day; fatigue and the glass of vodka
were obviously telling on him. He dozed, rocking to and fro,
and his red eyelids dropped more frequently over the naked
eyes. I could not help asking all the same, "Grandfather, is
there such a thing as hell, do you think?"

He raised his head and said sternly and reproachfully, "Hell?
How can that be? How can you? God—and hell? Is that possible? The two don't go together, friend. It's a fraud. You people who can read invented this to frighten folk; it's all priests'
nonsense. Why one should want to frighten people, I cannot
see. Besides, no one is really afraid of that hell of yours. . . ."

"And what about the devil? Where does he live, in that case?"

"Don't you joke about that. . . ."

"I'm not joking. . . ."

"Well—well . . ."

He waved the skirts of his coat once more over the fire, and
said softly, "Don't sneer at him. To everyone his own burden.
The little Frenchie might have been right about the devil
bowing down to the Lord in due time. A priest told me the story
of the prodigal son from the Scriptures one day—I can remember it well. It seems to me that it is the story of the devil himself. It's he, no other but he, that is the prodigal son. . . ."

He swayed over the fire.

"Hadn't you better go to sleep?" I suggested.

The old man agreed, "Yes, it's time . . ."

He readily turned on his side, curled himself up, pulled the
coat over his head—and was silent. The branches cracked and

hissed on the coals, the smoke rose in fanciful streamers into the darkness of the night.

I watched the old man and thought to myself, "Is he a saint, owning the treasure of limitless love for the world?"

I remembered the lame girl with the sorrowful eyes, in the motley frock, and life itself appeared to me in the image of that girl: she was standing in front of a hideous little god and he, who knew only how to love, put all the enchanting power of that love into one word of consolation: "Dee-ear. . . ."

CHARACTERS

Oedipus, *King of Thebes*
Priest of Zeus
Creon, *brother of Jocasta*
Teiresias, *the blind prophet*
Jocasta
First Messenger, *a shepherd from Corinth*
A Shepherd, *formerly in the service of Laius*
Second Messenger, *from the house*
Chorus of Theban Elders

*A train of suppliants (old men, youths, and
children). The children* Antigone *and* Ismene,
daughters of Oedipus *and* Jocasta

SCENE: *Before the Royal Palace at Thebes*

Sophocles

OEDIPUS THE KING*

SOPHOCLES, one of the greatest tragedians in the history of literature, lived in classic Greece during its golden age (c. 496 to 406 B.C.). He
is said to have written 113 plays, of which seven have survived. *Oedipus
King* (also known as *Oedipus Tyranus* or *Oedipus Rex*) was part of a
trilogy. Called "the most famous of Greek dramas," it has been translated
into many languages, including numerous translations into English. Not
only did it lend its name to the famous Oedipus complex which was
fundamental to the early development of psychoanalysis, but the drama
undoubtedly had a profound influence on psychoanalytic thinking.

Oedipus. My children, latest-born to Cadmus who was of
old, why are ye set before me thus with wreathed branches of
suppliants, while the city reeks with incense, rings with prayers
for health and cries of woe? I deemed it unmeet, my children,
to hear these things at the mouth of others, and have come
hither myself, I, Oedipus renowned of all.

Tell me, then, thou venerable man—since it is thy natural
part to speak for these—in what mood are ye placed here, with
what dread or what desire? Be sure that I would gladly give all
aid; hard of heart were I, did I not pity such suppliants as
these.

Priest of Zeus. Nay, Oedipus, ruler of my land, thou seest of
what years we are who beset thy altars, some, nestlings still too
tender for far flights, some, bowed with age, priests, as I of
Zeus—and these, the chosen youth; while the rest of the folk sit
with wreathed branches in the market places, and before the
two shrines of Pallas, and where Ismenus gives answer by fire.

For the city, as thou thyself seest, is now too sorely vexed,

* Translated into English prose by Sir Richard Claverhouse Jebb. (Houghton
Mifflin Company) 1916.

and can no more lift her head from beneath the angry waves of death; a blight is on her in the fruitful blossoms of the land, in the herds among the pastures, in the barren pangs of women; and withal the flaming god, the malign plague, hath swooped on us, and ravages the town; by whom the house of Cadmus is made waste, but dark Hades rich in groans and tears.

It is not as deeming thee ranked with gods that I and these children are suppliants at thy hearth, but as deeming thee first of men, both in life's common chances, and when mortals have to do with more than man: seeing that thou camest to the town of Cadmus, and didst quit us of the tax that we rendered to the hard songstress; and this, though thou knewest nothing from us that could avail thee, nor hadst been schooled; no, by a god's aid, 'tis said and believed, didst thou uplift our life.

And now, Oedipus, King glorious in all eyes, we beseech thee, all we suppliants, to find for us some succor, whether by the whisper of a god thou knowest it, or haply as in the power of man; for I see that, when men have been proved in deeds past, the issues of their counsels, too, most often have effect.

On, best of mortals, again uplift our State! On, guard thy fame, since now this land calls thee savior for thy former zeal; and never be it our memory of thy reign that we were first restored and afterward cast down: nay, lift up this State in such wise that it fall no more!

With good omen didst thou give us that past happiness; now also show thyself the same. For if thou art to rule this land, even as thou art now its lord, 'tis better to be lord of men than of a waste: since neither walled town nor ship is anything, if it is void and no men dwell with thee therein.

Oedipus. Oh my piteous children, known, well known to me are the desires wherewith ye have come: well wot I that ye suffer all; yet, sufferers as ye are, there is not one of you whose suffering is as mine. Your pain comes on each one of you for himself alone, and for no other; but my soul mourns at once for the city, and for myself, and for thee.

So that ye rouse me not, truly, as one sunk in sleep: no, be sure that I have wept full many tears, gone many ways in wanderings of thought. And the sole remedy which, well ponder-

ing, I could find, this I have put into act. I have sent the son of
Menoeceus, Creon, mine own wife's brother, to the Pythian
house of Phoebus, to learn by what deed or word I might deliver this town. And already, when the lapse of days is reck-
oned, it troubles me what he doth; for he tarries strangely, beyond the fitting space. But when he comes, then shall I be no
true man if I do not all that the god shows.

Priest. Nay, in season hast thou spoken; at this moment these
sign to me that Creon draws near.

Oedipus. O king Apollo, may he come to us in the brightness of saving fortune, even as his face is bright!

Priest. Nay, to all seeming, he brings comfort; else would he
not be coming crowned thus thickly with berry-laden bay.

Oedipus. We shall know soon: he is at range to hear. Prince,
my kinsman, son of Menoeceus, what news hast thou brought us
from the god?

[*Enter* Creon]

Creon. Good news: I tell thee that even troubles hard to
bear, if haply they find the right issue, will end in perfect peace.

Oedipus. But what is the oracle? So far, thy words make me
neither bold nor yet afraid.

Creon. If thou wouldest hear while these are nigh, I am
ready to speak; or else to go within.

Oedipus. Speak before all: the sorrow which I bear is for
these more than for mine own life.

Creon. With thy leave, I will tell what I heard from the god.
Phoebus our lord bids us plainly to drive out a defiling thing,
which (he saith) hath been harbored in this land, and not to
harbor it, so that it cannot be healed.

Oedipus. By what rite shall we cleanse us? What is the manner of the misfortune?

Creon. By banishing a man, or by bloodshed in quittance of
bloodshed, since it is that blood which brings the tempest on
our city.

Oedipus. And who is the man whose fate he thus reveals?

Creon. Laius, king, was lord of our land before thou wast
pilot of this State.

Oedipus. I know it well—by hearsay, for I saw him never.

Creon. He was slain; and the god now bids us plainly to wreak vengeance on his murderers—whosoever they be.

Oedipus. And where are they upon the earth? Where shall the dim track of this old crime be found?

Creon. In this land, said the god. What is sought for can be caught; only that which is not watched escapes.

Oedipus. And was it in the house, or in the field, or on strange soil that Laius met this bloody end?

Creon. 'Twas on a visit to Delphi, as he said, that he had left our land; and he came home no more, after he had once set forth.

Oedipus. And was there none to tell? Was there no comrade of his journey who saw the deed, from whom tidings might have been gained, and used?

Creon. All perished, save one who fled in fear, and could tell for certain but one thing of all that he saw.

Oedipus. And what was that? One thing might show the clue to many, could we get but a small beginning for hope.

Creon. He said that robbers met and fell on them, not in one man's might, but with full many hands.

Oedipus. How, then, unless there was some trafficking in bribes from here, should the robber have dared thus far?

Creon. Such things were surmised; but, Laius once slain, amid our troubles no avenger arose.

Oedipus. But, when royalty had fallen thus, what trouble in your path can have hindered a full search?

Creon. The riddling Sphinx had made us let dark things go, and was inviting us to think of what lay at our doors.

[*Exit* Creon]

Oedipus. Nay, I will start afresh, and once more make dark things plain. Right worthily hath Phoebus, and worthily hast thou, bestowed this care on the cause of the dead; and so, as is meet, ye shall find me too leagued with you in seeking vengeance for this land, and for the god besides. On behalf of no far-off friend, no, but in mine own cause, shall I dispel this taint. For whoever was the slayer of Laius might wish to take vengeance on me also with a hand as fierce. Therefore, in doing right to Laius, I serve myself.

Come, haste ye, my children, rise from the altar steps, and lift these suppliant boughs; and let some other summon hither the folk of Cadmus, warned that I mean to leave nought untried; for our health (with the god's help) shall be made certain—or our ruin.

Priest. My children, let us rise; we came at first to seek what this man promises of himself. And may Phoebus, who sent these oracles, come to us therewith, our savior and deliverer from the pest.

Chorus. O sweetly speaking message of Zeus, in what spirit hast thou come from golden Pytho unto glorious Thebes? I am on the rack, terror shakes my soul, O thou Delian healer to whom wild cries rise, in holy fear of thee, what thing thou wilt work for me, perchance unknown before, perchance renewed with the revolving years: tell me, thou immortal Voice, born of Golden Hope!

First, call I on thee, daughter of Zeus, divine Athena, and on thy sister, guardian of our land, Artemis, who sits on her throne of fame, above the circle of our Agora, and on Phoebus the far-darter: O shine forth on me, my threefold help against death! If ever aforetime, in arrest of ruin hurrying on the city, ye drove a fiery pest beyond our borders, come now also!

Woe is me, countless are the sorrows that I bear; a plague is on all our host, and thought can find no weapon for defense. The fruits of the glorious earth grow not; by no birth of children do women surmount the pangs in which they shriek; and life on life mayest thou see sped, like bird on nimble wing, aye, swifter than resistless fire, to the shore of the western god.

By such deaths, past numbering, the city perishes: unpitied, her children lie on the ground, spreading pestilence, with none to mourn: and meanwhile young wives, and gray-haired mothers with them, uplift a wail at the steps of the altars, some here, some there, entreating for their weary woes. The prayer to the Healer rings clear, and, blent therewith, the voice of lamentation: for these things, golden daughter of Zeus, send us the bright face of comfort.

And grant that the fierce god of death, who now with no brazen shields, yet amid cries as of battle, wraps me in the flame of his onset, may turn his back in speedy flight from our land, borne by a fair wind to the great deep of Amphitrite, or to those waters in which none find haven, even to the Thracian wave; for if night leave aught undone, day follows to accomplish this. O thou who wieldest the powers of the fire-fraught lightning, O Zeus our father, slay him beneath thy thunderbolt!

Lycean King, fain were I that thy shafts also, from thy bent bow's string of woven gold, should go abroad in their might, our champions in the face of the foe; yea, and the flashing fires of Artemis wherewith she glances through the Lycian hills. And I call him whose locks are bound with gold, who is named with the name of this land, ruddy Bacchus to whom Bacchants cry, the comrade of the Maenads, to draw near with the blaze of his blithe torch, our ally against the god unhonored among gods.

Oedipus. Thou prayest: and in answer to thy prayer, if thou wilt give a loyal welcome to my words and minister to thine own disease, thou mayest hope to find succor and relief from woes. These words will I speak publicly, as one who has been a stranger to this report, a stranger to the deed; for I should not be far on the track, if I were tracing it alone, without a clue. But as it is, since it was only after the time of the deed that I was numbered a Theban among Thebans, to you, the Cadmeans all, I do thus proclaim.

Whosoever of you knows by whom Laius son of Labdacus was slain, I bid him to declare all to me. And if he is afraid, I tell him to remove the danger of the charge from his path by denouncing himself; for he shall suffer nothing else unlovely, but only leave the land, unhurt. Or if any one knows an alien, from another land, as the assassin, let him not keep silence; for I will pay his guerdon, and my thanks shall rest with him besides.

But if ye keep silence—if any one, through fear, shall seek to screen friend or self from my behest—hear ye what I then shall do. I charge you that no one of this land, whereof I hold the empire and the throne, give shelter or speak word unto that murderer, whosoever he be,—make him partner of his prayer or sacrifice or serve him with the lustral rite; but that all ban him their homes, knowing that this is our defiling thing, as the oracle of the Pythian god hath newly shown me. I then am on this wise the ally of the god and of the slain. And I pray solemnly that the slayer, whoso he be, whether his hidden guilt is lonely or hath partners, evilly, as he is evil, may wear out his unblest life. And for myself I pray that if, with my privity, he should become an inmate of my house, I may suffer the same things which even now I called down upon others. And on you I lay it to make all these words good, for my sake, and for the sake of the god, and for our land's thus blasted with barrenness by angry heaven.

For even if the matter had not been urged on us by a god, it was not meet that ye should leave the guilt thus unpurged, when one so noble, and he your king, had perished; rather were ye bound to search it out. And now, since 'tis I who hold the powers which once he held, who possess his bed and the wife who bare seed to him; and since, had his hope of issue not been frustrate, children born of one mother would have made ties betwixt him and me—but, as it was, fate swooped upon his head; by reason of these things will I uphold this cause, even as the cause of mine own sire, and will leave nought untried in seeking to find him whose hand shed that blood, for the honor of the son of Labdacus and of Polydorus and elder Cadmus and Agenor who was of old.

And for those who obey me not, I pray that the gods send them neither harvest of the earth nor fruit of the womb, but that they be wasted by their lot that now is, or by one yet more dire. But for all you, the loyal folk of Cadmus to whom these things seem good, may justice, our ally, and all the gods be with you graciously forever.

Chorus. As thou hast put me on my oath, on my oath, O king, I will speak. I am not the slayer, nor can I point to him who slew. As for the question, it was for Phoebus, who sent it, to tell us this thing—who can have wrought the deed.

Oedipus. Justly said; but no man on the earth can force the gods to what they will not.

Chorus. I would fain say what seems to me next best after this.

Oedipus. If there is yet a third course, spare not to show it.

Chorus. I know that our lord Teiresias is the seer most like to our lord Phoebus, from whom, O king, a searcher of these things might learn them most clearly.

Oedipus. Not even this have I left out of my cares. On the hint of Creon, I have twice sent a man to bring him; and this long while I marvel why he is not here.

Chorus. Indeed (his skill apart) the rumors are but faint and old.

Oedipus. What rumors are they? I look to every story.

Chorus. Certain wayfarers were said to have killed him.

Oedipus. I, too, have heard it, but none sees him who saw it.

Chorus. Nay, if he knows what fear is, he will not stay when he hears thy curses, so dire as they are.

Oedipus. When a man shrinks not from a deed, neither is he scared by a word.

Chorus. But there is one to convict him. For here they bring at last the godlike prophet, in whom alone of men doth live the truth.

[*Enter* Teiresias, *led by·a boy*]

Oedipus. Teiresias, whose soul grasps all things, the lore that may be told and the unspeakable, the secrets of heaven and the low things of earth, thou feelest, though thou canst not see, what a plague doth haunt our State, from which, great prophet, we find in thee our protector and only savior. Now, Phoebus—if indeed thou knowest it not from the messengers— sent answer to our question that the only riddance from this pest which could come was if we should learn aright the slayers of Laius, and slay them, or send them into exile from our land. Do thou, then, grudge neither voice of birds nor any other way of seer lore that thou hast, but rescue thyself and the State, rescue me, rescue all that is defined by the dead. For we are in thy hand; and man's noblest task is to help others by his best means and powers.

Teiresias. Alas, how dreadful to have wisdom where it profits not the wise! Aye, I knew this well, but let it slip out of mind; else would I never have come here.

Oedipus. What now? How sad thou hast come in!

Teiresias. Let me go home; most easily wilt thou bear thine own burden to the end, and I mine, if thou wilt consent.

Oedipus. Thy words are strange, nor kindly to this State which nurtured thee, when thou withholdest this response.

Teiresias. Nay, I see that thou, on thy part, openest not thy lips in season: therefore I speak not, that neither may I have thy mishap.

Oedipus. For the love of the gods, turn not away, if thou hast knowledge: all we suppliants implore thee on our knees.

Teiresias. Aye, for ye are all without knowledge; but never will I reveal my briefs—that I say not thine.

Oedipus. How sayest thou? Thou knowest the secret, and wilt not tell it, but art minded to betray us and to destroy the State?

Teireisas. I will pain neither myself nor thee. Why vainly ask these things? Thou wilt not learn them from me.

Oedipus. What, basest of the base, for thou wouldest anger a very stone, wilt thou never speak out? Can nothing touch thee? Wilt thou never make an end?

Teiresias. Thou blamest my temper, but seest not that to which thou thyself art wedded: no, thou findest fault with me.

Oedipus. And who would not be angry to hear the words with which thou now dost slight this city?

Teiresias. The future will come of itself, though I shroud it in silence.

Oedipus. Then, seeing that it must come, thou on thy part shouldst tell me thereof.

Teiresias. I will speak no further; rage, then, if thou wilt, with the fiercest wrath thy heart doth know.

Oedipus. Aye, verily, I will not spare—so wroth I am—to speak all my thought. Know that thou seemest to me e'en to have helped in plotting the deed, and to have done it, short of slaying with thy hands. Hadst thou eyesight, I would have said that the doing, also, of this thing was thine alone.

Teiresias. In sooth? I charge thee that thou abide by the decree of thine own mouth, and from this day speak neither to these nor to me: thou art the accursed defiler of this land.

Oedipus. So brazen with thy blustering taunt? And wherein dost thou trust to escape thy due?

Teiresias. I have escaped: in my truth is my strength.

Oedipus. Who taught thee this? It was not, at least, thine art.

Teiresias. Thou: for thou didst spur me into speech against my will.

Oedipus. What speech? Speak again that I may learn it better.

Teiresias. Didst thou not take my sense before? Or art thou tempting me in talk?

Oedipus. No, I took it not so that I can call it known. Speak again.

Teiresias. I say that thou art the slayer of the man whose slayer thou seekest.

Oedipus. Now thou shalt rue that thou hast twice said words so dire.

Teiresias. Wouldst thou have me say more, that thou mayest be more wroth?

Oedipus. What thou wilt; it will be said in vain.

Teiresias. I say that thou hast been living in unguessed shame with thy nearest kin, and seest not to what woe thou hast come.

Oedipus. Dost thou indeed think that thou shalt always speak thus without smarting?

Teiresias. Yes, if there is any strength in truth.

Oedipus. Nay, there is, for all save thee; for thee that strength is not, since thou art maimed in ear, and in wit, and in eye.

Teiresias. Aye, and thou art a poor wretch to utter taunts which every man here will soon hurl at thee.

Oedipus. Night, endless night hath thee in her keeping, so that thou canst never hurt me, or any man who sees the sun.

Teiresias. No, thy doom is not to fall by me: Apollo is enough, whose care it is to work that out.

Oedipus. Are these Creon's devices, or thine?

Teiresias. Nay, Creon is no plague to thee; thou art thine own.

Oedipus. O wealth, and empire, and skill surpassing skill in life's keen rivalries, how great is the envy that cleaves to you, if for the sake, yea, of this power which the city hath put into my hands, a gift unsought, Creon the trusty, Creon mine old friend, hath crept on me by stealth, yearning to thrust me out of it, and hath suborned such a scheming juggler as this, a tricky quack, who hath eyes only for his gains, but in his art is blind!

Come, now, tell me, where hast thou proved thyself a seer? Why, when the watcher was here who wove dark song, didst thou say nothing that could free this folk? Yet the riddle, at least, was not for the first comer to read; there was need of a seer's skill; and none such thou wast found to have, either by help of birds, or as known from any god: no, I came, I, Oedipus the ignorant, and made her mute, when I had seized the answer by my wit, untaught of birds. And it is I whom thou art trying to oust, thinking to stand close to Creon's throne. Methinks thou and the plotter of these things will rue your zeal to purge the land. Nay, didst thou not seem to be an old man, thou shouldst have learned to thy cost how bold thou art.

Chorus. To our thinking, both this man's words and thine, Oedipus, have been said in anger. Not for such words is our need, but to seek how we shall best discharge the mandates of the god.

Teiresias. King though thou art, the right of reply, at least, must be deemed the same for both; of that I too am lord. Not to thee do I live servant, but to Loxias; and so I shall not stand enrolled under Creon for my patron. And I tell thee— since thou hast taunted me even with blindness—that thou hast sight, yet seest not in what misery thou art, nor where thou dwellest, nor with whom. Dost thou know of what stock thou art? And thou hast been an unwitting foe to thine own kin, in the shades, and on the earth above; and the double lash of thy mother's and thy father's curse shall one day drive thee from this land in dreadful haste, with darkness then on the eyes that now see true.

And what place shall not be harbor to thy shriek, what of all Cithaeron shall not ring with it soon, when thou hast learnt the meaning of the nuptials in which, within that house, thou didst find a fatal haven, after a voyage so fair? And a throng of other ills thou guessest not, which shall make thee level with thy true self and with thine own brood.

Therefore heap thy scorns on Creon and on my message: for no one among men shall ever be crushed more miserably than thou.

Oedipus. Are these taunts to be indeed borne from him?— Hence, ruin take thee! Hence, this instant! Back! Away! Avaunt thee from these doors!

Teiresias. I had never come, not I, hadst thou not called me.

Oedipus. I knew not that thou wast about to speak folly, or it had been long ere I had sent for thee to my house.

Teiresias. Such am I, as thou thinkest, a fool; but for the parents who begat thee, sane.

Oedipus. What parents? Stay . . . and who of men is my sire?

Teiresias. This day shall show thy birth and shall bring thy ruin.

Oedipus. What riddles, what dark words thou always speakest!

Teiresias. Nay, art not thou most skilled to unravel dark speech?

Oedipus. Make that my reproach in which thou shalt find me great.

Teiresias. Yet 'twas just that fortune that undid thee.

Oedipus. Nay, if I delivered this town, I care not.

Teiresias. Then I will go: so do thou, boy, take me hence.

Oedipus. Aye, let him take thee: while here, thou art a hindrance, thou, a trouble: when thou hast vanished, thou wilt not vex me more.

Teiresias. I will go when I have done mine errand, fearless of thy frown: for thou canst never destroy me. And I tell thee —the man of whom thou hast this long while been in quest, uttering threats, and proclaiming a search into the murder of Laius—that man is here, in seeming, an alien sojourner, but anon he shall be found a native Theban, and shall not be glad of his fortune. A blind man, he who now hath sight, a beggar, who now is rich, he shall make his way to a strange land, feeling the ground before him with his staff. And he shall be found at once brother and father of the children with whom he consorts; son and husband of the woman who bore him; heir to his father's bed, shedder of his father's blood.

So go thou in and think on that; and if thou find that I have been at fault, say thenceforth that I have no wit in prophecy.

[Teiresias *is led out by the boy.* Oedipus *enters the palace*]

Chorus. Who is he of whom the divine voice from the Delphian rock hath spoken, as having wrought with red hands horrors that no tongue can tell?

It is time that he ply in flight a foot stronger than the feet of storm-swift steeds: for the son of Zeus is springing on him, all armed with fiery lightnings, and with him come the dread, unerring Fates.

Yea, newly given from snowy Parnassus, the message hath flashed forth to make all search for the unknown man. Into the wild wood's covert, among caves and rocks he is roaming, fierce as a bull, wretched and forlorn on his joyless path, still seeking to put from him the doom spoken at Earth's central shrine: but that doom ever lives, ever flits around him.

Dreadly, in sooth, dreadly doth the wise augur move me, who approve not, nor am able to deny. How to speak, I know not; I am fluttered with forebodings; neither in the present have I clear vision, nor of the future. Never in past days, nor in these, have I heard how the house of Labdacus or the son of Polybus had, either against other, any grief that I could bring as proof in assailing the public fame of Oedipus, and seeking to avenge the line of Labdacus for the undiscovered murder.

Nay, Zeus indeed and Apollo are keen of thought, and know the things of earth; but that mortal seer wins knowledge above mine, of this there can be no sure test; though man may surpass man in lore. Yet, until I see the word made good, never will I assent when men blame Oedipus. Before all eyes, the winged maiden came against him of old, and he was seen to be wise; he bore the test, in welcome service to our State; never, therefore, by the verdict of my heart shall he be adjudged guilty of crime.

[*Enter* Creon]

Creon. Fellow citizens, having learned that Oedipus the king lays dire charges against me, I am here, indignant. If, in the present troubles, he thinks that he has suffered from me, by word or deed, aught that tends to harm, in truth I crave not my full term of years, when I must bear such blame as this. The wrong of this rumor touches me not in one point alone, but has the largest scope, if I am to be called a traitor in the city, a traitor, too, by thee and by my friends.

Chorus. Nay, but this taunt came under stress, perchance, of anger, rather than from the purpose of the heart.

Creon. And the saying was uttered, that my counsels won the seer to utter his falsehoods?

Chorus. Such things were said—I know not with what meaning.

Creon. And was this charge laid against me with steady eyes and steady mind?

Chorus. I know not; I see not what my masters do: but here comes our lord forth from the house.

[*Enter* Oedipus]

Oedipus. Sirrah, how camest thou here? Hast thou a front so bold that thou hast come to my house, who art the proved assassin of its master, the palpable robber of my crown? Come, tell me, in the name of the gods, was it cowardice or folly that thou sawest in me, that thou didst plot to do this thing? Didst thou think that I would not note this deed of thine creeping on me by stealth, or, aware, would not ward it off? Now is not thine attempt foolish—to seek, without followers or friends, a throne, a prize which followers and wealth must win?

Creon. Mark me now, in answer to thy words, hear a fair reply, and then judge for thyself on knowledge.

Oedipus. Thou art apt in speech, but I have a poor wit for thy lessons, since I have found thee my malignant foe.

Creon. Now first hear how I will explain this very thing—

Oedipus. Explain me not one thing—that thou art not false.

Creon. If thou deemest that stubbornness without sense is a good gift, thou art not wise.

Oedipus. If thou deemest that thou canst wrong a kinsman and escape the penalty, thou art not sane.

Creon. Justly said, I grant thee: but tell me what is the wrong that thou sayest thou hast suffered from me.

Oedipus. Didst thou advise, or didst thou not, that I should send for that reverend seer?

Creon. And now I am still of the same mind.

Oedipus. How long is it, then, since Laius—

Creon. Since Laius . . . ? I take not thy drift . . .

Oedipus. —was swept from men's sight by a deadly violence?

Creon. The count of years would run far into the past.

Oedipus. Was this seer, then, of the craft in those days?

Creon. Yea, skilled as now, and in equal honor.

Oedipus. Made he, then, any mention of me at that time?

Creon. Never, certainly, when I was within hearing.

Oedipus. But held ye not a search touching the murder?

Creon. Due search we held, of course—and learned nothing.

Oedipus. And how was it that this sage did not tell his story then?

Creon. I know not; where I lack light, 'tis my wont to be silent.

Oedipus. Thus much, at least, thou knowest, and couldst declare with light enough.

Creon. What is that? If I know it, I will not deny.

Oedipus. That, if he had not conferred with thee, he would never have named my slaying of Laius.

Creon. If so he speaks, thou best knowest; but I claim to learn from thee as much as thou hast now from me.

Oedipus. Learn thy fill: I shall never be found guilty of the blood.

Creon. Say, then—thou hast married my sister?

Oedipus. The question allows not of denial.

Creon. And thou rulest the land as she doth, with like sway?

Oedipus. She obtains from me all her desire.

Creon. And rank not I as a third peer of you twain?

Oedipus. Aye, 'tis just therein that thou art seen a false friend.

Creon. Not so, if thou wouldst reason with thine own heart as I with mine. And first weigh this—whether thou thinkest that any one would choose to rule amid terrors rather than in unruffled peace—granting that he is to have the same powers. Now I, for one, have no yearning in my nature to be a king rather than to do kingly deeds, no, nor hath any man who knows how to keep a sober mind. For now I win all boons from thee without fear; but, were I ruler myself, I should be doing much e'en against mine own pleasure.

How, then, could royalty be sweeter for me to have than painless rule and influence? Not yet am I so misguided as to desire other honors than those which profit. Now, all wish me joy; now, every man has a greeting for me; now, those who have a suit to thee crave speech with me, since therein is all their hope of success. Then why should I resign these things, and take those? No mind will become false, while it is wise. Nay, I am no lover of such policy, and, if another put it into deed, never could I bear to act with him.

And, in proof of this, first, go to Pytho, and ask if I brought thee true word of the oracle; then next, if thou find that I have planned aught in concert with the soothsayer, take and slay me, by the sentence not of one mouth, but of twain—by mine own, no less than thine. But make me not guilty in a corner, on unproved surmise. It is not right to adjudge bad men good at random, or good men bad. I count it a like thing for a man to cast off a true friend as to cast away the life in his own bosom, which most he loves. Nay, thou wilt learn these things with sureness in time, for time alone shows a just man; but thou couldst discern a knave even in one day.

Chorus. Well hath he spoken, O king, for one who giveth heed not to fall: the quick in counsel are not sure.

Oedipus. When the stealthy plotter is moving on me in quick sort, I, too, must be quick with my counterplot. If I await him in repose, his ends will have been gained, and mine missed.

Creon. What wouldst thou, then? Cast me out of the land?

Oedipus. Not so: I desire thy death—not thy banishment—that thou mayest show forth what manner of thing is envy.

Creon. Thou speakest as resolved not to yield or to believe?

Creon. No, for I find thee not sane.

Oedipus. Sane, at least, in mine own interest.

Creon. Nay, thou shouldst be so in mine also.

Oedipus. Nay, thou art false.

Creon. But if thou understandest nought?

Oedipus. Yet must I rule.

Creon. Not if thou rule ill.

Oedipus. Hear him, O Thebes!

Creon. Thebes is for me also—not for thee alone.

Chorus. Cease, princes; and in good time for you I see Jocasta coming yonder from the house, with whose help ye should compose your present feud.

[*Enter* Jocasta]

Jocasta. Misguided men, why have ye raised such foolish strife of tongues? Are ye not ashamed, while the land is thus sick, to stir up troubles of your own? Come, go thou into the house,—and thou, Creon, to thy home,—and forbear to make much of a petty grief.

Creon. Kinswoman, Oedipus thy lord claims to do dread things unto me, even one or other of two ills, to thrust me from the land of my fathers, or to slay me amain.

Oedipus. Yea; for I have caught him, lady, working evil, by ill arts, against my person.

Creon. Now may I see no good, but perish accursed, if I have done aught to thee of that wherewith thou chargest me!

Jocasta. Oh, for the gods' love, believe it, Oedipus—first, for the awful sake of this oath unto the gods,—then for my sake and for theirs who stand before thee?

Chorus. Consent, reflect, hearken, O my king, I pray thee!

Oedipus. What grace, then, wouldest thou have me grant thee?

Chorus. Respect him who aforetime was not foolish, and who now is strong in his oath.

Oedipus. Now dost thou know what thou cravest?

Chorus. Yea.

Oedipus. Declare, then, what thou meanest.

Chorus. That thou shouldest never use an unproved rumor to cast a dishonoring charge on the friend who has bound himself with a curse.

Oedipus. Then be very sure that, when thou seekest this, for me thou art seeking destruction, or exile from this land.

Chorus. No, by him who stands in the front of all the heavenly host; no, by the sun! Unblest, unfriended, may I die by the uttermost doom, if I have that thought! But my unhappy soul is worn by the withering of the land, and again by the thought that our old sorrows should be crowned by sorrows springing from you twain.

Oedipus. Then let him go, though I am surely doomed to death, or to be thrust dishonored from the land. Thy lips, not his, move my compassion by their plaint; but he, where'er he be, shall be hated.

Creon. Sullen in yielding art thou seen, even as vehement in the excesses of thy wrath; but such natures are justly sorest for themselves to bear.

Oedipus. Then wilt thou not leave me in peace, and get thee gone?

Creon. I will go my way; I have found thee undiscerning, but in the sight of these I am just.

[*Exit*]

Chorus. Lady, why dost thou delay to take yon man into the house?

Jocasta. I will do so, when I have learned what hath chanced.

Chorus. Blind suspicion, bred of talk, arose; and, on the other part, injustice wounds.

Jocasta. It was on both sides?

Chorus. Aye.

Jocasta. And what was the story?

Chorus. Enough, methinks, enough—when our land is already vexed—that the matter should rest where it ceased.

Oedipus. Seest thou to what thou hast come, for all thy honest purpose, in seeking to slack and blunt my zeal?

Chorus. King, I have said it not once alone—be sure that I should have been shown a madman, bankrupt in sane counsel, if I put thee away—thee, who gavest a true course to my beloved country when distraught by troubles—thee, who now also art like to prove our prospering guide.

Jocasta. In the name of the gods, tell me also, O king, on what account thou hast conceived this steadfast wrath.

Oedipus. That will I; for I honor thee, lady, above yonder men—the cause is Creon, and the plots that he hath laid against me.

Jocasta. Speak on—if thou canst tell clearly how the feud began.

Oedipus. He says that I stand guilty of the blood of Laius.

Jocasta. As on his own knowledge? Or on hearsay from another?

Oedipus. Nay, he hath made a rascal seer his mouthpiece; as for himself, he keeps his lips wholly pure.

Jocasta. Then absolve thyself of the things whereof thou speakest; hearken to me, and learn for thy comfort that nought of mortal birth is a sharer in the science of the seer. I will give thee pithy proof of that.

An oracle came to Laius once—I will not say from Phoebus himself, but from his ministers—that the doom should overtake him to die by the hand of his child, who should spring from him and me.

Now Laius—as, at least, the rumor saith—was murdered one day by foreign robbers at a place where three highways meet. And the child's birth was not three days past, when Laius pinned its ankles together, and had it thrown, by others' hands, on a trackless mountain.

So, in that case, Apollo brought it not to pass that the babe should become the slayer of his sire, or that Laius should die— the dread thing which he feared—by his child's hand. Thus did the messages of seer-craft map out the future. Regard them, thou, not at all. Whatsoever needful things the god seeks, he himself will easily bring to light.

Oedipus. What restlessness of soul, lady, what tumult of the mind hath just come upon me since I heard thee speak!

Jocasta. What anxiety hath startled thee, that thou sayest this?

Oedipus. Methought I heard this from thee—that Laius was slain where three highways meet.

Jocasta. Yea, that was the story; nor hath it ceased yet.

Oedipus. And where is the place where this befell?

Jocasta. The land is called Phocis; and branching roads lead to the same spot from Delphi and from Daulia.

Oedipus. And what is the time that hath passed since these things were?

Jocasta. The news was published to the town shortly before thou wast first seen in power over this land.

Oedipus. O Zeus, what hast thou decreed to do unto me?

Jocasta. And wherefore, Oedipus, doth this thing weigh upon thy soul?

Oedipus. Ask me not yet; but say what was the stature of Laius, and how ripe his manhood.

Jocasta. He was tall, the silver just lightly strewn among his hair; and his form was not greatly unlike to thine.

Oedipus. Unhappy that I am! Methinks I have been laying myself even now under a dread curse, and knew it not.

Jocasta. How sayest thou? I tremble when I look on thee, my king.

Oedipus. Dread misgivings have I that the seer can see. But thou wilt show better if thou wilt tell me one thing more.

Jocasta. Indeed—though I tremble—I will answer all thou askest, when I hear it.

Oedipus. Went he in small force, or with many armed followers, like a chieftain?

Jocasta. Five they were in all, a herald one of them; and there was one carriage, which bore Laius.

Oedipus. Alas! 'Tis now clear indeed. Who was he who gave you these tidings, lady?

Jocasta. A servant—the sole survivor who came home.

Oedipus. Is he haply at hand in the house now?

Jocasta. No, truly; so soon as he came thence, and found thee reigning in the stead of Laius, he supplicated me, with hand laid on mine, that I would send him to the fields, to the pastures of the flocks, that he might be far from the sight of this town. And I sent him; he was worthy, for a slave, to win e'en a larger boon than that.

Oedipus. Would, then, that he could return to us without delay!

Jocasta. It is easy: but wherefore dost thou enjoin this?

Oedipus. I fear, lady, that mine own lips have been unguarded; and therefore am I fain to behold him.

Jocasta. Nay, he shall come. But I, too, methinks, have a claim to learn what lies heavy on thy heart, my king.

Oedipus. Yea, and it shall not be kept from thee, now that my forebodings have advanced so far. Who, indeed, is more to me than thou, to whom I should speak in passing through such a fortune as this?

My father was Polybus of Corinth, my mother, the Dorian Merope; and I was held the first of all the folk in that town, until a chance befell me, worthy, indeed, of wonder, though not worthy of mine own heat concerning it. At a banquet, a man full of wine cast it at me in his cups that I was not the true son of my sire. And I, vexed, restrained myself for that day as best I might; but on the next I went to my mother and father and questioned them; and they were wroth for the taunt with him who had let that word fly. So on their part I had comfort; yet was this thing ever rankling in my heart; for it still crept abroad with strong rumor. And, unknown to mother or father, I went to Delphi; and Phoebus sent me forth disappointed of that knowledge for which I came, but in his response set forth other things, full of sorrow and terror and woe; even that I was fated to defile my mother's bed; and that I should show unto men a brood which they could not endure to behold; and that I should be the slayer of the sire who begat me.

And I, when I had listened to this, turned to flight from the land of Corinth, thenceforth wotting of its region by the stars alone, to some spot where I should never see fulfillment of the infamies foretold in mine evil doom. And on my way I came to the regions in which thou sayest that this prince perished. Now, lady, I will tell thee the truth. When in my journey I was near to those three roads, there met me a herald, and a man seated in a carriage drawn by colts, as thou hast described; and he who was in front, and the old man himself, were for thrusting me rudely from the path. Then, in anger, I struck him who pushed me aside—the driver; and the old man, seeing it, watched the moment when I was passing, and, from the carriage, brought his goad with two teeth down full upon my head. Yet was he paid with interest; by one swift blow from the staff in this hand he was rolled right out of the carriage, on his back; and I slew every man of them.

But if this stranger had any tie of kinship with Laius, who is now more wretched than the man before thee? What mortal could prove more hated of heaven? Whom no stranger, no citizen, is allowed to receive in his house; whom it is unlawful that any one accost; whom all must repel from their homes! And this—this curse—was laid on me by no mouth but mine own! And I pollute the bed of the slain man with the hands by which he perished. Say, am I vile? Oh, am I not utterly unclean?—seeing that I must be banished, and in banishment see not mine own people, nor set foot in mine own land, or else be joined in wedlock to my mother, and slay my sire, even Polybus, who begat and reared me.

Then would not he speak aright of Oedipus, who judged these things sent by some cruel power above man? Forbid, forbid, ye pure and awful gods, that I should see that day! No, may I be swept from among men, ere I behold myself visited with the brand of such a doom!

Chorus. To us, indeed, these things, O king, are fraught with fear; yet have hope, until at least thou hast gained full knowledge from him who saw the deed.

Oedipus. Hope, in truth, rests with me thus far alone; I can await the man summoned from the pastures.

Jocasta. And when he has appeared—what wouldst thou have of him?

Oedipus. I will tell thee. If his story be found to tally with thine, I, at least, shall stand clear of disaster.

Jocasta. And what of special note didst thou hear from me?

Oedipus. Thou wast saying that he spoke of Laius as slain by robbers. If, then, he still speaks, as before, of several, I was not the slayer: a solitary man could not be held the same with that band. But if he names one lonely wayfarer, then beyond doubt this guilt leans to me.

Jocasta. Nay, be assured that thus, at least, the tale was first told; he cannot revoke that, for the city heard it, not I alone. But even if he should diverge somewhat from his former story, never, king, can he show that the murder of Laius, at least, is truly square to prophecy; of whom Loxias plainly said that he must die by the hand of my child. Howbeit that poor innocent never slew him, but perished first itself. So henceforth, for what touches divination, I would not look to my right hand or my left.

Oedipus. Thou judgest well. But nevertheless send some one to fetch the peasant, and neglect not this matter.

Jocasta. I will send without delay. But let us come into the house: nothing will I do save at thy good pleasure.

[*Exeunt* Oedipus *and* Jocasta]

Chorus. May destiny still find me winning the praise of reverent purity in all words and deeds sanctioned by those laws of range sublime, called into life throughout the high clear heaven, whose father is Olympus alone; their parent was no race of mortal men, no, nor shall oblivion ever lay them to sleep; the god is mighty in them, and he grows not old.

Insolence breeds the tyrant; Insolence, once bainly surfeited on wealth that is not meet nor good for it, when it hath scaled the topmost ramparts, is hurled to a dire doom, wherein no service of the feet can serve. But I pray that the god never quell such rivalry as benefits the State; the god will I ever hold for our protector.

But if any man walks haughtily in deed or word, with no fear of justice, no reverence for the images of gods, may an evil doom seize him for his ill-starred pride, if he will not win his vantage fairly, nor keep him from unholy deeds, but must lay profaning hands on sanctities.

Where such things are, what mortal shall boast any more that he can ward the arrows of the gods from his life? Nay, if such deeds are in honor, wherefore should we join in the sacred dance?

No more will I go reverently to earth's central and inviolate shrine, no more to Abae's temple or Olympia, if these oracles fit not the issue, so that all men shall point at them with the finger. Nay, king, if thou art rightly called, Zeus all-ruling, may it not escape thee and thine ever-deathless power!

The old prophecies concerning Laius are fading; already men

are setting them at nought, and nowhere is Apollo glorified with honors; the worship of the gods is perishing.

[*Enter* Jocasta]

Jocasta. Princes of the land, the thought has come to me to visit the shrines of the gods, with this wreathed branch in my hands, and these gifts of incense. For Oedipus excites his soul over much with all manner of alarm, nor, like a man of sense, judges the new things by the old, but is at the will of the speaker, if he speak terrors.

Since, then, by counsel I can do no good, to thee, Lycean Apollo, for thou art nearest, I have come, a suppliant with these symbols of prayer, that thou mayest find us some riddance from uncleanness. For now we are all afraid, seeing him affrighted, even as they who see fear in the helmsman of their ship.

[*Enter* Messenger]

Messenger. Might I learn from you, strangers, where is the house of the king Oedipus? Or, better still, tell me where he himself is—if ye know.

Chorus. This is his dwelling, and he himself, stranger, is within; and this lady is the mother of his children.

Messenger. Then may she be ever happy in a happy home, since she is his heaven-blest queen.

Jocasta. Happiness to thee also, stranger! 'Tis the due of thy fair greeting. But say what thou hast come to seek or to tell.

Messenger. Good tidings, lady, for thy house and for thy husband.

Jocasta. What are they? And from whom hast thou come?

Messenger. From Corinth: and at the message which I will speak anon thou wilt rejoice—doubtless; yet haply grieve.

Jocasta. And what is it? How hath it thus a double potency?

Messenger. The people will make him king of the Isthmian land, as 'twas said there.

Jocasta. How then? Is the aged Polybus no more in power?

Messenger. No, verily: for death holds him in the tomb.

Jocasta. How sayest thou? Is Polybus dead, old man?

Messenger. If I speak not the truth, I am content to die.

Jocasta. O handmaid, away with all speed, and tell this to thy master! O ye oracles of the gods, where stand ye now! This is the man whom Oedipus long feared and shunned, lest he should slay him; and now this man hath died in the course of destiny, not by his hand.

[Enter Oedipus]

Oedipus. Jocasta, dearest wife, why hast thou summoned me forth from these doors?

Jocasta. Hear this man, and judge, as thou listenest, to what the awful oracles of the gods have come.

Oedipus. And he—who may he be, and what news hath he for me?

Jocasta. He is from Corinth, to tell that thy father Polybus lives no longer, but hath perished.

Oedipus. How, stranger? Let me have it from thine own mouth.

Messenger. If I must first make these tidings plain, know indeed that he is dead and gone.

Oedipus. By treachery, or by visit of disease?

Messenger. A light thing in the scale brings the aged to their rest.

Oedipus. Ah, he died, it seems, of sickness?

Messenger. Yea, and of the long years that he had told.

Oedipus. Alas, alas! Why, indeed, my wife, should one look to the hearth of the Pythian seer, or to the birds that scream above our heads, on whose showing I was doomed to slay my sire? But he is dead, and hid already beneath the earth; and here am I, who have not put hand to spear. Unless, perchance, he was killed by longing for me: thus, indeed, I should be the cause of his death. But the oracles as they stand, at least, Polybus hath swept with him to his rest in Hades: they are worth nought.

Jocasta. Nay, did I not so foretell to thee long since?

Oedipus. Thou didst, but I was misled by my fear.

Jocasta. Now no more lay aught of those things to heart.

Oedipus. But surely I must needs fear my mother's bed?

Jocasta. Nay, what should mortal fear, for whom the decrees of fortune are supreme, and who hath clear foresight of nothing? 'Tis best to live at random, as one may. But fear not thou touching wedlock with thy mother. Many men ere now have so fared in dreams also, but he to whom these things are as nought bears his life most easily.

Oedipus. All these bold words of thine would have been well, were not my mother living; but as it is, since she lives, I must needs fear—though thou sayest well.

Jocasta. Howbeit thy father's death is a great sign to cheer us.

Oedipus. Great, I know; but my fear is of her who lives.

Messenger. And who is the woman about whom ye fear?

Oedipus. Merope, old man, the consort of Polybus.

Messenger. And what is it in her that moves your fear?

Oedipus. A heaven-sent oracle of dread import, stranger.

Messenger. Lawful, or unlawful, for another to know?

Oedipus. Lawful, surely. Loxias once said that I was doomed to espouse mine own mother, and to shed with mine own hands my father's blood. Wherefore my home in Corinth was long kept by me afar; with happy event, indeed, yet still 'tis sweet to see the face of parents.

Messenger. Was it indeed for fear of this that thou wast an exile from that city?

Oedipus. And because I wished not, old man, to be the slayer of my sire.

Messenger. Then why have I not freed thee, king, from this fear, seeing that I came with friendly purpose?

Oedipus. Indeed thou shouldst have guerdon due from me.

Messenger. Indeed 'twas chiefly for this that I came—that, on thy return home, I might reap some good.

Oedipus. Nay, I will never go near my parents.

Messenger. Ah my son, 'tis plain enough that thou knowest not what thou doest.

Oedipus. How, old man? For the gods' love, tell me.

Messenger. If for these reasons thou shrinkest from going home.

Oedipus. Aye, I dread lest Phoebus prove himself true for me.

Messenger. Thou dreadest to be stained with guilt through thy parents?

Oedipus. Even so, old man—this it is that ever affrights me.

Messenger. Dost thou know, then, that thy fears are wholly vain?

Oedipus. How so, if I was born of those parents?

Messenger. Because Polybus was nothing to thee in blood.

Oedipus. What sayest thou? Was Polybus not my sire?

Messenger. No more than he who speaks to thee, but just so much.

Oedipus. And how can my sire be level with him who is as nought to me?

Messenger. Nay, he begat thee not, any more than I.

Oedipus. Nay, wherefore, then, called he me his son?

Messenger. Know that he had received thee as a gift from my hands of yore.

Oedipus. And yet he loved me so dearly, who came from another's hand?

Messenger. Yea, his former childlessness won him thereto.

Oedipus. And thou—hadst thou bought me or found me by chance, when thou gavest me to him?

Messenger. Found thee in Cithaeron's winding glens.

Oedipus. And wherefore wast thou roaming in those regions?

Messenger. I was there in charge of mountain flocks.

Oedipus. What, thou wast a shepherd—a vagrant hireling?

Messenger. But thy preserver, my son, in that hour.

Oedipus. And what pain was mine when thou didst take me in thine arms?

Messenger. The ankles of thy feet might witness.

Oedipus. Ah me, why dost thou speak of that old trouble?

Messenger. I freed thee when thou hadst thine ankles pinned together.

Oedipus. Aye, 'twas a dread brand of shame that I took from my cradle.

Messenger. Such, that from that fortune thou wast called by the name which still is thine.

Oedipus. Oh, for the gods' love—was the deed my mother's or father's? Speak!

Messenger. I know not; he who gave thee to me wots better of that than I.

Oedipus. What, thou hadst me from another. Thou didst not light on me thyself?

Messenger. No. Another shepherd gave thee up to me.

Oedipus. Who was he? Art thou in case to tell clearly?

Messenger. I think he was called one of the household of Laius.

Oedipus. The king who ruled this country long ago?

Messenger. The same. 'Twas in his service that the man was a herd.

Oedipus. Is he still alive, that I might see him?

Messenger. Nay, ye folk of the country should know best.

[*Exit*]

Oedipus. Is there any of you here present that knows the herd of whom he speaks—that hath seen him in the pastures or the town? Answer! The hour hath come that these things should be finally revealed.

Chorus. Methinks he speaks of no other than the peasant whom thou wast already fain to see; but our lady Jocasta might best tell that.

Oedipus. Lady, wottest thou of him whom we lately summoned? Is it of him that this man speaks?

Jocasta. Why ask of whom he spoke? Regard it not . . . waste not a thought on what he said . . . 'twere idle.

Oedipus. It must not be that, with such clues in my grasp, I should fail to bring my birth to light.

Jocasta. For the gods' sake, if thou hast any care for thine own life, forbear this search! My anguish is enough.

Oedipus. Be of good courage; though I be found the son of servile mother—aye, a slave by three descents—thou wilt not be proved base born.

Jocasta. Yet hear me, I implore thee: do not thus.

Oedipus. I must not hear of not discovering the whole truth.

Jocasta. Yet I wish thee well—I counsel thee for the best.

Oedipus. These best counsels, then, vex my patience.

Jocasta. Ill-fated one! Mayst thou never come to know who thou art!

Oedipus. Go, some one, fetch me the herdsman hither, and leave yon woman to glory in her princely stock.

Jocasta. Alas, alas, miserable!—that word alone can I say unto thee, and no other word henceforth forever.

[*She rushes into the palace*]

Chorus. Why hath the lady gone, Oedipus, in a transport of wild grief? I misdoubt, a storm of sorrow will break forth from this silence.

Oedipus. Break forth what will! Be my race never so lowly, I must crave to learn it. Yon woman, perchance, for she is proud with more than a woman's pride, thinks shame of my base source. But I, who hold myself son of fortune that gives good, will not be dishonored. She is the mother from whom I spring; and the months, my kinsmen, have marked me sometimes lowly, sometimes great. Such being my lineage, never more can I prove false to it, or spare to search out the secret of my birth.

Chorus. If I am a seer or wise of heart, O Cithaeron, thou shalt not fail—by yon heaven, thou shalt not!—to know at to-morrow's full moon that Oedipus honors thee as native to him, as his nurse, and his mother, and that thou art celebrated in our dance and song, because thou art well pleasing to our prince. O Phoebus to whom we cry, may these things find favor in thy sight!

Who was it, my son, who of the race whose years are many that bore thee in wedlock with Pan, the mountain-roaming father? Or was it a bride of Loxias that bore thee? For dear to him are all the upland pastures. Or perchance 'twas Cyllene's lord, or the Bacchants' god, dweller on the hill-tops, that received thee, a newborn joy, from one of the nymphs of Helicon, with whom he most doth sport.

Oedipus. Elders, if 'tis for me to guess, who have never met with him, I think I see the herdsman of whom we have long been in quest; for in his venerable age he tallies with yon stranger's years, and withal I know those who bring him, methinks, as servants of mine own. But perchance thou mayest have the advantage of me in knowledge, if thou hast seen the herdsman before.

Chorus. Aye, I know him, be sure; he was in the service of Laius—trusty as any man, in his shepherd's place.

[*The* Herdsman *is brought in*]

Oedipus. I ask thee first, Corinthian stranger, is this he whom thou meanest?

Messenger. This man whom thou beholdest.

Oedipus. Ho thou, old man—I would have thee look this way, and answer all that I ask thee. Thou wast once in the service of Laius?

Herdsman. I was—a slave not bought, but reared in his house.

Oedipus. Employed in what labor, or what way of life?

Herdsman. For the best part of my life I tended flocks.

Oedipus. And what the regions that thou didst chiefly haunt?

Herdsman. Sometimes it was Cithaeron, sometimes the neighboring ground.

Oedipus. Then wottest thou of having noted yon man in these parts—

Herdsman. Doing what? What man dost thou mean?

Oedipus. This man here—or of having ever met him before?

Herdsman. Not so that I could speak at once from memory.

Messenger. And no wonder, master. But I will bring clear recollection to his ignorance. I am sure that he well wots of the time when we abode in the region of Cithaeron—he with two flocks, I, his comrade, with one—three full half-years, from spring to Arcturus; and then for the winter I used to drive my flock to mine own fold, and he took his to the fold of Laius. Did aught of this happen as I tell, or did it not?

Herdsman. Thou speakest the truth—though 'tis long ago.

Messenger. Come, tell me now—wottest thou of having given me a boy in those days, to be reared as mine own foster son?

Herdsman. What now? Why dost thou ask the question?

Messenger. Yonder man, my friend, is he who then was young.

Herdsman. Plague seize thee—be silent once for all!

Oedipus. Ha! chide him not, old man—thy words need chiding more than his.

Herdsman. And wherein, most noble master, do I offend?

Oedipus. In not telling of the boy concerning whom he asks.

Herdsman. He speaks without knowledge—he is busy to no purpose.

Oedipus. Thou wilt not speak with a good grace, but thou shalt on pain.

Herdsman. Nay, for the gods' love, misuse not an old man!

Oedipus. Ho, some one—pinion him this instant!

Herdsman. Alas, wherefore? What more wouldst thou learn?

Oedipus. Didst thou give this man the child of whom he asks?

Herdsman. I did—and would I had perished that day!

Oedipus. Well, thou wilt come to that, unless thou tell the honest truth.

Herdsman. Nay, much more am I lost, if I speak.

Oedipus. The fellow is bent, methinks, on more delays . . .

Herdsman. No, no! I said before that I gave it to him.

Oedipus. Whence hadst thou got it? In thine own house, or from another?

Herdsman. Mine own it was not—I had received it from a man.

Oedipus. From whom of the citizens here? From what home?

Herdsman. Forbear, for the gods' love, master, forbear to ask more!

Oedipus. Thou art lost if I have to question thee again.

Herdsman. It was a child, then, of the house of Laius.

Oedipus. A slave—or one born of his own race?

Herdsman. Ah me—I am on the dreaded brink of speech.

Oedipus. And I of hearing; yet must I hear.

Herdsman. Thou must know, then, that 'twas said to be his own child, but thy lady within could best say how these things are.

Oedipus. How? She gave it to thee?

Herdsman. Yea, O king.

Oedipus. For what end?

Herdsman. That I should make away with it.

Oedipus. Her own child, the wretch?

Herdsman. Aye, from fear of evil prophecies.

Oedipus. What were they?

Herdsman. The tale ran that he must slay his sire.

Oedipus. Why, then, didst thou give him up to this old man?

Herdsman. Through pity, master, as deeming that he would bear him away to another land, whence he himself came; but he saved him for the direst woe. For if thou art what this man saith, know that thou wast born to misery.

[*Exit* Herdsman]

Oedipus. Oh, oh! All brought to pass—all true! Thou light, may I now look my last on thee—I who have been found accursed in birth, accursed in wedlock, accursed in the shedding of blood!

[*He rushes into the palace*]

Chorus. Alas, ye generations of men, how mere a shadow do I count your life! Where, where is the mortal who wins more of happiness than just the seeming, and, after the semblance, a falling away? Thine is a fate that warns me—thine, thine, unhappy Oedipus—to call no earthly creature blest.

For he, O Zeus, sped his shaft with peerless skill, and won the prize of an all-prosperous fortune; he slew the maiden with crooked talons who sang darkly; he arose for our land as a tower against death. And from that time, Oedipus, thou hast been called our king, and hast been honored supremely, bearing sway in great Thebes.

But now whose story is more grievous in men's ears? Who is a more wretched captive to fierce plagues and troubles, with all his life reversed?

Alas, renowned Oedipus! The same bounteous place of rest sufficed thee, as child and as sire also, that thou shouldst make thereon thy nuptial couch. Oh, how can the soil wherein thy father sowed, unhappy one, have suffered thee in silence so long?

Time the all-seeing hath found thee out in thy despite: he judgeth the monstrous marriage wherein begetter and begotten have long been one.

Alas, thou child of Laius, would, would that I had never seen thee! I wail as one who pours a dirge from his lips; sooth to speak, 'twas thou that gavest me new life, and through thee darkness hath fallen upon mine eyes.

[*Enter* Second Messenger *from the house*]

Second Messenger. Ye who are ever most honored in this land, what deeds shall ye hear, what deeds behold, what burden of sorrow shall be yours, if, true to your race, ye still care for the house of Labdacus! For I ween that not Ister nor Phasis could wash this house clean, so many are the ills that it shrouds, or will soon bring to light, ills wrought not unwittingly, but of purpose. And those griefs smart most which are seen to be of our own choice.

Chorus. Indeed those which we knew before fall not short of claiming sore lamentation: besides them, what dost thou announce?

Second Messenger. This is the shortest tale to tell and to hear: our royal lady Jocasta is dead.

Chorus. Alas, hapless one! From what cause?

Second Messenger. By her own hand. The worst pain in what hath chanced is not for you, for yours it is not to behold. Nevertheless, so far as mine own memory serves, ye shall learn that unhappy woman's fate.

When, frantic, she had passed within the vestibule, she rushed straight toward her nuptial couch, clutching her hair with the fingers of both hands; once within the chamber, she dashed the doors together at her back; then called on the name of Laius, long since a corpse, mindful of that son, begotten long ago, by whom the sire was slain, leaving the mother to breed accursed offspring with his own.

And she bewailed the wedlock wherein, wretched, she had born a twofold brood, husband by husband, children by her child. And how thereafter she perished, is more than I know. For with a shriek Oedipus burst in, and suffered us not to watch her woe unto the end; on him, as he rushed around, our eyes were set. To and fro he went, asking us to give him a sword, asking where he should find the wife who was no wife, but a mother whose womb had borne alike himself and his children. And, in his frenzy, a power above man was his guide; for 'twas none of us mortals who were nigh. And with a dread shriek, as though some one beckoned him on, he sprang at the double doors, and from their sockets forced the bending bolts, and rushed into the room.

There beheld we the woman hanging by the neck in a twisted noose of swinging cords. But he, when he saw her, with a dread, deep cry of misery, loosed the halter whereby she hung. And when the hapless woman was stretched upon the ground, then was the sequel dread to see. For he tore from her raiment the golden brooches wherewith she was decked, and lifted them, and smote full on his own eyeballs, uttering words like these: "No more shall ye behold such horrors as I was suffering and working! long enough have ye looked on those whom ye ought never to have seen, failed in knowledge of those whom I yearned to know—henceforth ye shall be dark!"

To such dire refrain, not once alone but oft struck he his eyes with lifted hand; and at each blow the ensanguined eyeballs bedewed his beard, nor sent forth sluggish drops of gore, but all at once a dark shower of blood came down like hail.

From the deeds of twain such ills have broken forth, not on one alone, but with mingled woe for man and wife. The old happiness of their ancestral fortune was aforetime happiness indeed; but today—lamentation, ruin, death, shame, all earthly ills that can be named—all, all are theirs.

Chorus. And hath the sufferer now any respite from pain?

Second Messenger. He cries for some one to unbar the gates and show to all the Cadmeans his father's slayer, his mother's —the unholy word must not pass my lips—as purposing to cast himself out of the land, and abide no more, to make the house accursed under his own curse. Howbeit he lacks strength, and one to guide his steps; for the anguish is more than man may bear. And he will show this to thee also; for lo, the bars of the gates are withdrawn, and soon thou shalt behold a sight which even he who abhors it must pity.

[*Enter* Oedipus]

Chorus. O dread fate for men to see, O most dreadful of all that have met mine eyes! Unhappy one, what madness hath come on thee? Who is the unearthly foe that, with a bound of more than mortal range, hath made thine ill-starred life his prey?

Alas, alas, thou hapless one! Nay, I cannot e'en look on thee, though there is much that I would fain ask, fain learn, much that draws my wistful gaze, with such a shuddering dost thou fill me!

Oedipus. Woe is me! Alas, alas, wretched that I am! Whither, whither am I borne in my misery? How is my voice swept abroad on the wings of the air? O my Fate, how far hast thou sprung!

Chorus. To a dread place, dire in men's ears, dire in their sight.

Oedipus. O thou horror of darkness that enfoldest me, visitant unspeakable, resistless, sped by a wind too fair!

Ay me! and once again, ay me!

How is my soul pierced by the stab of these goads, and withal by the memory of sorrows!

Chorus. Yea, amid woes so many a twofold pain may well be thine to mourn and to bear.

Oedipus. Ah, friend, thou still art steadfast in thy tendance of me, thou still hast patience to care for the blind man! Ah me! Thy presence is not hid from me—no, dark though I am, yet know I thy voice full well.

Chorus. Man of dread deeds, how couldst thou in such wise quench thy vision? What more than human power urged thee?

Oedipus. Apollo, friends, Apollo was he that brought these my woes to pass, these my sore, sore woes: but the hand that struck the eyes was none save mine, wretched that I am! Why was I to see, when sight could show me nothing sweet?

Chorus. These things were even as thou sayest.

Oedipus. Say, friends, what can I more behold, what can I love, what greeting can touch mine ear with joy? Haste, lead me from the land, friends, lead me hence, the utterly lost, the thrice accursed, yea, the mortal most abhorred of heaven!

Chorus. Wretched alike for thy fortune and for thy sense thereof, would that I had never so much as known thee!

Oedipus. Perish the man, whoe'er he was, that freed me in the pastures from the cruel shackle on my feet, and saved me from death, and gave me back to life—a thankless deed! Had I died then, to my friends and to mine own soul I had not been so sore a grief.

Chorus. I also would have had it thus.

Oedipus. So had I not come to shed my father's blood, nor been called among men the spouse of her from whom I sprang: but now am I forsaken of the gods, son of a defiled mother, successor to his bed who gave me mine own wretched being; and if there be yet a woe surpassing woes, it hath become the portion of Oedipus.

Chorus. I know not how I can say that thou hast counseled well, for thou wert better dead than living and blind.

Oedipus. Show me not at large that these things are not best done thus. Give me counsel no more. For, had I sight, I know not with what eyes I could e'en have looked on my father, when I came to the place of the dead, aye, or on my miserable mother, since against both I have sinned such sins as strangling could not punish. But deem ye that the sight of children, born as mine were born, was lovely for me to look upon? No, no, not lovely to mine eyes forever! No, nor was this town with its towered walls, nor the sacred statues of the gods, since I, thrice wretched that I am—I, noblest of the sons of Thebes—have doomed myself to know these no more, by mine own command that all should thrust away the impious one, even him whom gods have shown to be unholy, and of the race of Laius!

After bearing such a stain upon me, was I to look with steady eyes on this folk? No, verily. No, were there yet a way to choke the fount of hearing, I had not spared to make a fast prison of this wretched frame, that so I should have known nor sight nor sound. For 'tis sweet that our thought should dwell beyond the sphere of griefs.

Alas, Cithaeron, why hadst thou a shelter for me? When I was given to thee, why didst thou not slay me straightway, that so I might never have revealed my source to men? Ah, Polybus, ah, Corinth, and thou that wast called the ancient house of my fathers, how seeming-fair was I your nurseling, and what ills were festering beneath! For now I am found evil, and of evil birth. O ye three roads, and thou secret glen—thou coppice, and narrow way where three paths met—ye who drank from my hands that father's blood which was mine own—remember ye, perchance, what deeds I wrought for you to see—and then, when I came hither, what fresh deeds I went on to do?

O marriage rites, ye gave me birth, and when ye had brought me forth, again ye bore children to your child, ye created an incestuous kinship of fathers, brothers, sons, brides, wives, mothers—yea, all the foulest shame that is wrought among men! Nay, but 'tis unmeet to name what 'tis unmeet to do—haste ye, for the gods' love, hide me somewhere beyond the land, or slay me, or cast me into the sea, where ye shall never behold me more! Approach, deign to lay your hands on a wretched man; hearken, fear not, my plague can rest on no mortal beside.

Chorus. Nay, here is Creon, in meet season for thy requests, crave thy act or counsel; for he alone is left to guard the land in thy stead.

Oedipus. Ah me, how indeed shall I accost him? What claim to credence can be shown on my part? For in the past I have been found wholly false to him.

[*Enter* Creon]

Creon. I have not come in mockery, Oedipus, nor to reproach thee with any bygone fault. (To the attendants.) But ye, if ye respect the children of men no more, revere at least the all-nurturing flame of our lord the Sun—spare to show thus nakedly a pollution such as this—one which neither earth can welcome, nor the holy rain, nor the light. Nay, take him into the house as quickly as ye may; for it best accords with piety that kinsfolk alone should see and hear a kinsman's woes.

Oedipus. For the gods' love—since thou hast done a gentle violence to my presage, who hast come in a spirit so noble to me, a man most vile—grant me a boon, for thy good I will speak, not for mine own.

Creon. And what wish art thou so fain to have of me?

Oedipus. Cast me out of this land with all speed, to a place where no mortal shall be found to greet me more.

Creon. This would I have done, be thou sure, but that I craved first to learn all my duty from the god.

Oedipus. Nay, his behest hath been set forth in full, to let me perish, the parricide, the unholy one, that I am.

Creon. Such was the purport; yet, seeing to what a pass we have come, 'tis better to learn clearly what should be done.

Oedipus. Will ye, then, seek a response on behalf of such a wretch as I am?

Creon. Aye, for thou thyself wilt now surely put faith in the god.

Oedipus. Yea; and on thee lay I this charge, to thee will I make this entreaty: give to her who is within such burial as thou thyself wouldest; for thou wilt meetly render the last rites to thine own. But for me, never let this city of my sire be condemned to have me dwelling therein, while I live. No, suffer me to abide on the hills, where yonder is Cithaeron, famed as mine, which my mother and sire, while they lived, set for my appointed tomb, that so I may die by their decree who sought to slay me. Howbeit of thus much am I sure, that neither sickness nor aught else can destroy me; for never had I been snatched from death, but in reserve for some strange doom.

Nay, let my fate go wither it will, but as touching my children, I pray thee, Creon, take no care on thee for my sons; they are men, so that be they where they may, they can never lack the means to live. But my two girls, poor hapless ones, who never knew my table spread apart, or lacked their father's presence, but ever in all things shared my daily bread, I pray thee, care for them; and—if thou canst—suffer me to touch them with my hands, and to indulge my grief. Grant it, prince, grant it, thou noble heart! Ah, could I but once touch them with my hands, I should think that they were with me, even as when I had sight.

[Creon's *attendants lead in the children* Antigone *and* Ismene]

Ha? O ye gods, can it be my loved ones that I hear sobbing. Can Creon have taken pity on me and sent me my children— my darlings? Am I right?

Creon. Yea. 'Tis of my contriving, for I knew thy joy in them of old—the joy that now is thine.

Oedipus. Then blessed be thou, and, for guerdon of this errand, may heaven prove to thee a kinder guardian than it hath to me! My children, where are ye? Come hither, hither to the hands of him whose mother was your own, the hands whose offices have wrought that your sire's once bright eyes should be such orbs as these, his, who seeing nought, knowing nought, became your father by her from whom he sprang! For you also do I weep—behold you I cannot—when I think of the bitter life in days to come which men will make you live. To what company of the citizens will ye go, to what festival, from which ye shall not return home in tears, instead of sharing in the holiday? But when ye are now come to years ripe for marriage, who shall he be, who shall be the man, my daughters, that will hazard taking unto him such reproaches as must be baneful alike to my offspring and to yours? For what misery is wanting? Your sire slew his sire, he had seed of her who bare him, and begat you at the sources of his own being! Such are the taunts that will be cast at you; and who then will wed? The man lives not, no, it cannot be, my children, but ye must wither in barren maidenhood.

Ah, son of Menoeceus, hear me—since thou art the only father left to them, for we, their parents, are lost, both of us— allow them not to wander poor and unwed, who are thy kinswomen, nor abase them to the level of my woes. Nay, pity them, when thou seest them at this tender age so utterly forlorn, save for thee. Signify thy promise, generous man, by the touch of thy hand! To you, my children, I would have given much counsel, were your minds mature; but now I would have this to be your prayer—that ye live where occasion suffers, and that the life which is your portion may be happier than your sire's.

Creon. Thy grief hath had large scope enough. Nay, pass into the house.

Oedipus. I must obey, though 'tis in no wise sweet.

Creon. Yea, for it is in season that all things are good.

Oedipus. Knowest thou, then, on what conditions I will go?

Creon. Thou shalt name them; so shall I know them when I hear.

Oedipus. See that thou send me to dwell beyond this land.

Creon. Thou askest me for what the god must give.

Oedipus. Nay, to the gods I have become most hateful.

Creon. Then shalt thou have thy wish anon.

Oedipus. So thou consentest?

Creon. 'Tis not my wont to speak idly what I do not mean.

Oedipus. Then 'tis time to lead me hence.

Creon. Come, then, but let thy children go.

Oedipus. Nay, take not these from me!

Creon. Crave not to be master in all things: for the mastery which thou didst win hath not followed thee through life.

Chorus. Dwellers in our native Thebes, behold, this is Oedipus, who knew the famed riddle, and was a man most mighty; on whose fortunes what citizen did not gaze with envy? Behold into what a stormy sea of dread trouble he hath come!

Therefore, while our eyes wait to see the destined final day, we must call no one happy who is of mortal race, until he hath crossed life's border, free from pain.

DRAMATIS PERSONAE

Bonaventura, a friar
A Cardinal, nuncio to the Pope
Soranzo, a nobleman
Florio,
Donado, } Citizens of Parma
Grimaldi, a Roman gentleman
Giovanni, son of Florio
Bergetto, nephew of Donado
Richardetto, a supposed physician
Vasques, servant to Soranzo
Poggio, servant to Bergetto
Banditti, Officers, Attendants, Servants

Annabella, daughter of Florio
Hippolita, wife of Richardetto
Philotis, niece of Richardetto
Putana, tutoress to Annabella

SCENE—*Parma*

John Ford

'TIS PITY SHE'S A WHORE

JOHN FORD (1586-c.1640), born in England, after having achieved a reputation as an important dramatist, collaborated with Dekker and Rowley in writing *The Witch of Edmonton,* perhaps his most successful work. *'Tis Pity She's A Whore,* like several of his other works, takes up a problem with which Ford was deeply concerned: the conflict between man's overwhelming and often compulsive passions and the restraints that society imposes on these passions. It is probably the most outspoken and forthright study of incest ever written for the English-language stage, and has been the subject of critical studies by Havelock Ellis, Swinburne, and others.

ACT I

SCENE I—Friar Bonaventura's *Cell*

[*Enter* Friar *and* Giovanni]

Friar. Dispute no more in this; for know, young man,
These are no school-points; nice philosophy
May tolerate unlikely arguments,
But Heaven admits no jest: wits that presumed
On wit too much, by striving how to prove
There was no God with foolish grounds of art,
Discovered first the nearest way to hell,
And filled the world with devilish atheism.
Such questions, youth, are vain: far better 'tis
To bless the sun than reason why it shines;
Yet He thou talk'st of is above the sun.
No more! I may not hear it.
Gio.   Gentle father,
To you I have unclasped my burdened soul,

Emptied the storehouse of my thoughts and heart,
Made myself poor of secrets; have not left
Another word untold, which hath not spoke
All what I ever durst or think or know;
And yet is here the comfort I shall have?
Must I not do what all men else may,—love?
   Friar. Yes, you may love, fair son.
   Gio.   Must I not praise
That beauty which, if framed anew, the gods
Would make a god of, if they had it there,
And kneel to it, as I do kneel to them?
   Friar. Why, foolish madman—
   Gio.   Shall a trifling sound,
A customary form, from man to man,
Of brother and of sister, be a bar
'Twixt my perpetual happiness and me?
Say that we had one father; say one womb—
Curse to my joys!—gave both us life and birth;
Are we not therefore each to other bound
So much the more by nature? by the links
Of blood, of reason? nay, if you will have't,
Even of religion, to be ever one,
One soul, one flesh, one love, one heart, one all?
   Friar. Have done, unhappy youth! for thou art lost.
   Gio. Shall, then, for that I am her brother born,
My joys be ever banished from her bed?
No, father; in your eyes I see the change
Of pity and compassion; from your age,
As from a sacred oracle, distills
The life of counsel: tell me, holy man,
What cure shall give me ease in these extremes?
   Friar. Repentance, son, and sorrow for this sin:
For thou hast moved a Majesty above
With thy unrangèd almost blasphemy.
   Gio. O, do not speak of that, dear confessor!
   Friar. Art thou, my son, that miracle of wit
Who once, within these three months, wert esteemed
A wonder of thine age throughout Bononia?

How did the University applaud
Thy government, behavior, learning, speech,
Sweetness, and all that could make up a man!
I was proud of my tutelage, and chose
Rather to leave my books than part with thee;
I did so:—but the fruits of all my hopes
Are lost in thee, as thou art in thyself.
O, Giovanni![1] hast thou left the schools
Of knowledge to converse with lust and death?
For death waits on thy lust. Look through the world,
And thou shalt see a thousand faces shine
More glorious than this idol thou ador'st:
Leave her, and take thy choice, 'tis much less sin;
Though in such games as those they lose that win.

   Gio. It were more ease to stop the ocean
From floats and ebbs than to dissuade my vows.

   Friar. Then I have done, and in thy willful flames
Already see thy ruin; Heaven is just.
Yet hear my counsel.

   Gio.   As a voice of life.

   Friar. Hie to thy father's house; there lock thee fast
Alone within thy chamber; then fall down
On both thy knees, and grovel on the ground;
Cry to thy heart; wash every word thou utter'st
In tears—and if't be possible—of blood:
Beg Heaven to cleanse the leprosy of lust
That rots thy soul; acknowledge what thou art,
A wretch, a worm, a nothing; weep, sigh, pray
Three times a-day and three times every night:
For seven days' space do this; then, if thou find'st
No change in thy desires, return to me:
I'll think on remedy. Pray for thyself
At home, whilst I pray for thee here.—Away!
My blessing with thee! we have need to pray.

   Gio. All this I'll do, to free me from the rod
     Of vengeance; else I'll swear my fate's my god.

                                  [Exeunt]

---

1 Giovanni is here used by Ford as a quadrisyllable.

SCENE II—*The Street before* Florio's *House*

[*Enter* Grimaldi *and* Vasques, *with their swords drawn*]

Vas. Come, sir, stand to your tackling; if you prove craven,
I'll make you run quickly.

Grim. Thou art no equal match for me.

Vas. Indeed, I never went to the wars to bring home news;
nor cannot play the mountebank for a meal's meat, and swear
I got my wounds in the field. See you these gray hairs? they'll
not flinch for a bloody nose. Wilt thou to this gear?

Grim. Why, slave, thinkest thou I'll balance my reputation
with a cast-suit?[2] Call thy master; he shall know that I dare—

Vas. Scold like a cot-quean;[3]—that's your profession. Thou
poor shadow of a soldier, I will make thee know my master
keeps servants thy betters in quality and performance. Comest
thou to fight or prate?

Grim. Neither, with thee. I am a Roman and a gentleman;
one that have got mine honor with expense of blood.

Vas. You are a lying coward and a fool. Fight, or by these
hilts, I'll kill thee: brave my lord!—you'll fight?

Grim. Provoke me not, for if thou dost—

Vas.   Have at you!

[*They fight; Grimaldi is worsted*]
[*Enter* Florio, Donado, *and* Soranzo, *from opposite sides*]

Flo. What mean these sudden broils so near my doors?
Have you not other places but my house
To vent the spleen of your disordered bloods?
Must I be haunted still with such unrest
As not to eat or sleep in peace at home?
Is this your love, Grimaldi? Fie! 'tis naught.

Don. And, Vasques, I may tell thee, 'tis not well
To broach these quarrels; you are ever forward
In seconding contentions.

[*Enter* Annabella *and* Putana *above*]

Flo.   What's the ground?

Sor. That, with your patience, signiors, I'll resolve:

2 *i.e.* Cast-off.

3 A contemptuous term for one who concerns himself with female affairs.

This gentleman, whom fame reports a soldier,
For else I know not, rivals me in love
To Signior Florio's daughter; to whose ears
He still prefers his suit, to my disgrace;
Thinking the way to recommend himself
Is to disparage me in his report:
But know, Grimaldi, though, may be, thou art
My equal in thy blood, yet this betrays
A lowness in thy mind, which, wert thou noble,
Thou wouldst as much disdain as I do thee
For this unworthiness: and on this ground
I willed my servant to correct his tongue,
Holding a man so base no match for me.

Vas. And had not your sudden coming prevented us, I had
let my gentleman blood under the gills: I should have wormed
you, sir, for running mad.[4]

Grim. I'll be revenged, Soranzo.

Vas. On a dish of warm broth to stay your stomach—do,
honest, innocence, do! spoon-meat is a wholesomer diet than a
Spanish blade.

Grim. Remember this!

Sor.   I fear thee not, Grimaldi.

                                          [*Exit* Grimaldi]

Flo. My Lord Soranzo, this is strange to me,
Why you should storm, having my word engaged;
Owning her heart, what need you doubt her ear?
Losers may talk by law of any game.

Vas. Yet the villainy of words, Signior Florio, may be such as
would make any unspleened dove choleric. Blame not my lord
in this.

Flo. Be you more silent:
I would not for my wealth, my daughter's love
Should cause the spilling of one drop of blood.
Vasques, put up, let's end this fray in wine.   [*Exeunt*]

Put. How like you this, child? here's threatening, challenging,
quarreling, and fighting on every side; and all is for your sake:

4 The allusion is to the practice of cutting what is called the worm from under
a dog's tongue, as a preventive of madness.—*Gifford.*

you had need look to yourself, charge; you'll be stolen away
sleeping else shortly.

Ann. But, tutoress, such a life gives no content
To me; my thoughts are fixed on other ends.
Would you would leave me!

Put. Leave you! no marvel else; leave me no leaving, charge;
this is love outright. Indeed, I blame you not; you have choice
fit for the best lady in Italy.

Ann. Pray do not talk so much.

Put. Take the worst with the best, there's Grimaldi the soldier, a very well-timbered fellow. They say he is a Roman,
nephew to the Duke Montferrato; they say he did good service
in the wars against the Milanese; but, 'faith, charge, I do not
like him, an't be for nothing but for being a soldier: not one
amongst twenty of your skirmishing captains but have some
privy maim or other that mars their standing upright. I like
him the worse, he crinkles so much in the hams: though he
might serve if there were no more men, yet he's not the man
I would choose.

Ann. Fie, how thou pratest.

Put. As I am a very woman, I like Signior Soranzo well; he
is wise, and what is more, rich; and what is more than that,
kind; and what is more than all this, a nobleman: such a one,
were I the fair Annabella myself, I would wish and pray for.
Then he is bountiful; besides, he is handsome, and, by my
troth, I think, wholesome,—and that's news in a gallant of
three-and-twenty; liberal, that I know; loving, that you know;
and a man sure, else he could never ha' purchased such a good
name with Hippolita, the lusty widow, in her husband's lifetime: an 'twere but for that report, sweetheart, would 'a were
thine! Commend a man for his qualities, but take a husband
as he is a plain, sufficient, naked man: such a one is for your
bed, and such a one is Signior Soranzo, my life for't.

Ann. Sure the woman took her morning's draught too soon.

[*Enter* Bergetto *and* Poggio]

Put. But look, sweetheart, look what thing comes now! Here's
another of your ciphers to fill up the number: O, brave old ape
in a silken coat! Observe.

Berg. Didst thou think, Poggio, that I would spoil my new clothes, and leave my dinner, to fight?

Pog. No, sir, I did not take you for so arrant a baby.

Berg. I am wiser than so: for I hope, Poggio, thou never heardst of an elder brother that was a coxcomb; didst, Poggio?

Pog. Never, indeed, sir, as long as they had either land or money left them to inherit.

Berg. Is it possible, Poggio? O, monstrous! Why, I'll undertake with a handful of silver to buy a headful of wit at any time: but, sirrah, I have another purchase in hand; I shall have the wench, mine uncle says. I will but wash my face and shift socks, and then have at her, i'faith! Mark my pace, Poggio!

[Passes over the stage, and exit]

Pog. Sir,—I have seen an ass and a mule trot the Spanish pavin⁵ with a better grace, I know not how often.

[Aside, and follows him]

Ann. This idiot haunts me too.

Put. Ay, ay, he needs no description. The rich magnifico that is below with your father, charge, Signior Donado his uncle, for that he means to make this, his nephew, a golden calf, thinks that you will be a right Israelite, and fall down to him presently: but I hope I have tutored you better. They say a fool's bauble is a lady's playfellow; yet you, having wealth enough, you need not cast upon the dearth of flesh, at any rate. Hang him, idiot!

[Giovanni passes over the stage]

Ann. But see, Putana, see! what blessèd shape
Of some celestial creature now appears!—
What man is he, that with such sad aspéct
Walks careless of himself?

Put. Where?

Ann. Look below.

Put. O, 'tis your brother, sweet.

Ann. Ha!

Put. 'Tis your brother.

---

⁵ "A grave and majestic dance; the method of performing it was anciently by gentlemen dressed with a cap and sword; by those of the long robe, in their gowns; by princes, in their mantles; and by ladies, in gowns with long trains, the motion whereof in the dance resembled that of a peacock's tail."—*Hawkins.*

Ann. Sure, 'tis not he; this is some woeful thing
Wrapped up in grief, some shadow of a man.
Alas, he beats his breast and wipes his eyes,
Drowned all in tears: methinks I hear him sigh:
Let's down, Putana, and partake the cause.
I know my brother, in the love he bears me,
Will not deny me partage in his sadness.
My soul is full of heaviness and fear.   *[Aside]*

[Exit above with Putana]

    SCENE III—*A Hall in* Florio's *House*

[Enter Giovanni]

  Gio. Lost! I am lost! my fates have doomed my death:
The more I strive, I love; the more I love,
The less I hope: I see my ruin certain.
What judgment or endeavors could apply
To my incurable and restless wounds,
I thoroughly have examined, but in vain.
O, that it were not in religion sin
To make our love a god, and worship it!
I have even wearied Heaven with prayers, dried up
The spring of my continual tears, even starved
My veins with daily fasts: what wit or art
Could counsel, I have practiced; but, alas,
I find all these but dreams, and old men's tales,
To fright unsteady youth; I'm still the same:
Or I must speak, or burst. 'Tis not, I know,
My lust, but 'tis my fate that leads me on.
Keep fear and low faint-hearted shame with slaves!
I'll tell her that I love her, though my heart
Were rated at the price of that attempt.
O me! she comes.

[Enter Annabella *and* Putana]

  Ann.   Brother!
Gio. [Aside]   If such a thing
As courage dwell in men, ye heavenly powers,
Now double all that virtue in my tongue!
  Ann. Why, brother,

Will you not speak to me?

 Gio.   Yes: how d'ye sister?

 Ann. Howe'er I am, methinks you are not well.

 Put. Bless us! Why are you so sad, sir?

 Gio. Let me entreat you, leave us a while, Putana.

Sister, I would be private with you.

 Ann. Withdraw, Putana.

 Put. I will. If this were any other company for her,

I should think my absence an office of some credit: but

I will leave them together.   *[Aside, and exit]*

 Gio. Come, sister, lend your hand: let's walk together!

I hope you need not blush to walk with me;

Here's none but you and I.

 Ann.   How's this?

 Gio.   I'faith,

I mean no harm.

 Ann.   Harm?

 Gio.   No, good faith.

How is't with ye?

 Ann. *[Aside]* I trust he be not frantic.

I am very well, brother.

 Gio. Trust me, but I am sick; I fear so sick

'Twill cost my life.

 Ann. Mercy forbid it! 'tis not so, I hope.

 Gio. I think you love me, sister.

 Ann.   Yes, you know

I do.

 Gio. I know't, indeed. You're very fair.

 Ann. Nay, then I see you have a merry sickness.

 Gio. That's as it proves. The poets feign, I read,

That Juno for her forehead did exceed

All other goddesses; but I durst swear

Your forehead exceeds hers, as hers did theirs.

 Ann. 'Troth, this is pretty!

 Gio.   Such a pair of stars

As are thine eyes would, like Promethean fire,

If gently glanced, give life to senseless stones.

 Ann. Fie upon ye!

    Gio. The lily and the rose, most sweetly strange,
Upon your dimpled cheeks do strive for change:
Such lips would tempt a saint; such hands as those
Would make an anchorite lascivious.
    Ann. D'ye mock me or flatter me?
    Gio. If you would see a beauty more exact
Than art can counterfeit or nature frame,
Look in your glass, and there behold your own.
    Ann. O, you are a trim youth!
    Gio. Here!   *[Offers his dagger to her]*
    Ann.   What to do?
    Gio.   And here's my breast; strike home!
Rip up my bosom; there thou shalt behold
A heart in which is writ the truth I speak.
Why stand ye?
    Ann.   Are you earnest?
    Gio.   Yes, most earnest.
You cannot love?
    Ann.   Whom?
    Gio.   Me. My tortured soul
Hath felt affliction in the heat of death.
O, Annabella, I am quite undone!
The love of thee, my sister, and the view
Of thy immortal beauty have untuned
All harmony both of my rest and life.
Why d'ye not strike?
    Ann.   Forbid it, my just fears!
If this be true, 'twere fitter I were dead.
    Gio. True, Annabella! 'tis no time to jest.
I have too long suppressed the hidden flames
That almost have consumed me: I have spent
Many a silent night in sighs and groans;
Ran over all my thoughts, despised my fate,
Reasoned against the reasons of my love,
Done all that smoothed-cheeked virtue could advise;
But found all bootless: 'tis my destiny
That you must either love, or I must die.
    Ann. Comes this in earnestness from you?

Gio.   Let some mischief
Befall me soon, if I dissemble aught.
   Ann. You are my brother Giovanni.
   Gio.   You
My sister Annabella; I know this,
And could afford you instance why to love
So much the more for this; to which intent
Wise nature first in your creation meant
To make you mine; else't had been sin and foul
To share one beauty to a double soul.
Nearness in birth and blood doth but persuade
A nearer nearness in affection.
I have asked counsel of the holy church,
Who tells me I may love you; and 'tis just
That, since I may, I should; and will, yes, will.
Must I now live or die?
   Ann.   Live; thou hast won
The field, and never fought: what thou hast urged
My captive heart had long ago resolved.
I blush to tell thee, but I'll tell thee now,
For every sigh that thou hast spent for me
I have sighed ten; for every tear shed twenty:
And not so much for that I loved, as that
I dared not say I loved, nor scarcely think it.
   Gio. Let not this music be a dream, ye gods,
For pity's sake, I beg ye!
   Ann.   On my knees,   [*She kneels*]
Brother, even by our mother's dust, I charge you,
Do not betray me to your mirth or hate:
Love me or kill me, brother.
   Gio.   On my knees,   [*He kneels*]
Sister, even by my mother's dust, I charge you,
Do not betray me to your mirth or hate:
Love me or kill me, sister.
   Ann. You speak in truth, then?
   Gio.   In good faith, I do;
And so do you, I hope: say, I'm in earnest.
   Ann. I'll swear it, I.

Gio.   And I; and by this kiss,

                 [Kisses her.]

Once more, yet once more: now let's rise   *[They rise]*,
   by this,
I would not change this minute for Elysium.
What must we now do?
  Ann.   What you will.
  Gio.   Come, then;
After so many tears as we have wept,
Let's learn to court in smiles, to kiss, and sleep.

                 [Exeunt]

   SCENE IV—*A Street*

             [Enter Florio *and* Donado]
  Flo. Signior Donado, you have said enough,
I understand you; but would have you know
I will not force my daughter 'gainst her will.
You see I have but two, a son and her;
And he is so devoted to his book,
As I must tell you true, I doubt his health:
Should he miscarry, all my hopes rely
Upon my girl. As for worldly fortune,
I am, I thank my stars, blessed with enough.
My care is, how to match her to her liking:
I would not have her marry wealth, but love
And if she like your nephew, let him have her.
Here's all that I can say.
  Don.   Sir, you say well,
Like a true father; and, for my part, I,
If the young folks can like, 'twixt you and me,
Will promise to assure my nephew presently
Three thousand florins yearly during life,
And after I am dead my whole estate.
  Flo. 'Tis a fair proffer, sir; meantime your nephew
Shall have free passage to commence his suit:
If he can thrive, he shall have my consent.
So for this time I'll leave you, signior.   *[Exit]*
  Don.   Well,

Here's hope yet, if my nephew would have wit;
But he is such another dunce, I fear
He'll never win the wench. When I was young,
I could have done't, i'faith; and so shall he,
If he will learn of me; and, in good time,
He comes himself.

[*Enter* Bergetto *and* Poggio]

How now, Bergetto, whither away so fast?

Berg. O, uncle, I have heard the strangest news that ever came out of the mint! Have I not, Poggio?

Pog. Yes, indeed, sir.

Don. What news, Bergetto?

Berg. Why, look ye, uncle, my barber told me just now that there is a fellow come to town who undertakes to make a mill go without the mortal help of any water or wind, only with sand bags: and this fellow hath a strange horse, a most excellent beast, I'll assure you, uncle, my barber says; whose head, to the wonder of all Christian people, stands just behind where his tail is. —Is't not true, Poggio?

Pog. So the barber swore, indeed.

Don. And you are running thither?

Berg. Ay, indeed, uncle.

Don. Wilt thou be a fool still? Come, sir, you shall not go: you have more mind of a puppet play than on the business I told ye. Why, thou great baby, wilt never have wit? wilt make thyself a May-game to all the world?

Pog. Answer for yourself, master.

Berg. Why, uncle, should I sit at home still, and not go abroad to see fashions like other gallants?

Don. To see hobbyhorses! What wise talk, I pray, had you with Annabella, when you were at Signior Florio's house?

Berg. O, the wench, Ud's sa'me, uncle, I tickled her with a rare speech, that I made her almost burst her belly with laughing.

Don. Nay, I think so; and what speech was't?

Berg. What did I say, Poggio?

Pog. Forsooth, my master said, that he loved her almost as well as he loved Parmesan, and swore—I'll be sworn for him—

that she wanted but such a nose as his was, to be as pretty a young woman as any was in Parma.

Don. O, gross!

Berg. Nay, uncle: then she asked me whether my father had any more children than myself; and I said, "No; 'twere better he should have had his brains knocked out first."

Don. This is intolerable.

Berg. Then said she, "Will Signior Donado, your uncle, leave you all his wealth?"

Don. Ha! that was good; did she harp upon that string?

Berg. Did she harp upon that string! ay, that she did. I answered, "Leave me all his wealth! why, woman, he hath no other wit; if he had, he should hear on't to his everlasting glory and confusion: I know," quoth I, "I am his white-boy,[6] and will not be gulled": and with that she fell into a great smile, and went away. Nay, I did fit her.

Don. Ah, sirrah, then I see there is no changing of nature. Well, Bergetto, I fear thou wilt be a very ass still.

Berg. I should be sorry for that, uncle.

Don. Come, come you home with me: since you are no better a speaker, I'll have you write to her after some courtly manner, and enclose some rich jewel in the letter.

Berg. Ay, marry, that will be excellent.

Don. Peace, idiot!

Once in my time I'll set my wits to school:
If all fail, 'tis but the fortune of a fool.

Berg. Poggio, 'twill do, Poggio.   *[Exeunt]*

[6] A term of endearment. It is said that this and similar terms are still used in some parts of Ireland. Under the ancient Irish Geilfine system of land tenure the homestead itself, in the division of the family property, fell to the lot of the fifth son, who was called the fair-haired or white-headed boy, *geil* meaning white.

ACT II

SCENE I—*An apartment in* Florio's *house*

[*Enter* Giovanni *and* Annabella]

Giovanni. Come, Annabella, no more sister now,
But love, a name more gracious, do not blush,
Beauty's sweet wonder, but be proud to know
That yielding thou hast conquered, and inflamed
A heart whose tribute is thy brother's life.

Ann. And mine is his. O, how these stolen contents
Would print a modest crimson on my cheeks,
Had any but my heart's delight prevailed!

Gio. I marvel why the chaster of your sex
Should think this pretty toy called maidenhead
So strange a loss, when, being lost, 'tis nothing,
And you are still the same.

Ann.   'Tis well for you;
Now you can talk.

Gio.   Music as well consists
In the ear as in the playing.

Ann.   O, you're wanton!
Tell on't, you're best; do.

Gio.   Thou wilt chide me, then.
Kiss me—so! Thus hung Jove on Leda's neck,
And sucked divine ambrosia from her lips.
I envy not the mightiest man alive;
But hold myself in being king of thee,
More great than were I king of all the world.
But I shall lose you, sweetheart.

Ann.   But you shall not.

Gio. You must be married, mistress.

Ann.   Yes! to whom?

Gio. Some one must have you.

Ann.   You must.

Gio.   Nay, some other.

Ann. Now, prithee do not speak so: without jesting
You'll make me weep in earnest.

Gio.   What, you will not!
But tell me, sweet, canst thou be dared to swear
That thou wilt live to me, and to no other?

Ann. By both our loves I dare; for didst thou know,
My Giovanni, how all suitors seem
To my eyes hateful, thou wouldst trust me then.

Gio. Enough, I take thy word: sweet, we must part:
Remember what thou vow'st; keep well my heart.

Ann. Will you be gone?

Gio. I must.

Ann. When to return?

Gio.   Soon.

Ann.   Look you do.

Gio.   Farewell.

Ann. Go where thou wilt, in mind I'll keep thee here.
And where thou art, I know I shall be there.

                                                [*Exit* Giovanni]

Guardian!

                                                [*Enter* Putana]

Put. Child, how is't, child? well, thank Heaven, ha!

Ann. O guardian, what a paradise of joy
Have I passed over!

Put. Nay, what a paradise of joy have you passed under!
Why, now I commend thee, charge. Fear nothing, sweetheart:
what though he be your brother? your brother's a man, I hope;
and I say still, if a young wench feel the fit upon her, let her take
any body, father or brother, all is one.

Ann. I would not have it known for all the world.

Put. Nor I, indeed; for the speech of the people: else 'twere
nothing.

Flo. [*Within*] Daughter Annabella!

Ann. O me, my father!—Here, sir!—Fetch my work.

Flo. [*Within*] What are you doing?

Ann.   So: let him come now.

[*Enter* Florio, *followed by* Richardetto *as a* Doctor of
Physic, *and* Philotis *with a lute*]

Flo. So hard at work! that's well; you lose no time.
Look, I have brought you company; here's one,
A learnèd doctor lately come from Padua,
Much skilled in physic; and, for that I see
You have of late been sickly, I entreated
This reverend man to visit you some time.

  Ann. You're very welcome, sir.
  Rich.   I thank you, mistress.
Loud fame in large report hath spoke your praise
As well for virtue as beauty
For which I have been bold to bring with me
A kinswoman of mine, a maid, for song
And music one perhaps will give content:
Please you to know her.

  Ann.   They are parts I love.
And she for them most welcome.

  Phi.   Thank you, lady.
  Flo. Sir, now you know my house, pray make not strange;
And if you find my daughter need your art,
I'll be your paymaster.

  Rich.   Sir, what I am
She shall command.

  Flo.   Sir, you shall bind me to you.
Daughter, I must have conference with you
About some matters that concern us both.
Good Master Doctor, please you but walk in,
We'll crave a little of your cousin's skill
I think my girl hath not quite forgot
To touch an instrument; she could have done't:
We'll hear them both.

  Rich.   I'll wait upon you, sir.   [*Exeunt*]

  SCENE II—*A Room in* Soranzo's *House*

                                        [*Enter* Soranzo *with a book*]
  Sor. [*Reads*] "Love's measure is extreme, the comfort pain,
The life unrest, and the reward disdain."

What's here? look't o'er again. 'Tis so; so writes
This smooth, licentious poet in his rhymes:
But, Sannazar, thou liest; for, had thy bosom
Felt such oppression as is laid on mine,
Thou wouldst have kissed the rod that made thee smart.—
To work, then, happy Muse, and contradict
What Sannazar hath in his envy writ.   [*Writes*]
"Love's measure is the mean, sweet his annoys,
His pleasures life, and his reward all joys."
Had Annabella lived when Sannazar
Did, in his brief Encomium,[7] celebrate
Venice, that queen of cities, he had left
That verse which gained him such a sum of gold,
And for one only look from Annabel
Had writ of her and her diviner cheeks.
O, how my thoughts are—
      Vas. [*Within*] Pray, forbear; in rules of civility, let me give
notice on't: I shall be taxed of my neglect of duty and service.
      Sor. What rude intrusion interrupts my peace?
Can I be nowhere private?
      Vas. [*Within*] You wrong your modesty.
      Sor. What's the matter, Vasques? who is't?
                                          [*Enter* Hippolita *and* Vasques]
      Hip.   'Tis I;
Do you know me now? Look, perjured man, on her
Whom thou and thy distracted lust have wronged.
Thy sensual rage of blood hath made my youth
A scorn to men and angels; and shall I
Be now a foil to thy unsated change?
Thou know'st, false wanton, when my modest fame
Stood free from stain or scandal, all the charms
Of hell or sorcery could not prevail
Against the honor of my chaster bosom.
Thine eyes did plead in tears, thy tongue in oaths,
Such and so many, that a heart of steel

---

[7] This is the well-known epigram, beginning
            "Viderat Hadriacis Venetam Neptunus in undis
                  Stare urbem."

Would have been wrought to pity, as was mine:
And shall the conquest of my lawful bed,
My husband's death, urged on by his disgrace,
My loss of womanhood, be ill-rewarded
With hatred and contempt? No; know, Soranzo.
I have a spirit doth as much distaste
The slavery of fearing thee, as thou
Dost loathe the memory of what hath passed.
   Sor. Nay, dear Hippolita,
   Hip.   Call me not dear,
Nor think with supple words to smooth the grossness
Of my abuses: 'tis not your new mistress,
Your goodly madam merchant, shall triumph
On my dejection; tell her thus from me,
My birth was nobler and by much more free.
   Sor. You are too violent.
   Hip.   You are too double
In your dissimulation. Seest thou this,
This habit, these black mourning weeds of care?
'Tis thou art cause of this; and hast divorced
My husband from his life, and me from him,
And made me widow in my widowhood.
   Sor. Will you yet hear?
   Hip.   More of thy perjuries?
Thy soul is drowned too deeply in those sins;
Thou need'st not add to the number.
   Sor.   Then I'll leave you;
You're past all rules of sense.
   Hip.   And thou of grace.
   Vas. Fie, mistress, you are not near the limits of reason: if my
lord had a resolution as noble as virtue itself, you take the
course to unedge it all. Sir, I beseech you do not perplex her;
griefs, alas, will have a vent: I dare undertake Madam Hippolita
will now freely hear you.
   Sor. Talk to a woman frantic! Are these the fruits of your
love?
   Hip. They are the fruits of thy untruth, false man!
Didst thou not swear, whilst yet my husband lived,

That thou wouldst wish no happiness on earth
More than to call me wife? didst thou not vow,
When he should die, to marry me? for which
The devil in my blood, and thy protests,
Caused me to counsel him to undertake
A voyage to Ligorne, for that we heard
His brother there was dead, and left a daughter
Young and unfriended, who, with much ado,
I wished him to bring hither: he did so,
And went; and, as thou know'st, died on the way.
Unhappy man, to buy his death so dear,
With my advice! yet thou, for whom I did it,
Forgett'st thy vows, and leav'st me to my shame.
    Sor. Who could help this?
    Hip.   Who! perjured man, thou couldst,
If thou hadst faith or love.
    Sor.   You are deceived:
The vows I made, if you remember well,
Were wicked and unlawful; 'twere more sin
To keep them than to break them: as for me,
I cannot mask my penitence. Think thou
How much thou hast digressed from honest shame
In bringing of a gentleman to death
Who was thy husband; such a one as he,
So noble in his quality, condition,
Learning, behavior, entertainment, love,
As Parma could not show a braver man.
    Vas. You do not well; this was not your promise.
    Sor. I care not; let her know her monstrous life.
Ere I'll be servile to so black a sin,
I'll be a curse.—Woman, come here no more;
Learn to repent, and die; for, by my honor,
I hate thee and thy lust: you've been too foul.   [*Exit*]
    Vas. [*Aside*] This part has been scurvily played.
    Hip. How foolishly this beast contemns his fate,
And shuns the use of that which I more scorn
Than I once loved, his love! But let him go;

My vengeance shall give comfort to his woe.[8]   [*Going*]

Vas. Mistress, mistress, Madam Hippolita! pray, a word or two.

Hip. With me, sir?

Vas. With you, if you please.

Hip. What is't?

Vas. I know you are infinitely moved now, and you think you have cause: some I confess you have, but sure not so much as you imagine.

Hip. Indeed!

Vas. O, you were miserably bitter, which you followed even to the last syllable; 'faith, you were somewhat too shrewd: by my life, you could not have took my lord in a worse time since I first knew him; tomorrow you shall find him a new man.

Hip. Well, I shall wait his leisure.

Vas. Fie, this is not a hearty patience; it comes sourly from you: 'troth, let me persuade you for once.

Hip. [*Aside*] I have it, and it shall be so; thanks, opportunity! —Persuade me! to what?

Vas. Visit him in some milder temper. O, if you could but master a little your female spleen, how might you win him!

Hip. He will never love me. Vasques, thou hast been a too trusty servant to such a master, and I believe thy reward in the end will fall out like mine.

Vas. So perhaps too.

Hip. Assure thyself it will. Had I one so true, so truly honest, so secret to my counsels, as thou hast been to him and his, I should think it a slight acquittance, not only to make him master of all I have, but even of myself.

Vas. O, you are a noble gentlewoman!

Hip. Wilt thou feed always upon hopes? Well, I know thou art wise, and seest the reward of an old servant daily, what it is.

Vas. Beggary and neglect.

Hip. True; but, Vasques, wert thou mine, and wouldst be private to me and my designs, I here protest, myself and all what I can else call mine should be at thy dispose.

8 *i.e.* To the woe occasioned by his falsehood

Vas. [*Aside*] Work you that way, old mole? then I have the wind of you.—I were not worthy of it by any desert that could lie within my compass: if I could—

Hip. What then?

Vas. I should then hope to live in these my old years with rest and security.

Hip. Give me thy hand: now promise but thy silence,
And help to bring to pass a plot I have,
And here, in sight of heaven, that being done,
I make thee lord of me and mine estate.

Vas. Come, you are merry; this is such a happiness that I can neither think or believe.

Hip. Promise thy secrecy, and 'tis confirmed.

Vas. Then here I call our good genii for witnesses, whatsoever your designs are, or against whomsoever, I will not only be a special actor therein, but never disclose it till it be effected.

Hip. I take thy word, and, with that, thee for mine;
Come, then, let's more confer of this anon.
On this delicious bane my thoughts shall banquet;
Revenge shall sweeten what my griefs have tasted.

                                        [*Aside, and exit with* Vasques]

SCENE III—*The Street*

                                        [*Enter* Richardetto *and* Philotis]

Rich. Thou seest, my lovely niece, these strange mishaps,
How all my fortunes turn to my disgrace;
Wherein I am but as a looker-on,
Whiles others act my shame, and I am silent.

Phi. But, uncle, wherein can this borrowed shape
Give you content?

Rich.   I'll tell thee, gentle niece:
Thy wanton aunt in her lascivious riots
Lives now secure, thinks I am surely dead
In my late journey to Ligorne for you,
As I have caused it to be rumoured out.
Now would I see with what an impudence
She gives scope to her loose adultery,
And how the common voice allows hereof:

Thus far I have prevailed.

   Phi.   Alas, I fear

You mean some strange revenge.

   Rich.   O, be not troubled;

Your ignorance shall plead for you in all:

But to our business. What! you learned for certain

How Signor Florio means to give his daughter

In marriage to Soranzo?

   Phi.   Yes, for certain.

   Rich. But how find you young Annabella's love

Inclined to him?

   Phi.   For aught I could perceive,

She neither fancies him or any else.

   Rich. There's mystery in that, which time must show.

She used you kindly?

   Phi.   Yes.

   Rich.   And craved your company?

   Phi. Often.

   Rich.   'Tis well; it goes as I could wish.

I am the doctor now; and as for you,

None knows you: if all fail not, we shall thrive.

But who comes here? I know him; 'tis Grimaldi,

A Roman and a soldier, near allied

Unto the Duke of Montferrato, one

Attending on the nuncio of the pope

That now resides in Parma; by which means

He hopes to get the love of Annabella.

                                [*Enter* Grimaldi]

   Grim. Save you, sir.

   Rich.   And you, sir.

   Grim.   I have heard

Of your approvèd skill, which through the city

Is freely talked of, and would crave your aid.

   Rich. For what, sir?

   Grim. Marry, sir, for this—

But I would speak in private.

   Rich.   Leave us, cousin.[9] [*Exit* Philotis]

9 "Cousin" was frequently used for nephew or niece

Grim. I love fair Annabella, and would know
Whether in art there may not be receipts
To move affection.
    Rich.   Sir, perhaps there may;
But these will nothing profit you.
    Grim.   Not me?
    Rich. Unless I be mistook, you are a man
Greatly in favor with the cardinal.
    Grim. What of that?
    Rich.   In duty to his grace,
I will be bold to tell you, if you seek
To marry Florio's daughter, you must first
Remove a bar 'twixt you and her.
    Grim.   Who's that?
    Rich. Soranzo is the man that hath her heart;
And while he lives, be sure you cannot speed.
    Grim. Soranzo! what, mine enemy? is't he?
    Rich. Is he your enemy?
    Grim.   The man I hate
Worse than confusion; I will to him straight.
    Rich. Nay, then, take mine advice,
Even for his grace's sake the cardinal:
I'll find a time when he and she do meet,
Of which I'll give you notice; and, to be sure
He shall not 'scape you, I'll provide a poison
To dip your rapier's point in: if he had
As many heads as Hydra had, he dies.
    Grim. But shall I trust thee, doctor?
    Rich.   As yourself;
Doubt not in aught. [*Exit* Grimaldi]—Thus shall the fates
    decree
By me Soranzo falls, that ruined me.   [*Exit.*]

    SCENE IV—*Another part of the Street*

        [*Enter* Donado *with a letter,* Bergetto, *and* Poggio]
    Don. Well, sir, I must be content to be both your secretary
and your messenger myself. I cannot tell what this letter may

work; but, as sure as I am alive, if thou come once to talk with her, I fear thou wilt mar whatsoever I make.

Ber. You make, uncle! why, am not I big enough to carry mine own letter, I pray?

Don. Ay, ay, carry a fool's head o' thy own! why, thou dunce, wouldst thou write a letter, and carry it thyself?

Ber. Yes, that I would, and read it to her with my own mouth; for you must think, if she will not believe me myself when she hears me speak, she will not believe another's hand-writing. O, you think I am a blockhead, uncle. No, sir, Poggio knows I have indited a letter myself; so I have.

Pog. Yes, truly, sir; I have it in my pocket.

Don. A sweet one, no doubt; pray let's see't.

Ber. I cannot read my own hand very well, Poggio; read it, Poggio.

Don. Begin.

Pog. [*Reads*] "Most dainty and honey-sweet mistress; I could call you fair, and lie as fast as any that loves you; but my uncle being the elder man, I leave it to him, as more fit for his age and the color of his beard. I am wise enough to tell you I can jest where I see occasion; or if you like my uncle's wit better than mine you shall marry me; if you like mine better than his, I will marry you, in spite of your teeth. So, commending my best parts to you, I rest

Yours upwards and downwards, or you may choose,

Bergetto."

Ber. Ah, ha! here's stuff, uncle!

Don. Here's stuff indeed—to shame us all. Pray, whose advice did you take in this learned letter?

Pog. None, upon my word, but mine own,

Ber. And mine, uncle, believe it, nobody's else; 'twas mine own brain, I thank a good wit for't.

Don. Get you home, sir, and look you keep within doors till I return.

Ber. How! that were a jest indeed! I scorn it, i'faith.

Don. What! you do not?

Ber. Judge me, but I do now.

Pog. Indeed, sir, 'tis very unhealthy.

Don. Well, sir, if I hear any of your apish running to motions[10] and fopperies, till I come back, you were as good no; look to't.   [*Exit*]

Ber. Poggio, shall's steal to see this horse with the head in's tail?

Pog. Ay, but you must take heed of whipping.

Ber. Dost take me for a child, Poggio? Come, honest Poggio.
                                                      [*Exeunt*]

SCENE v—Friar Bonaventura's *Cell*

[*Enter* Friar *and* Giovanni]

Friar. Peace! thou hast told a tale whose every word
Threatens eternal slaughter to the soul;
I'm sorry I have heard it: would mine ears
Had been one minute deaf, before the hour
That thou cam'st to me! O young man, castaway,
By the religious number[11] of mine order,
I day and night have waked my agèd eyes
Above my strength, to weep on thy behalf;
But Heaven is angry, and be thou resolved [12]
Thou art a man remarked [13] to taste a mischief.
Look for't; though it come late, it will come sure,
     Gio. Father, in this you are uncharitable;
What I have done I'll prove both fit and good.
It is a principle which you have taught,
When I was yet your scholar, that the frame
And composition of the mind doth follow
The frame and composition of the body:
So, where the body's furniture is beauty,
The mind's must needs be virtue; which allowed,
Virtue itself is reason but refined,
And love the quintessence of that: this proves,
My sister's beauty being rarely fair

10 Puppet-shows
11 Gifford proposed "founder"
12 Satisfied
13 Marked out

Is rarely virtuous; chiefly in her love,
And chiefly in that love, her love to me:
If hers to me, then so is mine to her;
Since in like causes are effects alike.

   Friar. O ignorance in knowledge! Long ago,
How often have I warned thee this before!
Indeed, if we were sure there were no Deity,
Nor Heaven nor Hell, then to be led alone
By Nature's light—as were philosophers
Of elder times—might instance some defense.
But 'tis not so: then, madman, thou wilt find
That Nature is in Heaven's positions blind.

   Gio. Your age o'errules you; had you youth like mine,
You'd make her love your heaven, and her divine.

   Friar. Nay, then I see thou'rt too far sold to hell:
It lies not in the compass of my prayers
To call thee back, yet let me counsel thee;
Persuade thy sister to some marriage.

   Gio. Marriage! why, that's to damn her; that's to prove
Her greedy variety of lust.

   Friar. O, fearful! if thou wilt not, give me leave
To shrive her, lest she should die unabsolved.

   Gio. At your best leisure, father: then she'll tell you
How dearly she doth prize my matchless love;
Then you will know what pity 'twere we two
Should have been sundered from each other's arms.
View well her face, and in that little round
You may observe a world of variety;
For color, lips; for sweet perfumes, her breath;
For jewels, eyes; for threads of purest gold,
Hair; for delicious choice of flowers, cheeks;
Wonder in every portion of that form.
Hear her but speak, and you will swear the spheres
Make music to the citizens in Heaven.
But, father, what is else for pleasure framed
Lest I offend your ears, shall go unnamed.

   Friar. The more I hear, I pity thee the more,
That one so excellent should give those parts

All to a second death. What I can do
Is but to pray; and yet—I could advise thee,
Wouldst thou be ruled.
    Gio.   In what?
    Friar.   Why leave her yet;
The throne of mercy is above your trespass;
Yet time is left you both—
    Gio.   To embrace each other,
Else let all time be struck quite out of number:
She is like me, and I like her, resolved.
    Friar. No more! I'll visit her. This grieves me most,
Things being thus, a pair of souls are lost.   *[Exeunt]*

    SCENE VI—*A Room in* Florio's *House*

                [Enter Florio, Donado, Annabella, *and* Putana]
    Flo. Where's Giovanni?
    Ann.   Newly walked abroad,
And, as I heard him say, gone to the friar,
His reverend tutor.
    Flo.   That's a blessèd man,
A man made up of holiness: I hope
He'll teach him how to gain another world.
    Don. Fair gentlewoman, here's a letter sent
To you from my young cousin; I dare swear
He loves you in his soul: would you could hear
Sometimes what I see daily, sighs and tears,
As if his breast were prison to his heart!
    Flo. Receive it, Annabella.
    Ann. Alas, good man!   *[Takes the letter]*
    Don. What's that she said?
    Put. An't please you, sir, she said, "Alas, good man!" Truly
I do commend him to her every night before her first sleep, be-
cause I would have her dream of him; and she hearkens to that
most religiously.
    Don. Sayest so? God-a'-mercy, Putana! there's something for
thee [*Gives her money*]: and prithee do what thou canst on his
behalf; 'shall not be lost labor, take my word for't.

Put. Thank you most heartily, sir: now I have a feeling of
your mind, let me alone to work.

Ann. Guardian,

Put. Did you call?

Ann. Keep this letter.

Don. Signior Florio, in any case bid her read it instantly.

Flo. Keep it! for what? pray, read it me hereright.

Ann. I shall, sir.   [*She reads the letter*]

Don. How d'ye find her inclined, signior?

Flo. Troth, sir, I know not how; not all so well
As I could wish.

Ann. Sir, I am bound to rest your cousin's debtor.
That jewel I'll return; for if he love,
I'll count that love a jewel.

Don.   Mark you that?
Nay, keep them both, sweet maid.

Ann.   You must excuse me,
Indeed I will not keep it.

Flo.   Where's the ring,
That which your mother, in her will, bequeathed,
And charged you on her blessing not to give 't
To any but your husband? send back that.

Ann. I have it not.

Flo.   Ha! have it not! where is't?

Ann. My brother in the morning took it from me,
Said he would wear't today.

Flo.   Well, what do you say
To young Bergetto's love? are you content to
Match with him? speak.

Don.   There is the point, indeed.

Ann. [*Aside*] What shall I do? I must say something now.

Flo. What say? why d'ye not speak?

Ann.   Sir, with your leave—
Please you to give me freedom?

Flo.   Yes, you have it.

Ann. Signior Donado, if your nephew mean
To raise his better fortunes in his match,

The hope of me will hinder such a hope:
Sir, if you love him, as I know you do,
Find one more worthy of his choice than I:
In short, I'm sure I shall not be his wife.

   Don. Why, here's plain dealing; I commend thee for't;
And all the worst I wish thee is, Heaven bless thee!
Your father yet and I will still be friends:
Shall we not, Signior Florio?

   Flo.   Yes; why not?
Look, here your cousin comes.

                               [Enter Bergetto *and* Poggio]
   Don. [Aside] O, coxcomb! what doth he make here?

   Ber. Where's my uncle, sirs?

   Don. What's the news now?

   Ber. Save you, uncle, save you! You must not think I come
for nothing, masters. And how, and how is't? what, you have
read my letter? ah, there I—tickled you, i'faith.

   Pog. [Aside to Bergetto] But 'twere better you had tickled
her in another place.

   Ber. Sirrah sweetheart, I'll tell thee a good jest; and riddle
what 'tis.

   Ann. You say you'll tell me.

   Ber. As I was walking just now in the street, I met a swagger-
ing fellow would needs take the wall of me; and because he did
thrust me, I very valiantly called him rogue. He hereupon bade
me draw; I told him I had more wit than so; but when he saw
that I would not, he did so maul me with the hilts of his rapier,
that my head sung whilst my feet capered in the kennel.

   Don. [Aside] Was ever the like ass seen!

   Ann. And what did you all this while?

   Ber. Laugh at him for a gull, till I saw the blood run about
mine ears, and then I could not choose but find in my heart to
cry; till a fellow with a broad beard—they say he is a newcome
doctor—called me into his house, and gave me a plaster, look
you, here 'tis: and, sir, there was a young wench washed my face
and hands most excellently; i' faith, I shall love her as long as I
live for't.—Did she not, Poggio?

   Pog. Yes, and kissed him too.

Ber. Why, la, now, you think I tell a lie, uncle, I warrant.

Don. Would he that beat thy blood out of thy head had beaten some wit into it! for I fear thou never wilt have any.

Ber. O, uncle, but there was a wench would have done a man's heart good to have looked on her. By this light, she had a face methinks worth twenty of you, Mistress Annabella.

Don. [*Aside*] Was ever such a fool born!

Ann. I am glad she pleased you sir.

Ber. Are you so? by my troth, I thank you, forsooth.

Flo. Sure, 'twas the doctor's niece, that was last day with us here.

Ber. 'Twas she, 'twas she.

Don. How do you know that, simplicity?

Ber. Why, does not he say so? if I should have said no, I should have given him the lie, uncle, and so have deserved a dry beating again: I'll none of that.

Flo. A very modest well-behaved young maid
As I have seen.

Don. Is she indeed?

Flo. Indeed she is, if I have any judgment.

Don. Well, sir, now you are free: you need not care for sending letters now; you are dismissed, your mistress here will none of you.

Ber. No! why, what care I for that? I can have wenches enough in Parma for half a crown apiece: cannot I, Poggio?

Pog. I'll warrant you, sir.

Don. Signior Florio,
I thank you for your free recourse you gave
For my admittance: and to you, fair maid,
That jewel I will give you 'gainst your marriage.
Come, will you go, sir?

Ber. Ay, marry, will I. Mistress, farewell, mistress;
I'll come again to-morrow; farewell, mistress.
                              [*Exeunt* Donado, Bergetto *and* Poggio]
                                        [*Enter* Giovanni]

Flo. Son, where have you been? What, alone, alone still?
I would not have it so; you must forsake
This over-bookish humor. Well, your sister

Hath shook the fool off.

Gio.   'Twas no match for her.

Flo. 'Twas not indeed; I meant it nothing less;
Soranzo is the man I only like:
Look on him, Annabella. Come, 'tis supper-time,
And it grows late.   [*Exit*]

Gio. Whose jewel's that?

Ann. Some sweetheart's.

Gio.   So I think.

Ann.   A lusty youth,
Signior Donado, gave it me to wear
Against my marriage.

Gio.   But you shall not wear it:
Send it back again.

Ann.   What, you are jealous?

Gio. That you shall know anon, at better leisure.
Welcome sweet night! the evening crowns the day.

                                                  [*Exeunt*]

ACT III

SCENE I—*A Room in* Donado's *House*

                              [*Enter* Bergetto *and* Poggio]

Bergetto. Does my uncle think to make me a baby still? No,
Poggio; he shall know I have a head now.

Pog. Ay, let him not bob you off like an ape with an apple.

Ber. 'Sfoot, I will have the wench, if he were ten uncles, in
despite of his nose, Poggio.

Pog. Hold him to the grindstone, and give not a jot of
ground: she hath in a manner promised you already.

Ber. True, Poggio; and her uncle, the doctor, swore I should
marry her.

Pog. He swore; I remember.

Ber. And I will have her, that's more: didst see the codpiece-
point she gave me and the box of marmalade?

Pog. Very well; and kissed you, that my chops watered at the
sight on't. There's no way but to clap up a marriage in a hugger-
mugger.

Ber. I will do't; for I tell thee, Poggio, I begin to grow valiant
methinks, and my courage begins to rise.

Pog. Should you be afraid of your uncle?

Ber. Hang him, old doting rascal! no: I say I will have her.

Pog. Lose no time, then.

Ber. I will beget a race of wise men and constables that shall
cart whores at their own charges; and break the duke's peace ere
I have done myself. Come away.

[*Exeunt*]

SCENE II—*A Room in* Florio's *House*

[*Enter* Florio, Giovanni, Soranzo, Annabella, Putana,
and Vasques]

Flo. My Lord Soranza, though I must confess
The proffers that are made me have been great
In marriage of my daughter, yet the hope
Of your still rising honors have prevailed
Above all other jointures: here she is;
She knows my mind; speak for yourself to her,
And hear, you, daughter, see you use him nobly:
For any private speech I'll give you time.
Come, son, and you the rest; let them alone;
Agree they as they may.

Sor.   I thank you, sir.

Gio. [*Aside to* Annabella]. Sister, be not all woman; think on
me.

Sor. Vasques,—

Vas.   My lord?

Sor.   Attend me without.

[*Exeunt all but* Soranzo *and* Annabella]

Ann. Sir, what's your will with me?

Sor.   Do you not know
What I should tell you?

Ann.   Yes; you'll say you love me.

Sor. And I will swear it too; will you believe it?

Ann. 'Tis no point of faith.

                    [*Enter* Giovanni *in the gallery above*]

Sor.   Have you not will to love?

Ann. Not you.

Sor.   Whom then?

Ann.   That's as the fates infer.

Gio. [*Aside*] Of those I'm regent now.

Sor.   What mean you, sweet?

Ann. To live and die a maid.

Sor.   O, that's unfit.

Gio. [*Aside*] Here's one can say that's but a woman's note.

Sor. Did you but see my heart, then would you swear—

Ann. That you were dead.

Gio. [*Aside*]   That's true, or somewhat near it.

Sor. See you these true love's tears?

Ann.   No.

Gio. [*Aside*]   Now she winks.

Sor. They plead to you for grace.

Ann.   Yet nothing speak.

Sor. O, grant my suit!

Ann.   What is it?

Sor.   To let me live—

Ann. Take it.

Sor.   Still yours.

Ann.   That is not mine to give.

Gio. [*Aside*] One such another word would kill his hopes.

Sor. Mistress, to leave those fruitless strifes of wit,

Know I have loved you long and loved you truly:

Not hope of what you have, but what you are,

Hath drawn me on; then let me not in vain

Still feel the rigor of your chaste disdain:

I'm sick, and sick to the heart.

Ann.   Help, aqua-vitae!

Sor. What mean you?

Ann.   Why, I thought you had been sick.

Sor. Do you mock my love?

Gio. [*Aside*]   There, sir, she was too nimble.

Sor. [*Aside*] 'Tis plain she laughs at me.—These scornful taunts
Neither become your modesty or years.

Ann. You are no looking-glass: or if you were,
I'd dress my language by you.

Gio. [*Aside*]   I'm confirmed.

Ann. To put you out of doubt, my lord, methinks
Your common sense should make you understand
That if I love you, or desired your love,
Some way I should have given you better taste:
But since you are a nobleman, and one
I would not wish should spend his youth in hopes,
Let me advise you to forbear your suit,
And think I wish you well, I tell you this.

Sor. Is't you speak this?

Ann.   Yes, I myself; yet know,
Thus far I give you comfort, if mine eyes
Could have picked out a man amongst all those
That sued to me to make a husband of,
You should have been that man: let this suffice;
Be noble in your secrecy and wise.

Gio. [*Aside*] Why, now I see she loves me.

Ann.   One word more.
As ever virtue lived within your mind,
As ever noble courses were your guide,
As ever you would have me know you loved me,
Let not my father know hereof by you:
If I hereafter find that I must marry,
It shall be you or none.

Sor.   I take that promise.

Ann. O, O my head!

Sor. What's the matter? not well?

Ann. O, I begin to sicken!

Gio.   Heaven forbid!
                    [*Aside, and exit from above*]

Sor. Help, help, within there, ho!
                    [*Re-enter* Florio, Giovanni, *and* Putana]
Look to your daughter, Signior Florio.

Flo. Hold her up, she swoons.

Gio. Sister, how d'ye?

Ann. Sick, brother, are you there?

Flo. Convey her to her bed instantly, whilst I send for a physician: quickly, I say.

Put. Alas, poor child!

[*Exeunt all but* Soranzo]

[*Re-enter* Vasques]

Vas. My lord.

Sor. O, Vasques, now I doubly am undone
Both in my present and my future hopes!
She plainly told me that she could not love,
And thereupon soon sickened; and I fear
Her life's in danger.

Vas. [*Aside*] By'r lady, sir, and so is yours, if you knew all.—
'Las, sir, I am sorry for that: may be 'tis but maid's sickness, an overflux of youth; and then, sir, there is no such present remedy as present marriage. But hath she given you an absolute denial?

Sor. She hath, and she hath not; I'm full of grief:
But what she said I'll tell thee as we go.

[*Exeunt*]

SCENE III—*Another Room in the same*

[*Enter* Giovanni *and* Putana]

Put. O, sir, we are all undone, quite undone, utterly undone, and shamed for ever! your sister, O, your sister!

Gio. What of her? for Heaven's sake, speak; how does she?

Put. O, that ever I was born to see this day!

Gio. She is not dead, ha? is she?

Put. Dead! no, she is quick; 'tis worse, she is with child. You know what you have done; Heaven forgive ye! 'tis too late to repent now, Heaven help us!

Gio. With child? how dost thou know't?

Put. How do I know't! am I at these years ignorant what the meanings of qualms and water-pangs be? of changing of colors, queasiness of stomachs, pukings, and another thing that I could name? Do not, for her and your credit's sake, spend the time in asking how, and which way, 'tis so: she is quick, upon my word: if you let a physician see her water, you're undone.

Gio. But in what case is she?

Put. Prettily amended: 'twas but a fit, which I soon espied,
and she much look for often henceforward.

Gio. Commend me to her, bid her take no care;[14]
Let not the doctor visit her, I charge you;
Make some excuse, till I return. O, me!
I have a world of business in my head.
Do not discomfort her.
How do these news perplex me! If my father
Come to her, tell him she's recovered well;
Say 'twas but some ill diet—d'ye hear, woman?
Look you to't.

    Put. I will, sir.   [*Exeunt*]

    SCENE IV—*Another Room in the same*
                      [*Enter* Florio *and* Richardetto]
    Flo. And how d'ye find her, sir?
    Rich.   Indifferent well;
I see no danger, scarce perceive she's sick,
But that she told me she had lately eaten
Melons, and, as she thought, those disagreed
With her young stomach.
    Flo.   Did you give her aught?
    Rich. An easy surfeit-water, nothing else.
You need not doubt her health: I rather think
Her sickness is a fullness of the blood,
You understand me?
    Flo.   I do; you counsel well;
And once, within these few days, will so order 't
She shall be married ere she know the time.
    Rich. Yet let not haste, sir, make unworthy choice;
That were dishonor.
    Flo.   Master Doctor, no;
I will not do so neither: in plain words,
My lord Soranzo is the man I mean.
    Rich. A noble and a virtuous gentleman.
    Flo. As any is in Parma. Not far hence
Dwells Father Bonaventure, a grave friar,

14 Not be too anxious

Once tutor to my son: now at his cell
I'll have 'em married.
    Rich.   You have plotted wisely.
    Flo. I'll send one straight to speak with him to-night.
    Rich. Soranzo's wise; he will delay no time.
    Flo. It shall be so.

                            [*Enter* Friar *and* Giovanni]
    Friar.   Good peace be here and love!
    Flo. Welcome, religious friar; you are one
That still bring blessing to the place you come to.
    Gio. Sir, with what speed I could, I did my best
To draw this holy man from forth his cell
To visit my sick sister; that with words
Of ghostly comfort, in this time of need,
He might absolve her, whether she live or die.
    Flo. 'Twas well done, Giovanni; thou herein
Hast showed a Christian's care, a brother's love.
Come, father, I'll conduct you to her chamber,
And one thing would entreat you.
    Friar.   Say on, sir.
    Flo. I have a father's dear impression
And wish, before I fall into my grave,
That I might see her married, as 'tis fit:
A word from you, grave man, will win her more
Than all our best persuasions.
    Friar.   Gentle sir,
Al this I'll say, that Heaven may prosper her.   [*Exeunt*]

    SCENE v—*A Room in* Richardetto's *House*
                              [*Enter* Grimaldi]
    Grim. Now if the doctor keep his word, Soranzo,
Twenty to one you miss your bride. I know
'Tis an unnoble act, and not becomes
A soldier's valor; but in terms of love,
Where merit cannot sway, policy must:
I am resolved, if this physician
Play not on both hands, then Soranzo falls.
                            [*Enter* Richardetto]

 Rich. You're come as I could wish; this very night
Soranzo, 'tis ordained, must be affied [15]
To Annabella, and, for aught I know,
Married.
 Grim. How!
 Rich.   Yet your patience:—
The place, 'tis Friar Bonaventure's cell.
Now I would wish you to bestow this night
In watching thereabouts; 'tis but a night:
If you miss now, tomorrow I'll know all.
 Grim. Have you the poison?
 Rich.   Here 'tis, in this box:
Doubt nothing, this will do't; in any case,
As you respect your life, be quick and sure.
 Grim. I'll speed him.
 Rich.   Do. Away; for 'tis not safe
You should be seen much here. Ever my love!
 Grim. And mine to you.   *[Exit]*
 Rich. So! if this hit, I'll laugh and hug revenge;
And they that now dream of a wedding feast
May chance to mourn the lusty bridegroom's ruin.
But to my other business. Niece Philotis!
          [Enter Philotis]

 Phi. Uncle?
 Rich. My lovely niece!
You have bethought ye?
 Phi.   Yes, and, as you counseled,
Fashioned my heart to love him: but he swears
He will tonight be married: for he fears
His uncle else, if he should know the drift,
Will hinder all, and call his coz to shrift.
 Rich. Tonight! why, best of all: but, let me see—
Ay—ha! yes, so it shall be—in disguise
We'll early to the friar's; I have thought on't.
 Phi. Uncle, he comes.
        [Enter Bergetto and Poggio]
 Rich.   Welcome, my worthy coz.

15 Contracted

Ber. Lass, pretty lass, come buss, lass! A-ha, Poggio!

[Kisses her]

Rich. [*Aside.*] There's hope of this yet.—
You shall have time enough; withdraw a little;
We must confer at large.

Ber. Have you not sweetmeats or dainty devices for me?

Phi. You shall have enough, sweetheart.

Ber. Sweetheart! mark that, Poggio. By my troth, I cannot
choose but kiss thee once more for that word, "sweetheart."
Poggio, I have a monstrous swelling about my stomach, whatsoever the matter be.

Pog. You shall have physic for't, sir.

Rich. Time runs apace.

Ber. Time's a blockhead.

Rich. Be ruled: when we have done what's fit to do,
Then you may kiss your fill, and bed her too.   *[Exeunt]*

SCENE VI—Annabella's *Chamber*

> *A table with wax lights;* Annabella *at confession be-*
> *fore the* Friar; *she weeps and wrings her hands.*

Friar. I'm glad to see this penance; for, believe me,
You have unripped a soul so foul and guilty,
As, I must tell you true, I marvel how
The earth hath borne you up: but weep, weep on,
These tears may do you good; weep faster yet,
Whiles I do read a lecture.

Ann.   Wretched creature!

Friar. Ay, you are wretched, miserably wretched,
Almost condemned alive. There is a place,—
List, daughter!—in a black and hollow vault,
Where day is never seen; there shines no sun,
But flaming horror of consuming fires,
A lightless sulphur, choked with smoky fogs
Of an infected darkness: in this place
Dwell many thousand thousand sundry sorts
Of nerve-dying deaths: there damnèd souls
Roar without pity; there are gluttons fed
With toads and adders; there is burning oil

Poured down the drunkard's throat; the usurer
Is forced to sup whole draughts of molten gold;
There is the murderer forever stabbed,
Yet can he never die; there lies the wanton
On racks of burning steel, whiles in his soul
He feels the torment of his raging lust.

    Ann. Mercy! O, mercy!

    Friar.   There stand these wretched things
Who have dreamed out whole years in lawless sheets
And secret incests, cursing one another.
Then you will wish each kiss your brother gave
Had been a dagger's point; then you shall hear
How he will cry, "O, would my wicked sister
Had first been damned, when she did yield to lust!"
But soft, methinks I see repentance work
New motions in your heart: say, how is't with you?

    Ann. Is there no way left to redeem my miseries?

    Friar. There is, despair not; Heaven is merciful,
And offers grace even now. 'Tis thus agreed:
First, for your honor's safety, that you marry
My lord Soranzo; next, to save your soul,
Leave off this life, and henceforth live to him.

    Ann. Ay me!

    Friar.   Sigh not; I know the baits of sin
Are hard to leave; O, 'tis a death to do't:
Remember what must come. Are you content?

    Ann. I am.

    Friar.   I like it well; we'll take the time.
Who's near us there?

                            [*Enter* Florio *and* Giovanni]

    Flo.   Did you call, father?

    Friar. Is Lord Soranzo come?

    Flo.   ' He stays below.

    Friar. Have you acquainted him at full?

    Flo.   I have,
And he is overjoyed.

    Friar.   And so are we.
Bid him come near.

Gio. [*Aside*]   My sister weeping! Ha!
I fear this friar's falsehood. I will call him.   [*Exit*]
   Flo. Daughter, are you resolved?
   Ann.   Father, I am.
              [*Re-enter* Giovanni *with* Soranzo *and* Vasques]
   Flo. My lord Soranzo, here
Give me your hand; for that I give you this.
                                        [*Joins their hands*]
   Sor. Lady, say you so too?
   Ann.   I do, and vow
To live with you and yours.
   Friar.   Timely resolved:
My blessing rest on both! More to be done,
You may perform it on the morning sun.   [*Exeunt*]

SCENE VII—*The Street before the Monastery*

     [*Enter* Grimaldi *with his rapier drawn and a dark lan-
     tern*]
   Grim. 'Tis early night as yet, and yet too soon
To finish such a work; here I will lie
To listen who comes next.   [*He lies down*]
          [*Enter* Bergetto *and* Philotis *disguised, followed at
          a short distance by* Richardetto *and* Poggio]
   Ber. We are almost at the place, I hope, sweetheart.
   Grim. [*Aside*] I hear them near, and heard one say "sweet-
     heart."
'Tis he; now guide my hand, some angry justice,
Home to his bosom! Now have at you, sir!
                              [*Stabs* Bergetto *and exit*]
   Ber. O, help, help! here's a stitch fallen in my guts:
O for a flesh-tailor quickly! Poggio!
   Phi. What ails my love?
   Ber. I am sure I cannot piss forward and backward, and yet
I am wet before and behind. Lights! lights! ho, lights!
   Phi. Alas, some villain here has slain my love!
   Rich. O, Heaven forbid it! Raise up the next neighbors
Instantly, Poggio, and bring lights.   [*Exit* Poggio]

How is't, Bergetto? slain! It cannot be;
Are you sure you're hurt?

Ber. O, my belly seethes like a porridge pot! Some cold water,
I shall boil over else; my whole body is in a sweat, that you may
wring my shire; feel here. Why, Poggio!

[*Re-enter* Poggio *with* Officers *and lights*]

Pog. Here. Alas, how do you?

Rich. Give me a light. What's here? all blood! O, sirs,
Signior Donado's nephew now is slain.
Follow the murderer with all the haste
Up to the city, he cannot be far hence:
Follow, I beseech you.

Officers.   Follow, follow, follow!   [*Exeunt*]

Rich. Tear off thy linen, coz, to stop his wounds.
Be of good comfort, man.

Ber. Is all this mine own blood? nay, then, good night with
me. Poggio, commend me to my uncle, dost hear? Bid him, for
my sake, make much of this wench. O, I am going the wrong
way sure, my belly aches so. O, farewell, Poggio! O, O!   [*Dies*]

Phi. O, he is dead!

Pog.   How! dead!

Rich.   He's dead indeed:
'Tis now too late to weep: let's have him home,
And with what speed we may find out the murderer.

Pog. O, my master! my master! my master!

[*Exeunt*]

SCENE VIII—*A Room in* Hippolita's *House*

[*Enter* Vasques *and* Hippolita]

Hip. Betrothed?

Vas. I saw it.

Hip. And when's the marriage day?

Vas.   Some two days hence.

Hip. Two days! why, man, I would but wish two
   hours
To send him to his last and lasting sleep;
And, Vasques, thou shalt see I'll do it bravely.

Vas. I do not doubt your wisdom, nor, I trust, you my secrecy;
I am infinitely yours.

Hip. I will be thine in spite of my disgrace.
So soon? O wicked man, I dare be sworn
He'd laugh to see me weep.

Vas. And that's a villainous fault in him.

Hip. No, let him laugh; I'm armed in my resolves:
Be thou still true.

Vas. I should get little by treachery against so hopeful a preferment as I am like to climb to.

Hip. Even to—my bosom, Vasques. Let my youth
Revel in these new pleasures: if we thrive,
He now hath but a pair of days to live.   [*Exeunt*]

SCENE IX—*The street before the* Cardinal's *gates*

> [*Enter* Florio, Donado, Richardetto, Poggio *and*
> Officers]

Flo. 'Tis bootless now to show yourself a child,
Signior Donado; what is done, is done:
Spend not the time in tears, but seek for justice.

Rich. I must confess somewhat I was in fault
That had not first acquainted you what love
Passed 'twixt him and my niece; but, as I live,
His fortune grieves me as it were mine own.

Don. Alas, poor creature! he meant no man harm,
That I am sure of.

Flo.   I believe that too.
But stay, my masters: are you sure you saw
The murderer pass here?

1st Off. An it please you, sir, we are sure we saw a ruffian,
with a naked weapon in his hand all bloody, get into my lord
cardinal's grace's gate; that we are sure of; but for fear of his
grace—bless us!—we dared go no farther.

Don. Know you what manner of man he was?

1st Off. Yes, sure, I know the man; they say he is a soldier;
he that loved your daughter, sir, an't please ye; 'twas he for
certain.

Flo. Grimaldi, on my life!

1st Off.   Ay, ay, the same.

Rich. The cardinal is noble; he no doubt
Will give true justice.

Don.   Knock some one at the gate.

Pog. I'll knock, sir.   [*Knocks*]

Serv. [*Within.*] What would ye?

Flo. We require speech with the lord cardinal
About some present business: pray inform
His grace that we are here.

                    [*Enter the* Cardinal, *followed by* Grimaldi]

Car. Why, how now, friends! what saucy mates are
     you
That know not duty nor civility?
Are we a person fit to be your host;
Or is our house become your common inn,
To beat our doors at pleasure? What such haste
Is yours, as that it cannot wait fit times?
Are you the masters of this commonwealth,
And know no more discretion? O, your news
Is here before you; you have lost a nephew,
Donado, last night by Grimaldi slain:
Is that your business? well, sir, we have knowledge on't;
Let that suffice.

Grim.   In presence of your grace,
In thought I never meant Bergetto harm:
But, Florio, you can tell with how much scorn
Soranzo, backed with his confederates,
Hath often wronged me! I to be revenged,
For that I could not win him else to fight,
Had thought by way of ambush to have killed him
But was unluckily therein mistook;
Else he had felt what late Bergetto did:
And though my fault to him were merely chance,
Yet humbly I submit me to your grace,   [*Kneeling*]
To do with me as you please.

Car.   Rise up, Grimaldi.   [*He rises*]
You citizens of Parma, if you seek
For justice, know, as nuncio from the pope,

For this offence I here receive Grimaldi
Into his holiness' protection:
He is no common man, but nobly born,
Of princes' blood, though you, Sir Florio,
Thought him too mean a husband for your daughter.
If more you seek for, you must go to Rome,
For he shall thither: learn more wit, for shame.
Bury your dead. Away, Grimaldi; leave 'em!

                              [*Exeunt* Cardinal *and* Grimaldi]

   Don. Is this a churchman's voice? dwells justice here?
   Flo. Justice is fled to Heaven, and comes no nearer.
Soranzo!—was't for him? O, impudence!
Had he the face to speak it, and not blush?
   Come, come, Donado, there's no help in this,
   When cardinals think murder's not amiss.
   Great men may do their wills, we must obey;
   But Heaven will judge them for't another day.   [*Exeunt*]

ACT IV

SCENE I—*A Room in* Florio's *House*

A banquet set out; hautboys.

                    [*Enter the* Friar, Giovanni, Annabella, Philotis,
                    Soranzo, Donado, Florio, Richardetto Putana,
                    and Vasques]

   Friar. These holy rites performed, now take your times
To spend the remnant of the day in feast:
Such fit repasts are pleasing to the saints,
Who are your guests, though not with mortal eyes
To be beheld. Long prosper in this day,
You happy couple, to each other's joy!
   Sor. Father, your prayer is heard; the hand of good-
     ness
Hath been a shield for me against my death:
And, more to bless me, hath enriched my life
With this most precious jewel; such a prize

As earth hath not another like to this.
Cheer up, my love: and, gentlemen my friends
Rejoice with me in mirth: this day we'll crown
With lusty cups to Annabella's health.

  Gio. [*Aside*] O torture! were the marriage yet undone,
Ere I'd endure this sight, to see my love
Clipt[16] by another, I would dare confusion,
And stand the horror of ten thousand deaths.

  Vas. Are you not well, sir?
  Gio.   Prithee, fellow, wait;
I need not thy officious diligence.

  Flo. Signior Donado, come, you must forget
Your late mishaps, and drown your cares in wine.

  Sor. Vasques!
  Vas.   My lord?
  Sor.   Reach me that weighty bowl.
Here, brother Giovanni, here's to you;
Your turn come next, though now a bachelor;
Here's to your sister's happiness and mine!
                  [*Drinks and offers him the bowl*]

  Gio. I cannot drink.
  Sor.   What!
  Gio.   'Twill indeed offend me.
  Ann. Pray, do not urge him, if he be not willing.
                        [*Hautboys*]

  Flo. How now! what music is this?
  Vas. O, sir, I had forgot to tell you; certain young maidens
of Parma, in honor to Madam Annabella's marriage, have sent
their loves to her in a masque, for which they humbly crave
your patience and silence.

  Sor. We are much bound to them; so much the more as it
comes unexpected: guide them in.
        [*Enter* Hippolita, *followed by* ladies *in white robes*
        with garlands of willows, all masked. Music and a
        dance]
Thanks, lovely virgins! now might we but know
To whom we've been beholding for this love,

16 Embraced

We shall acknowledge it.

    Hip.   Yes, you shall know.   [*Unmasks*]
What think you now?

    All.   Hippolita!

    Hip.   'Tis she;
Be not amazed; nor blush, young lovely bride;
I come not to defraud you of your man:
'Tis now no time to reckon up the talk
What Parma long hath rumored of us both:
Let rash report run on; the breath that vents it
Will, like a bubble, break itself at last.
But now to you, sweet creature; lend's your hand;
Perhaps it hath been said that I would claim
Some interest in Soranzo, now your lord;
What I have right to do, his soul knows best:
But in my duty to your noble worth,
Sweet Annabella, and my care of you,
Here, take, Soranzo, take this hand from me;
I'll once more join what by the holy church
Is finished and allowed. Have I done well?

    Sor. You have too much engaged us.

    Hip.   One thing more.
That you may know my single[17] charity,
Freely I here remit all interest
I e'er could claim, and give you back your vows;
And to confirm't, reach me a cup of wine,

                    [Vasques *gives her a poisoned cup*]
My lord Soranzo, in this draught I drink
Long rest t'ye! [*She drinks*].—[*Aside to* Vasques] Look to it,
    Vasques.

    Vas. [*Aside to* Hippolita] Fear nothing.

    Sor. Hippolita, I thank you; and will pledge
This happy union as another life.
Wine, there!

    Vas. You shall have none; neither shall you pledge her.

    Hip. How!

[17] Single-minded

Vas. Know now, Mistress She-devil, your own mischievous treachery hath killed you; I must not marry you.

Hip. Villain!

All. What's the matter?

Vas. Foolish woman, thou art now like a firebrand that hath kindled others and burnt thyself: *troppo sperar, inganna,*[18] thy vain hope hath deceived thee; thou art but dead; if thou hast any grace, pray.

Hip. Monster!

Vas. Die in charity, for shame. This thing of malice, this woman, had privately corrupted me with promise of marriage, under this politic reconciliation, to poison my lord, whiles she might laugh at his confusion on his marriage day. I promised her fair; but I knew what my reward should have been, and would willingly have spared her life, but that I was acquainted with the danger of her disposition; and now have fitted her a just payment in her own coin: end thy days in peace, vile woman; as for life, there's no hope; think not on't.

All. Wonderful justice!

Rich. Heaven, thou art righteous.

Hip.   O, 'tis true;
I feel my minute coming. Had that slave
Kept promise, O, my torment! thou this hour
Hadst died, Soranzo; heat above hell-fire!
Yet, ere I pass away, cruel, cruel flames!
Take here my curse amongst you: may thy bed
Of marriage be a rack unto thy heart,
Burn blood, and boil in vengeance; O, my heart,
My flame's intolerable! mayst thou live
To father bastards; may her womb bring forth
Monsters, and die together in your sins,
Hated, scorned, and unpitied! O, O!   [*Dies*]

Flo. Was e'er so vile a creature!

Rich.   Here're the end
Of lust and pride.

Ann.   It is a fearful sight.

18 Too much hope brings disappointment.

Sor. Vasques, I know thee now a trusty servant,
And never will forget thee. Come, my love,
We'll home, and thank the heavens for this escape.
Father and friends, we must break up this mirth;
It is too sad a feast.
      Don.   Bear hence the body.
      Friar. [*Aside to* Giovanni] Here's an ominous change!
Mark this, my Giovanni, and take heed!
      I fear the event: that marriage seldom's good
Where the bride banquet so begins in blood.   [*Exeunt*]

SCENE II—*A Room in* Richardetto's *House*

[*Enter* Richardetto *and* Philotis]
      Rich. My wretched wife, more wretched in her shame
Than in her wrongs to me, hath paid too soon
The forfeit of her modesty and life.
And I am sure, my niece, though vengeance hover,
Keeping aloof yet from Soranzo's fall,
Yet he will fall, and sink with his own weight.
I need not now—my heart persuades me so—
To further his confusion; there is One
Above begins to work: for, as I hear,
Debates already 'twixt his wife and him
Thicken and run to head; she, as 'tis said,
Slightens his love, and he abandons hers:
Much talk I hear. Since things go thus, my niece,
In tender love and pity of your youth,
My counsel is, that you should free your years
From hazard of these woes by flying hence
To fair Cremona, there to vow your soul
In holiness, a holy votaress:
Leave me to see the end of these extremes.
All human worldly courses are uneven;
No life is blessèd but the way to Heaven.
      Phi. Uncle, shall I resolve to be a nun?
      Rich. Ay, gentle niece; and in your hourly prayers
Remember me, your poor unhappy uncle.
Hie to Cremona now, as fortune leads,

Your home your cloister, your best friends your beads:
Your chaste and single life shall crown your birth:
Who dies a virgin lives a saint on earth.

    Phi. Then farewell, world, and wordly thoughts, adieu!
Welcome, chaste vows; myself I yield to you.   *[Exeunt]*

SCENE III—*A Chamber in* Soranzo's *House*

                      [Enter Soranzo *unbraced, and dragging in*
                      Annabella]

    Sor. Come, strumpet, famous whore! were every drop
Of blood that runs in thy adulterous veins
A life, this sword—dost see't?—should in one blow
Confound them all. Harlot, rare, notable harlot,
That with thy brazen face maintain'st thy sin,
Was there no man in Parma to be bawd
To your loose cunning whoredom else but I?
Must your hot itch and plurisy of lust,
The heydey of your luxury,[19] be fed
Up to a surfeit, and could none but I
Be picked out to be cloak to your close tricks,
Your belly sports? Now I must be the dad
To all that gallimaufry that is stuffed
In thy corrupted bastard-bearing womb!
Say, must I?

    Ann.   Beastly man! why, 'tis thy fate.
I sued not to thee; for, but that I thought
Your over-loving lordship would have run
Mad on denial, had ye lent me time,
I would have told ye in what case I was:
But you would needs be doing.

    Sor.   Whore of whores!
Darest thou tell me this?

    Ann.   O, yes; why not?
You were deceived in me; 'twas not for love
I chose you, but for honor: yet know this,
Would you be patient yet, and hide your shame,
I'd see whether I could love you.

19 Luxury was commonly used in the sense of lust.

Sor.   Excellent quean!
Why, art thou not with child?
    Ann.   What needs all this,
When 'tis superfluous? I confess I am.
    Sor. Tell me by whom.
    Ann.   Soft! 'twas not in my bargain.
Yet somewhat, sir, to stay your longing stomach,
I am content t' acquaint you with; the man,
The more than man, that got this sprightly boy,
For 'tis a boy, and therefore glory, sir,
Your heir shall be a son—
    Sor.   Damnable monster!
    Ann. Nay, an you will not hear, I'll speak no more.
    Sor. Yes, speak, and speak thy last.
    Ann.   A match! a match!
This noble creature was in every part
So angel-like, so glorious, that a woman
Who had not been but human, as was I,
Would have kneeled to him, and have begged for love.
You! why, you are not worthy once to name
His name without true worship, or, indeed,
Unless you kneeled, to hear another name him.
    Sor. What was he called?
    Ann.   We are not come to that;
Let it suffice that you shall have the glory
To father what so brave a father got.
In brief, had not this chance fall'n out as't doth,
I never had been troubled with a thought
That you had been a creature: but for marriage,
I scarce dream yet of that.
    Sor.   Tell me his name.
    Ann. Alas, alas, there's all! will you believe?
    Sor. What?
    Ann.   You shall never know.
    Sor.   How!
    Ann.   Never: if
You do, let me cursed!
    Sor. Not know it, strumpet! I'll rip up thy heart,

And find it there.

    Ann.   Do, do.

    Sor.   And with my teeth

Tear the prodigious lecher joint by joint.

    Ann. Ha, ha, ha! the man's merry.

    Sor.   Dost thou laugh?

Come, whore, tell me your lover, or, by truth,

I'll hew thy flesh to shreds; who is't?

    Ann. [*Sings*] *Che morte più dolce che morire per amore?*[20]

    Sor. Thus will I pull thy hair, and thus I'll drag

Thy lust-belepered body through the dust.

                       [*Hales her up and down*]

Yet tell his name.

    Ann. [*Sings*] *Morendo in grazia dee morire senza dolore.*[21]

    Sor. Dost thou triúmph? The treasures of the earth

Shall not redeem thee; were there kneeling kings

Did beg thy life, or angels did come down

To plead in tears, yet should not all prevail

Against my rage: dost thou not tremble yet?

    Ann. At what? to die! no, be a gallant hangman;

I dare thee to the worst: strike, and strike home;

I leave revenge behind, and thou shalt feel't.

    Sor. Yet tell me ere thou diest, and tell me truly,

Knows thy old father this?

    Ann.   No, by my life.

    Sor. Wilt thou confess, and I will spare thy life?

    Ann. My life! I will not buy my life so dear.

    Sor. I will not slack my vengeance.   [*Draws his sword*]

                         [*Enter* Vasques]

    Vas.   What d'ye mean, sir?

    Sor. Forbear, Vasques; such a damnèd whore

Deserves no pity.

    Vas.   Now the gods forbid.

And would you be her executioner, and kill her in your rage

too? O, 'twere most unmanlike. She is your wife: what faults

have been done by her before she married you were not against

20 What death sweeter than to die for love?
21 To die in grace is to die without sorrow.

you: alas, poor lady, what hath she committed, which any lady
in Italy, in the like case, would not? Sir, you must be ruled by
your reason, and not by your fury; that were unhuman and
beastly.

Sor. She shall not live.

Vas. Come, she must. You would have her confess the author
of her present misfortunes, I warrant ye; 'tis an unconscionable
demand, and she should lose the estimation that I, for my part,
hold of her worth, if she had done it: why, sir, you ought not,
of all men living, to know it. Good sir, be reconciled: alas, good
gentlewoman!

Ann. Pish, do not beg for me; I prize my life
As nothing; if the man will needs be mad,
Why, let him take it.

Sor. Vasques, hear'st thou this?

Vas. Yes, and commend her for it; in this she shows the noble-
ness of a gallant spirit, and beshrew my heart, but it becomes
her rarely.—[*Aside to* Soranzo] Sir, in any case, smother your
revenge; leave the scenting out your wrongs to me: be ruled,
as you respect your honor, or you mar all. [*Aloud*] Sir, if ever
my service were of any credit with you, be not so violent in your
distractions: you are married now; what a triumph might the
report of this give to other neglected suitors! 'Tis as manlike to
bear extremities as godlike to forgive.

Sor. O, Vasques, Vasques, in this piece of flesh,
This faithless face of hers, had I laid up
The treasure of my heart! Hadst thou been virtuous,
Fair, wicked woman, not the matchless joys
Of life itself had made me wish to live
With any saint but thee: deceitful creature,
How hast thou mocked my hopes, and in the shame
Of thy lewd womb even buried me alive!
I did too dearly love thee.

Vas. [*Aside to* Soranzo] This is well; follow this temper with
some passion: be brief and moving; 'tis for the purpose.

Sor. Be witness to my words thy soul and thoughts;
And tell me, didst not think that in my heart
I did too superstitiously adore thee?

Ann. I must confess I know you loved me well.

Sor. And wouldst thou use me thus! O Annabella,
Be thou assured, who'er the villain was
That thus hath tempted thee to this disgrace,
Well he might lust, but never loved as I:
He doted on the picture that hung out
Upon thy cheeks to please his humorous eye;
Not on the part I loved, which was thy heart,
And, as I thought, thy virtues.

Ann.   O, my lord!
These words wound deeper than your sword could do.

Vas. Let me not ever take comfort, but I begin to weep myself, so much I pity him: why, madam, I knew, when his rage
was over-past, what it would come to.

Sor. Forgive me, Annabella. Though thy youth
Hath tempted thee above thy strength to folly,
Yet will not I forget what I should be,
And what I am—a husband; in that name
Is hid divinity: if I do find
That thou wilt yet be true, here I remit
All former faults, and take thee to my bosom.

Vas. By my troth, and that's a point of noble charity.

Ann. Sir, on my knees,

Sor.   Rise up, you shall not kneel.
Get you to your chamber; see you make no show
Of alteration; I'll be with you straight:
My reason tells me now that " 'tis as common
To err in frailty as to be a woman."
Go to your chamber.   [*Exit* Annabella]

Vas. So! this was somewhat to the matter: what do you think
of your heaven of happiness now, sir?

Sor. I carry hell about me; all my blood
Is fired in swift revenge.

Vas. That may be; but know you how, or on whom? Alas, to
marry a great woman, being made great in the stock to your
hand, is a usual sport in these days; but to know what ferret it
was that hunted your cony-berry, there's the cunning.

Sor. I'll make her tell herself, or—

Vas. Or what? you must not do so; let me yet persuade your sufferance a little while: go to her, use her mildly; win her, if it be possible, to a voluntary, to a weeping tune: for the rest, if all hit, I will not miss my mark. Pray, sir, go in: the next news I tell you shall be wonders.

Sor. Delay in vengeance gives a heavier blow.   [*Exit*]

Vas. Ah, sirrah, here's work for the nonce! I had a suspicion of a bad matter in my head a pretty whiles ago; but after my madam's scurvy looks here at home, her waspish perverseness and loud fault-finding, then I remembered the proverb, that "where hens crow, and cocks hold their peace, there are sorry houses." 'Sfoot, if the lower parts of a she-tailor's cunning can cover such a swelling in the stomach, I'll never blame a false stitch in a shoe whiles I live again. Up, and up so quick? and so quickly too? 'twere a fine policy to learn by whom: this must be known; and I have thought on't:

[*Enter* Putana *in tears*]

Here's the way, or none. What, crying, old mistress! alas, alas, I cannot blame ye; we have a lord, Heaven help us, is so mad as the devil himself, the more shame for him.

Put. O, Vasques, that ever I was born to see this day! Doth he use thee so too sometimes, Vasques?

Vas. Me? why he makes a dog of me: but if some were of my mind, I know what we would do. As sure as I am an honest man, he will go near to kill my lady with unkindness: say she be with child, is that such a matter for a young woman of her years to be blamed for?

Put. Alas, good heart, it is against her will full sore.

Vas. I dare be sworn all his madness is for that she will not confess whose 'tis, which he will know; and when he doth know it, I am so well acquainted with his humor, that he will forget all straight. Well, I could wish she would in plain terms tell all, for that's the way, indeed.

Put. Do you think so?

Vas. Foh, I know't; provided that he did not win her to 't by force. He was once in a mind that you could tell, and meant to have wrung it out of you; but I somewhat pacified him for that: yet, sure, you know a great deal.

Put. Heaven forgive us all! I know a little, Vasques.

Vas. Why should you not? who else should? Upon my conscience, she loves you dearly; and you would not betray her to any affliction for the world.

Put. Not for all the world, by my faith and troth, Vasques.

Vas. 'Twere pity of your life if you should; but in this you should both relieve her present discomforts, pacify my lord, and gain yourself everlasting love and preferment.

Put. Dost think so, Vasques?

Vas. Nay, I know't; sure 'twas some near and entire friend.

Put. 'Twas a dear friend indeed; but—

Vas. But what? fear not to name him; my life between you and danger: 'faith, I think 'twas no base fellow.

Put. Thou wilt stand between me and harm?

Vas. 'Ud's pity, what else? you shall be rewarded too, trust me.

Put. 'Twas even no worse than her own brother.

Vas. Her brother Giovanni, I warrant ye!

Put. Even he, Vasques; as brave a gentleman as ever kissed fair lady. O, they love most perpetually.

Vas. A brave gentleman indeed! why, therein I commend her choice. [*Aside*] Better and better. You are sure 'twas he?

Put. Sure; and you shall see he will not be long from her too.

Vas. He were to blame if he would: but may I believe thee?

Put. Believe me! why, dost think I am a Turk or a Jew? No, Vasques, I have known their dealings too long to belie them now.

Vas. Where are you there? within, sirs!

[*Enter* Banditti]

Put. How now! What are these?

Vas. You shall know presently. Come, sirs, take me this old damnable hag, gag her instantly, and put out her eyes, quickly, quickly!

Put. Vasques! Vasques!

Vas. Gag her, I say; 'sfoot, d'ye suffer her to prate? what d'ye fumble about? let me come to her. I'll help your old gums, you toad-bellied bitch! [*They gag her.*] Sirs, carry her closely into the coal house, and put out her eyes instantly; if she roars, slit her nose: d'ye hear, be speedy and sure. [*Exeunt* Banditti *with* Putana.] Why, this is excellent and above expectation—her own brother! O, horrible! to what a height of liberty in damnation hath the devil trained our age! her brother, well! there's yet but a beginning; I must to my lord, and tutor him better in his points of vengeance: now I see how a smooth tale goes beyond a smooth tail. But soft! what thing comes next? Giovanni! as I would wish: my belief is strengthened, 'tis as firm as winter and summer.

[*Enter* Giovanni]

Gio. Where's my sister?

Vas. Troubled with a new sickness, my lord; she's somewhat ill.

Gio. Took too much of the flesh, I believe.

Vas. Troth, sir, and you, I think, have e'en hit it: but my virtuous lady—

Gio. Where's she?

Vas. In her chamber; please you visit her; she is alone. [Giovanni *gives him money*.] Your liberality hath doubly made me your servant, and ever shall, ever.

[*Exit* Giovanni]
[*Re-enter* Soranzo]

Sir, I am made a man; I have plied my cue with cunning and success: I beseech you let's be private.

Sor. My lady's brother's come; now he'll know all.

Vas. Let him know't; I have made some of them fast enough. How have you dealt with my lady?

Sor. Gently, as thou hast counseled; O, my soul
Runs circular in sorrow for revenge:
But, Vasques, thou shalt know—

Vas. Nay, I will know no more, for now comes your turn to know: I would not talk so openly with you. [*Aside*] Let my young master take time enough, and go at pleasure; he is sold to death, and the devil shall not ransom him. Sir, I beseech you, your privacy.

Sor. No conquest can gain glory of my fear. [*Exeunt*]

ACT V

SCENE I—*The Street before* Soranzo's *House*

[Annabella *appears at a window above*]

Ann. Pleasures, farewell, and all ye thriftless minutes
Wherein false joys have spun a weary life!
To these my fortunes now I take my leave.
Thou, precious Time, that swiftly rid'st in post
Over the world, to finish up the race
Of my last fate, here stay thy restless course,
And bear to ages that are yet unborn
A wretched, woeful woman's tragedy!
My conscience now stands up against my lust
With depositions characterized in guilt,

[*Enter* Friar *below*]

And tells me I am lost: now I confess
Beauty that clothes the outside of the face
Is cursèd if it be not clothed with grace.
Here like a turtle mewed-up in a cage,
Unmated, I converse with air and walls,
And descant on my vile unhappiness.
O, Giovanni, thou hast had the spoil
Of thine own virtues and my modest fame,
Would thou hadst been less subject to those stars
That luckless reigned at my nativity!
O, would the scourge due to my black offense
Might pass from thee, that I alone might feel
The torment of an uncontrollèd flame!

Friar [*Aside.*] What's this I hear?

Ann.   That man, that blessèd friar,
Who joined in ceremonial knot my hand
To him whose wife I now am, told me oft
I trod the path to death, and showed me how.

But they who sleep in lethargies of lust
Hug their confusion, making Heaven unjust;
And so did I.
    Friar [*Aside.*] Here's music to the soul!
    Ann. Forgive me, my good genius, and this once
Be helpful to my ends: let some good man
Pass this way, to whose trust I may commit
This paper, double-lined with tears and blood;
Which being granted, here I sadly vow
Repentance, and a leaving of that life
I long have died in.
    Friar.   Lady, Heaven hath heard you,
And hath by providence ordained that I
Should be his minister for your behoof.
    Ann. Ha, what are you?
    Friar.   Your brother's friend, the friar;
Glad in my soul that I have lived to hear
This free confession 'twixt your peace and you.
What would you, or to whom? fear not to speak.
    Ann. Is Heaven so bountiful? then I have found
More favor than I hoped. Here, holy man:
                        [Throws down a letter]
Commend me to my brother; give him that.
That letter; bid him read it, and repent.
Tell him that I, imprisoned in my chamber,
Barred of all company, even of my guardian,
Who gives me cause of much suspect, have time
To blush at what hath passed; bid him be wise,
And not believe the friendship of my lord:
I fear much more than I can speak: good father,
The place is dangerous, and spies are busy.
I must break off. You'll do't?
    Friar.   Be sure I will,
And fly with speed. My blessing ever rest
With thee, my daughter; live, to die more blest!   *[Exit]*
    Ann. Thanks to the heavens, who have prolonged my breath
To this good use! now I can welcome death.
                    [Withdraws from the window]

SCENE II—*A Room in* Soranzo's *House*

[*Enter* Soranzo *and* Vasques]

Vas. Am I to be believed now? first marry a strumpet, that cast herself away upon you but to laugh at your horns, to feast on your disgrace, riot in your vexations, cuckold you in your bride bed, waste your estate upon panders and bawds!

Sor. No more, I say, no more!

Vas. A cuckold is a goodly tame beast, my lord.

Sor. I am resolved; urge not another word;
My thoughts are great, and all as resolute
As thunder: in meantime I'll cause our lady
To deck herself in all her bridal robes;
Kiss her, and fold her gently in my arms.
Begone, yet, hear you, are the banditti ready
To wait in ambush.

Vas. Good sir, trouble not yourself about other business than your own resolution: remember that time lost cannot be recalled.

Sor. With all the cunning words thou canst, invite
The states[22] of Parma to my birthday's feast
Haste to my brother-rival and his father,
Entreat them gently, bid them not to fail.
Be speedy, and return.

Vas. Let not your pity betray you till my coming back; think upon incest and cuckoldry.

Sor. Revenge is all the ambition I aspire
To that I'll climb or fall: my blood's on fire.   [*Exeunt*]

SCENE III—*A Room in* Florio's *House*

[*Enter* Giovanni]

Gio. Busy opinion is an idle fool,
That, as a school rod keeps a child in awe,
Frights the inexperienced temper of the mind
So did it me, who, ere my precious sister
Was married, thought all taste of love would die
In such a contract; but I find no change

22 *i.e.* Nobles

Of pleasure in this formal law of sports.
She is still one to me, and every kiss
As sweet and as delicious as the first
I reaped, when yet the privilege of youth
Entitled her a virgin. O, the glory
Of two united hearts like hers and mine!
Let poring bookmen dream of other worlds;
My world and all of happiness is here,
And I'd not change it for the best to come:
A life of pleasure is elysium.

                                          [*Enter* Friar]

Father, you enter on the jubilee
Of my retired delights: now I can tell you,
The hell you oft have prompted is nought else
But slavish and fond superstitious fear;
And I could prove it too—
    Friar.   Thy blindness slays thee:
Look there, 'tis writ to thee.   [*Gives him the letter*]
    Gio. From whom?
    Friar. Unrip the seals and see;
The blood's yet seething hot, that will anon
Be frozen harder than congealèd coral.
Why d'ye change color, son?
    Gio.   'Fore Heaven, you make
Some petty devil factor 'twixt my love
And your religion-maskèd sorceries.
Where had you this?
    Friar.   Thy conscience, youth, is seared,
Else thou wouldst stoop to warning.
    Gio.   'Tis her hand,
I know't; and 'tis all written in her blood.
She writes I know not what. Death! I'll not fear
An armèd thunderbolt aimed at my heart.
She writes, we are discovered: Pox on dreams
Of low faint-hearted cowardice! discovered?
The devil we are! which way is't possible?
Are we grown traitors to our own delights?
Confusion take such dotage! 'tis but forged:

This is your peevish chattering, weak old man.

[*Enter* Vasques]

Now, sir, what brings you?

Vas. My lord, according to his yearly custom, keeping this day a feast in honor of his birthday, by me invites you thither. Your worthy father, with the pope's reverend nuncio, and other magnificoes of Parma, have promised their presence: will't please you to be of the number?

Gio. Yes, tell him I dare come.

Vas. "Dare come!"

Gio. So I said; and tell him more, I will come.

Vas. These words are strange to me.

Gio. Say, I will come.

Vas. You will not miss?

Gio. Yet more! I'll come, sir. Are you answered?

Vas. So I'll say. My service to you.   [*Exit*]

Friar. You will not go, I trust.

Gio.   Not go! for what?

Friar. O, do not go: this feast, I'll gage my life,
Is but a plot to train you to your ruin.
Be ruled, you shall not go.

Gio.   Not go! stood Death
Threatening his armies of confounding plagues
With hosts of dangers hot as blazing stars,
I would be there: not go! yes, and resolve
To strike as deep in slaughter as they all;
For I will go.

Friar.   Go where thou wilt: I see
The wildness of thy fate draws to an end,
To a bad, fearful end. I must not stay
To know thy fall: back to Bononia I
With speed will haste, and shun this coming blow.
Parma, farewell; would I had never known thee,
Or aught of thine! Well, young man, since no prayer
Can make thee safe, I leave thee to despair.   [*Exit*]

Gio. Despair, or tortures of a thousand hells;
All's one to me: I have set up my rest.[23]

[23] I have taken my resolution.

Now, now, work serious thoughts on baneful plots;
Be all a man, my soul; let not the curse
Of old prescription rend from me the gall
Of courage, which enrolls a glorious death:
If I must totter like a well-grown oak,
Some under-shrubs shall in my weighty fall
Be crushed to splits; with me they all shall perish!

                                                 [*Exit*]

SCENE IV—*A hall in* Soranzo's *house*

            [*Enter* Soranzo, Vasques *with masks, and* Banditti]
Sor. You will not fail, or shrink in the attempt?

Vas. I will undertake for their parts. Be sure, my masters, to be bloody enough, and as unmerciful as if you were preying upon a rich booty on the very mountains of Liguria: for your pardons trust to my lord; but for reward you shall trust none but your own pockets.

Band. We'll make a murder.

Sor. Here's gold [*Gives them money*]; here's more; want
    nothing; what you do
Is noble, and an act of brave revenge:
I'll make ye rich, banditti, and all free.

Band. Liberty! liberty!

Vas. Hold, take every man a vizard [*Gives them masks*]: when ye are withdrawn, keep as much silence as you can possibly. You know the watchword; till which be spoken, move not; but when you hear that, rush in like a stormy flood; I need not instruct ye in your own profession.

Band. No, no, no.

Vas. In, then: your ends are profit and preferment: away!
                      [*Exeunt* Banditti]
Sor. The guests will all come, Vasques?

Vas. Yes, sir. And now let me a little edge your resolution: you see nothing is unready to this great work, but a great mind in you; call to your remembrance your disgraces, your loss of honor, Hippolita's blood, and arm your courage in your own wrongs; so shall you best right those wrongs in vengeance, which you may truly call your own.

Sor. 'Tis well: the less I speak, the more I burn.
And blood shall quench that flame.

Vas. Now you begin to turn Italian. This beside: when my
young incest-monger comes, he will be sharp set on his old bit:
give him time enough, let him have your chamber and bed at
liberty; let my hot hare have law ere he be hunted to his death,
that, if it be possible, he post to hell in the very act of his
damnation.

Sor. It shall be so; and see, as we would wish,
He comes himself first.

> [*Enter* Giovanni]
> Welcome, my much-loved brother:

Now I perceive you honor me; you're welcome.
But where's my father?

Gio.   With the other states,[24]
Attending on the nuncio of the pope,
To wait upon him hither. How's my sister?

Sor. Like a good housewife, scarcely ready yet;
You're best walk to her chamber.

Gio.   If you will.

Sor. I must expect my honorable friends;
Good brother, get her forth.

Gio.   You're busy, sir.   [*Exit*]

Vas. Even as the great devil himself would have it! let him
go and glut himself in his own destruction.—[*Flourish.*] Hark,
the nuncio is at hand: good sir, be ready to receive him.

> [*Enter* Cardinal, Florio, Donado, Richardetto, *and*
> Attendants]

Sor. Most reverend lord, this grace hath made me proud,
That you vouchsafe my house; I ever rest
Your humble servant for this noble favor.

Car. You are our friend, my lord: his holiness
Shall understand how zealously you honor
Saint Peter's vicar in his substitute:
Our special love to you.

Sor.   Signiors, to you
My welcome, and my ever best of thanks

24 Nobles.

For this so memorable courtesy.
Pleaseth your grace walk near?
   Car.   My lord, we come
To celebrate your feast with civil mirth,
As ancient custom teacheth: we will go.
   Sor. Attend his grace there! Signiors, keep your way.

                                     [Exeunt]

SCENE V—Annabella's *bed-chamber in the same*

          [Annabella *richly dressed and* Giovanni *discovered
          lying on a bed*]
   Gio. What, changed so soon! hath your new sprightly lord
Found out a trick in night games more than we
Could know in our simplicity? Ha! is't so?
Or does the fit come on you, to prove treacherous
To your past vows and oaths?
   Ann.   Why should you jest
At my calamity, without all sense
Of the approaching dangers you are in?
   Gio. What danger's half so great as thy revolt?
Thou art a faithless sister, else thou know'st
Malice, or any treachery beside,
Would stoop to my bent brows: why, I hold fate
Clasped in my fist, and could command the course
Of time's eternal motion, hadst thou been
One thought more steady than an ebbing sea.
And what? you'll now be honest, that's resolved?
   Ann. Brother, dear brother, know what I have been,
And know that now there's but a dining time
'Twixt us and our confusion: let's not waste
These precious hours in vain and useless speech.
Alas, these gay attires were not put on
But to some end; this sudden solemn feast
Was not ordained to riot in expense;
I, that have now been chambered here alone,
Barred of my guardian or of any else,
Am not for nothing at an instant freed
To fresh access. Be not deceived, my brother;

This banquet is a harbinger of death
To you and me; resolve yourself it is,
And be prepared to welcome it.
    Gio.   Well, then;
The schoolmen teach that all this globe of earth
Shall be consumed to ashes in a minute.
    Ann. So I have read too.
    Gio.   But 'twere somewhat strange
To see the waters burn: could I believe
This might be true, I could believe as well
There might be hell or Heaven.
    Ann.   That's most certain.
    Gio. A dream, a dream! else in this other world
We should know one another.
    Ann.   So we shall.
    Gio. Have you heard so?
    Ann.   For certain.
    Gio.   But d'ye think
That I shall see you there? You look on me.
May we kiss one another, prate or laugh,
Or do as we do here?
    Ann.   I know not that.
But, brother, for the present, what d'ye mean
To free yourself from danger? some way think
How to escape: I'm sure the guests are come.
    Gio. Look up, look here; what see you in my face?
    Ann. Distraction and a troubled conscience.
    Gio. Death, and a swift repining wrath: yet look;
What see you in mine eyes?
    Ann.   Methinks you weep.
    Gio. I do indeed: these are the funeral tears
Shed on your grave; these furrowed-up my cheeks
When first I loved and knew not how to woo.
Fair Annabella, should I here repeat
The story of my life, we might lose time.
Be record all the spirits of the air,
And all things else that are, that day and night,
Early and late, the tribute which my heart

Hath paid to Annabella's sacred love
Hath been these tears, which are her mourners now!
Never till now did Nature do her best
To show a matchless beauty to the world,
Which in an instant, ere it scarce was seen,
The jealous Destinies required again.
Pray, Annabella, pray! Since we must part,
Go thou, white in thy soul, to fill a throne
Of innocence and sanctity in Heaven.
Pray, pray, my sister!

 Ann.   Then I see your drift.
Ye blessèd angels, guard me!

 Gio.   So say I.
Kiss me. If ever aftertimes should hear
Of our fast-knit affections, though perhaps
The laws of conscience and of civil use
May justly blame us, yet when they but know
Our loves, that love will wipe away that rigor
Which would in other incests be abhorred.
Give me your hand: how sweetly life doth run
In these well-colored veins! how constantly
These palms do promise health! but I could chide
With Nature for this cunning flattery.
Kiss me again: forgive me.

 Ann.   With my heart.

 Gio. Farewell!

 Ann.   Will you be gone?

 Gio.   Be dark, bright sun,
And make this midday night, that thy gilt rays
May not behold a deed will turn their splendor
More sooty than the poets feign their Styx!—
One other kiss, my sister.

 Ann.   What means this?

 Gio. To save thy fame, and kill thee in a kiss.

               [Stabs her]

Thus die, and die by me, and by my hand!
Revenge is mine; honor doth love command.

 Ann. O, brother, by your hand!

Gio.   When thou art dead
I'll give my reasons for't; for to dispute
With thy—even in thy death—most lovely beauty,
Would make me stagger to perform this act,
Which I most glory in.
   Ann. Forgive him, Heaven—and me my sins! Farewell,
Brother unkind, unkind—Mercy, great Heaven! O, O!   [*Dies*]
   Gio. She's dead, alas, good soul! The hapless fruit
That in her womb received its life from me
Hath had from me a cradle and a grave.
I must not dally. This sad marriage bed,
In all her best, bore her alive and dead.
Soranzo, thou hast missed thy aim in this:
I have prevented now thy reaching plots,
And killed a love, for whose each drop of blood
I would have pawned my heart. Fair Annabella,
How over-glorious art thou in thy wounds,
Triumphing over infamy and hate!
Shrink not, courageous hand, stand up, my heart,
And boldly act my last and greater part!

                                   [*The scene closes*]

    SCENE VI—*A banqueting-room in the same*

            [*A banquet set out. Enter the* Cardinal, Florio,
            Donado, Soranzo, Richardetto, Vasques, *and*
            Attendants]
   Vas. [*Aside to* Soranzo] Remember, sir, what you have to do;
be wise and resolute.
   Sor. [*Aside to* Vasques] Enough: my heart is fixed. Pleaseth
   your grace
To taste these coarse confections: though the use
Of such set entertainments more consists
In custom than in cause, yet, reverend sir,
I am still made your servant by your presence.
   Car. And we your friend.
   Sor. But where's my brother Giovanni?
            [*Enter* Giovanni *with a heart upon his dagger*]
   Gio. Here, here, Soranzo! trimmed in reeking blood,

That triumphs over death, proud in the spoil
Of love and vengeance! Fate, or all the powers
That guide the motions of immortal souls,
Could not prevent me.
 Car. What means this?
 Flo. Son Giovanni!
 Sor. [*Aside*] Shall I be forestalled?
 Gio. Be not amazed: if your misgiving hearts
Shrink at an idle sight, what bloodless fear
Of coward passion would have seized your senses,
Had you beheld the rape of life and beauty
Which I have acted! My sister, O, my sister!
 Flo. Ha! what of her?
 Gio.   The glory of my deed
Darkened the midday sun, made noon as night.
You came to feast, my lords, with dainty fare:
I came to feast too; but I digged for food
In a much richer mine than gold or stone
Of any value balanced; 'tis a heart,
A heart, my lords, in which is mine entombed:
Look well upon't; d'ye know't?
 Vas. [*Aside*] What strange riddle's this?
 Gio. 'Tis Annabella's heart, 'tis: why d'ye startle?
I vow 'tis hers: this dagger's point ploughed under
Her fruitful womb, and left to me the fame
Of a most glorious executioner.
 Flo. Why, madman, art thyself?
 Gio. Yes, father; and, that times to come may know
How, as my fate, I honored my revenge,
List, father; to your ears I will yield up
How much I have deserved to be your son.
 Flo. What is't thou say'st?
 Gio.   Nine moons have had their changes
Since I first thoroughly viewed and truly loved
Your daughter and my sister,
 Flo.   How! Alas, my lords,
He is a frantic madman!
 Gio.   Father, no.

For nine months' space in secret I enjoyed
Sweet Annabella's sheets; nine months I lived
A happy monarch of her heart and her.
Soranzo, thou know'st this: thy paler cheek
Bears the confounding print of thy disgrace;
For her too-fruitful womb too soon betrayed
The happy passage of our stol'n delights,
And made her mother to a child unborn.

 Car. Incestuous villain!

 Flo.   O, his rage belies him.

 Gio. It does not, 'tis the oracle of truth;
I vow it is so.

 Sor.   I shall burst with fury,
Bring the strumpet forth!

 Vas. I shall, sir.   *[Exit]*

 Gio.   Do, sir. Have you all no faith
To credit yet my triumphs? Here I swear
By all that you call sacred, by the love
I bore my Annabella whilst she lived,
These hands have from her bosom ripped this heart.

        [Re-enter Vasques]

Is't true, or no, sir?

 Vas.   'Tis most strangely true.

 Flo. Cursèd man! Have I lived to—   *[Dies]*

 Car.   Hold up, Florio.
Monster of children! see what thou hast done,
Broke thy old father's heart. Is none of you
Dares venture on him?

 Gio.   Let 'em! O, my father,
How well his death becomes him in his griefs!
Why, this was done with courage: now survives
None of our house but I, gilt in the blood
Of a fair sister and a hapless father.

 Sor. Inhuman scorn of men, hast thou a thought
T' outlive thy murders?   *[Draws]*

 Gio.   Yes, I tell thee, yes;
For in my fists I bear the twists of life.
Soranzo, see this heart, which was thy wife's;

Thus I exchange it royally for thine.   [*They fight*]
And thus, and thus!   [Soranzo *falls*]
     Now brave revenge is mine.

 Vas. I cannot hold any longer. You, sir, are you grown insolent in your butcheries? have at you!

 Gio. Come, I am armed to meet thee.   [*They fight*]

 Vas. No! will it not be yet? if this will not, another shall. Not
yet? I shall fit you anon. Vengeance! [25]

       [*The* banditti *rush in*]

 Gio. Welcome! come more of you; whate'er you be,
I dare your worst.   [*They surround and wound him*]
O, I can stand no longer! feeble arms,
Have you so soon lost strength?   [*Falls*]

 Vas. Now you are welcome, sir!—[*Aside to* banditti.] Away,
my masters, all is done; shift for yourselves, your reward is your
own; shift for yourselves.

 Band. Away, away!   [*Exeunt*]

 Vas. How d'ye, my lord? See you this? [*Pointing to* Giovanni.]
How is't?

 Sor. Dead; but in death well pleased that I have lived
To see my wrongs revenged on that black devil.
O, Vasques, to thy bosom let me give
My last of breath; let not that lecher live.
O!   [*Dies*]

 Vas. The reward of peace and rest be with him, my ever dearest lord and master!

 Gio. Whose hand gave me this wound?

 Vas. Mine, sir; I was your first man: have you enough?

 Gio. I thank thee; thou hast done for me
But what I would have else done on myself.
Art sure thy lord is dead?

 Vas.   O, impudent slave!
As sure as I am sure to see thee die.

 Car. Think on thy life and end, and call for mercy.

 Gio. Mercy! why, I have found it in this justice.

 Car. Strive yet to cry to Heaven.

 Gio.   O, I bleed fast!

[25] The watchword previously agreed on.

Death, thou'rt a guest long looked for; I embrace
Thee and thy wounds: O, my last minute comes!
Where'er I go, let me enjoy this grace,
Freely to view my Annabella's face.   [*Dies*]

   Don. Strange miracle of justice!

   Car. Raise up the city; we shall be murdered all!

   Vas. You need not fear, you shall not: this strange task being
ended, I have paid the duty to the son which I have vowed to
the father.

   Car. Speak, wretched villain, what incarnate fiend
Hath led thee on to this?

   Vas. Honesty, and pity of my master's wrongs: for know, my
lord, I am by birth a Spaniard, brought forth my country in my
youth by Lord Soranzo's father, whom whilst he lived I served
faithfully: since whose death I have been to this man as I was to
him. What I have done was duty, and I repent nothing, but that
the loss of my life had not ransomed his.

   Car. Say, fellow, know'st thou any yet unnamed
Of counsel in this incest?

   Vas. Yes, an old woman, sometime guardian to this murdered
lady.

   Car. And what's become of her?

   Vas. Within this room she is! whose eyes, after her confession,
I caused to be put out, but kept alive, to confirm what from Giovanni's own mouth you have heard. Now, my lord, what I have
done you may judge of; and let your own wisdom be a judge in
your own reason.

   Car. Peace! First this woman, chief in these effects,
My sentence is, that forthwith she be ta'en
Out of the city, for example's sake,
There to be burnt to ashes.

   Don.   'Tis most just.

   Car. Be it your charge, Donado, see it done.

   Don. I shall.

   Vas. What for me? if death, 'tis welcome: I have been honest
to the son, as I was to the father.

   Car. Fellow, for thee, since what thou didst was done
Not for thyself, being no Italian,

We banish thee for ever; to depart
Within three days: in this we do dispense
With grounds of reason, not of thine offense.

    Vas. 'Tis well: this conquest is mine, and I rejoice that a
Spaniard outwent an Italian in revenge.   *[Exit]*

    Car. Take up these slaughtered bodies, see them buried;
And all the gold and jewels, or whatsoever,
Confiscate by the canons of the church,
We seize upon to the pope's proper use.

    Rich. [*Discovers himself.*] Your grace's pardon: thus long I
        lived disguised,
To see the effect of pride and lust at once
Brought both to shameful ends.

    Car. What! Richardetto, whom we thought for dead?

    Don. Sir, was it you—

    Rich.   Your friend.

    Car.   We shall have time
To talk at large of all: but never yet
Incest and murder have so strangely met.
Of one so young, so rich in nature's store,
Who could not say, 'Tis Pity She's a Whore?

                                  [Exeunt]

Herman Melville

PIERRE [*Excerpt from a Novel*]
Book XXV

HERMAN MELVILLE (1819-1891), author of *Pierre, or The Ambiguities*, was born in New York. The publication of *Moby Dick* in 1851
established Melville's reputation as one of the greatest figures of nineteenth
century American literature, an evaluation that is unchallenged today. The
following year there appeared *Pierre*, of which the final chapters are reprinted here. The ambiguity in which Pierre is caught is the struggle of
a man of faith in a world of corruption and compromise. "At times Melville seems to jeer at his hapless and feckless hero," writes Willard Thorp
of Princeton University, "but he is more certain than in Moby Dick that
the fault lies in heaven where the corrosion of evil first touched man's
nature. Heaven gives perplexed man no answer to this ambiguity."

1

A day or two after the arrival of Lucy, when she had quite
recovered from any possible ill effects of recent events,—events
conveying such a shock to both Pierre and Isabel, though to
each in a quite different way, but not, apparently at least, moving Lucy so intensely—as they were all three sitting at coffee,
Lucy expressed her intention to practice her crayon art professionally. It would be so pleasant an employment for her, besides
contributing to their common fund. Pierre well knew her
expertness in catching likenesses, and judiciously and truthfully
beautifying them; not by altering the features so much, as by
steeping them in a beautifying atmosphere. For even so, said
Lucy, thrown into the Lagoon, and there beheld—as I have
heard—the roughest stones, without transformation, put on the
softest aspects. If Pierre would only take a little trouble to bring
sitters to her room, she doubted not a fine harvest of heads might
easily be secured. Certainly, among the numerous inmates of

the old church, Pierre must know many who would have no objections to being sketched. Moreover, though as yet she had had small opportunity to see them; yet among such a remarkable company of poets, philosophers, and mystics of all sorts, there must be some striking heads. In conclusion, she expressed her satisfaction at the chamber prepared for her, inasmuch as having been formerly the studio of an artist, one window had been considerably elevated, while by a singular arrangement of the interior shutters, the light could in any direction be thrown about at will.

Already Pierre had anticipated something of this sort; the first sight of the easel having suggested it to him. His reply was therefore not wholly unconsidered. He said, that so far as she herself was concerned, the systematic practice of her art at present would certainly be a great advantage in supplying her with a very delightful occupation. But since she could hardly hope for any patronage from her mother's fashionable and wealthy associates; indeed, as such a thing must be very far from her own desires; and as it was only from the Apostles she could— for some time to come, at least—reasonably anticipate sitters; and as those Apostles were almost universally a very forlorn and penniless set—though in truth there were some wonderfully rich-looking heads among them—therefore, Lucy must not look for much immediate pecuniary emolument. Ere long she might indeed do something very handsome; but at the outset, it was well to be moderate in her expectations. This admonishment came, modifiedly, from that certain stoic, dogged mood of Pierre, born of his recent life, which taught him never to expect any good from anything; but always to anticipate ill; however not in unreadiness to meet the contrary; and then, if good came, so much the better. He added that he would that very morning go among the rooms and corridors of the Apostles, familiarly announcing that his cousin, a lady-artist in crayons, occupied a room adjoining his, where she would be very happy to receive any sitters.

"And now, Lucy, what shall be the terms? That is a very important point, thou knowest."

"I suppose, Pierre, they must be very low," said Lucy, looking at him meditatively.

"Very low, Lucy; very low, indeed."

"Well, ten dollars, then."

"Ten Banks of England, Lucy!" exclaimed Pierre. "Why, Lucy, that were almost a quarter's income for some of the Apostles!"

"Four dollars, Pierre."

"I will tell thee now, Lucy—but first, how long does it take to complete one portrait?"

"Two sittings, and two mornings' work by myself, Pierre."

"And let me see; what are thy materials? They are not very costly, I believe. 'Tis not like cutting glass—thy tools must not be pointed with diamonds, Lucy?"

"See, Pierre!" said Lucy, holding out her little palm, "see; this handful of charcoal, a bit of bread, a crayon or two, and a square of paper—that is all."

"Well, then, thou shalt charge one-seventy-five for a portrait."

"Only one-seventy-five, Pierre?"

"I am half afraid now we have set it far too high, Lucy. Thou must not be extravagant. Look: if thy terms were ten dollars, and thou didst crayon on trust; then thou wouldst have plenty of sitters, but small returns. But if thou puttest thy terms right down, and also sayest thou must have thy cash right down too— don't start so at that *cash*—then not so many sitters to be sure, but more returns. Thou understandest."

"It shall be just as thou say'st, Pierre."

"Well, then, I will write a card for thee, stating thy terms; and put it up conspicuously in thy room, so that every Apostle may know what he has to expect."

"Thank thee, thank thee, cousin Pierre," said Lucy, rising. "I rejoice at thy pleasant and not entirely unhopeful view of my poor little plan. But I must be doing something; I must be earning money. See, I have eaten ever so much bread this morning, but have not earned one penny."

With a humorous sadness Pierre measured the large remainder of the one only piece she had touched, and then would have spoken banteringly to her; but she had slid away into her own room.

He was presently roused from the strange reverie into which the conclusion of this scene had thrown him, by the touch of Isabel's hand upon his knee, and her large expressive glance upon his face. During all the foregoing colloquy, she had remained entirely silent; but an unoccupied observer would perhaps have noticed, that some new and very strong emotions were restrainedly stirring within her.

"Pierre!" she said, intently bending over toward him.

"Well, well, Isabel," stammeringly replied Pierre; while a mysterious color suffused itself over his whole face, neck, and brow; and involuntarily he started a little back from her self-proffering form.

Arrested by this movement Isabel eyed him fixedly; then slowly rose, and with immense mournful stateliness, drew herself up, and said, "If thy sister can ever come too nigh to thee, Pierre, tell thy sister so beforehand; for the September sun draws not up the valley vapor more jealously from the disdainful earth, than my secret god shall draw me up from thee, if ever I can come too nigh to thee."

Thus speaking, one hand was on her bosom, as if resolutely feeling of something deadly there concealed; but, riveted by her general manner more than by her particular gesture, Pierre, at the instant, did not so particularly note the all-significant movement of the hand upon her bosom, though afterward he recalled it, and darkly and thoroughly comprehended its meaning.

"Too nigh to me, Isabel? Sun or dew, thou fertilizest me! Can sunbeams or drops of dew come too nigh the thing they warm and water? Then sit down by me, Isabel, and sit close; wind in within my ribs,—if so thou canst,—that my one frame may be the continent of two."

"Fine feathers make fine birds, so I have heard," said Isabel, most bitterly—"but do fine sayings always make fine deeds? Pierre, thou didst but just now draw away from me!"

"When we would most dearly embrace, we first throw back

our arms, Isabel; I but drew away, to draw so much the closer
to thee."

"Well, all words are arrant skirmishers; deeds are the army's
self! be it as thou sayest. I yet trust to thee, Pierre."

"My breath waits thine; what is it, Isabel?"

"I have been more blockish than a block; I am mad to think
of it! More mad, that her great sweetness should first remind me
of mine own stupidity. But she shall not get the start of me!
Pierre, some way I must work for thee! See, I will sell this hair;
have these teeth pulled out; but some way I will earn money
for thee!"

Pierre now eyed her startledly. Touches of a determinate
meaning shone in her; some hidden thing was deeply wounded
in her. An affectionate soothing syllable was on his tongue; his
arm was out; when shifting his expression, he whisperingly and
alarmedly exclaimed, "Hark! she is coming.—Be still."

But rising boldly, Isabel threw open the connecting door, ex-
claiming half hysterically—"Look, Lucy, here is the strangest
husband, fearful of being caught speaking to his wife!"

With an artist's little box before her—whose rattling, perhaps, had startled Pierre—Lucy was sitting midway in her
room, opposite the opened door, so that at that moment, both
Pierre and Isabel were plainly visible to her. The singular tone
of Isabel's voice instantly caused her to look up intently. At
once, a sudden irradiation of some subtle intelligence—but
whether welcome to her, or otherwise, could not be determined
—shot over her whole aspect. She murmured some vague random reply; and then bent low over her box, saying she was very
busy.

Isabel closed the door, and sat down again by Pierre. Her
countenance wore a mixed and writhing, impatient look. She
seemed as one in whom the most powerful emotion of life is
caught in inextricable toils of circumstances, and while longing
to disengage itself, still knows that all struggles will prove worse
than vain; and so, for the moment, grows madly reckless and
defiant of all obstacles. Pierre trembled as he gazed upon her.
But soon the mood passed from her; her old, sweet mournful-

ness returned; again the clear unfathomableness was in her mystic eye.

"Pierre, ere now,—ere I ever knew thee—I have done mad things, which I have never been conscious of, but in the dim recalling. I hold such things no things of mine. What I now remember, as just now done, was one of them."

"Thou hast done nothing but shown thy strength, while I have shown my weakness, Isabel; yes, to the whole world thou art my wife—to her, too, thou art my wife. Have I not told her so, myself? I was weaker than a kitten, Isabel; and thou, strong as those high things angelical, from which utmost beauty takes not strength."

"Pierre, once such syllables from thee, were all refreshing, and bedewing to me; now, though they drop as warmly and as fluidly from thee, yet falling through another and an intercepting zone, they freeze on the way, and clatter on my heart like hail, Pierre. Thou didst not speak thus to her!"

"She is not Isabel."

The girl gazed at him with a quick and piercing scrutiny; then looked quite calm, and spoke. "My guitar, Pierre: thou know'st how complete a mistress I am of it; now, before thou gettest sitters for the portrait sketcher, thou shalt get pupils for the music teacher. Wilt thou?" and she looked at him with a persuasiveness and touchingness, which to Pierre, seemed more than mortal.

"My poor, poor Isabel!" cried Pierre; "thou art the mistress of the natural sweetness of the guitar, not of its invented regulated artifices; and these are all that the silly pupil will pay for learning. And what thou hast cannot be taught. Ah, thy sweet ignorance is all transporting to me! my sweet, my sweet!—dear, divine girl!" And impulsively he caught her in his arms.

While the first fire of his feeling plainly glowed upon him, but ere he had yet caught her to him, Isabel had backward glided close to the connecting door, which, at the instant of his embrace, suddenly opened, as by its own volition.

Before the eyes of seated Lucy, Pierre and Isabel stood locked, Pierre's lips upon her cheek.

2

Notwithstanding the maternal visit of Mrs. Tartan, and the peremptoriness with which it had been closed by her declared departure never to return, and her vow to teach all Lucy's relatives and friends, and Lucy's own brothers, and her suitor, to disown her, and forget her; yet Pierre fancied that he knew too much in general of the human heart, and too much in particular of the character of both Glen and Frederic, to remain entirely untouched by disquietude, concerning what those two fiery youths might now be plotting against him, as the imagined monster, by whose infernal tricks Lucy Tartan was supposed to have been seduced from every earthly seemliness. Not happily, but only so much the more gloomily, did he augur from the fact that Mrs. Tartan had come to Lucy unattended, and that Glen and Frederic had let eight-and-forty hours and more go by, without giving the slightest hostile or neutral sign. At first he thought that bridling their impulsive fierceness, they were resolved to take the slower, but perhaps the surer method, to wrest Lucy back to them, by instituting some legal process. But this idea was repulsed by more than one consideration.

Not only was Frederic of that sort of temper, peculiar to military men, which would prompt him, in so closely personal and intensely private and family a matter, to scorn the hireling publicity of the law's lingering arm; and impel him, as by the furiousness of fire, to be his own righter and avenger; for, in him, it was perhaps quite as much the feeling of an outrageous family affront to himself, through Lucy, as her own presumed separate wrong, however black, which stung him to the quick: not only were these things so respecting Frederic; but concerning Glen, Pierre well knew, that be Glen heartless as he might, to do a deed of love, Glen was not heartless to do a deed of hate; that though, on that memorable night of his arrival in the city, Glen had heartlessly closed his door upon him, yet now Glen might heartfully burst Pierre's open, if by that he at all believed, that permanent success would crown the fray.

Besides, Pierre knew this—that so invincible is the natural,

untamable, latent spirit of a courageous manliness in man, that
though now socially educated for thousands of years in an arbitrary homage to the law, as the one only appointed redress for
every injured person; yet immemorially and universally, among
all gentlemen of spirit, once to have uttered independent personal threats of personal vengeance against your foe, and then,
after that, to fall back slinking into a court, and hire with sops
a pack of yelping pettifoggers to fight the battle so valiantly
proclaimed; this, on the surface, is ever deemed very decorous,
and very prudent—a most wise second thought; but, at bottom,
a miserably ignoble thing. Frederic was not the watery man for
that,—Glen had more grapey blood in him.

Moreover, it seemed quite clear to Pierre, that only by making out Lucy absolutely mad, and striving to prove it by a thousand despicable little particulars, could the law succeed in tearing her from the refuge she had voluntarily sought, a course
equally abhorrent to all the parties possibly to be concerned on
either side.

What, then, would those two boiling bloods do? Perhaps
they would patrol the streets; and at the first glimpse of lonely
Lucy, kidnap her home. Or if Pierre were with her, then, smite
him down by hook or crook, fair play or foul; and then, away
with Lucy! Or if Lucy systematically kept her room, then fall
on Pierre in the most public way, fell him, and cover him from
all decent recognition beneath heaps on heaps of hate and in-
sult; so that broken on the wheel of such dishonor, Pierre might
feel himself unstrung, and basely yield the prize.

Not the gibbering of ghosts in any old haunted house; no
sulphurous and portentous sign at night beheld in heaven, will
so make the hair to stand, as when a proud and honorable man
is revolving in his soul the possibilities of some gross public and
corporeal disgrace. It is not fear; it is a pride-horror, which is
more terrible than any fear. Then, by tremendous imagery, the
murderer's mark of Cain is felt burning on the brow, and the
already acquitted knife blood-rusts in the clutch of the anticipating hand.

Certain that those two youths must be plotting something
furious against him; with the echoes of their scorning curses on

the stairs still ringing in his ears—curses, whose swift responses from himself, he, at the time, had had much ado to check; thoroughly alive to the supernaturalism of that mad frothing hate which a spirited brother forks forth at the insulter of a sister's honor—beyond doubt the most uncompromising of all the social passions known to man—and not blind to the anomalous fact, that if such a brother stab his foe at his own mother's table, all people and all juries would bear him out, accounting everything allowable to a noble soul made mad by a sweet sister's shame caused by a damned seducer;—imagining to himself his own feelings, if he were actually in the position which Frederic so vividly fancied to be his; remembering that in love matters jealousy is as an adder, and that the jealousy of Glen was double-addered by the extraordinary malice of the apparent circumstances under which Lucy had spurned Glen's arms, and fled to his always successful and now married rival, as if wantonly and shamelessly to nestle there;—remembering all these intense incitements of both those foes of his, Pierre could not but look forward to wild work very soon to come. Nor was the storm of passion in his soul unratified by the decision of his coolest possible hour. Storm and calm both said to him, Look to thyself, oh Pierre!

Murders are done by maniacs; but the earnest thoughts of murder, these are the collected desperadoes. Pierre was such; fate, or what you will, had made him such. But such he was. And when these things now swam before him; when he thought of all the ambiguities which hemmed him in; the stony walls all round that he could not overleap; the million aggravations of his most malicious lot; the last lingering hope of happiness licked up from him as by flames of fire, and his one only prospect a black, bottomless gulf of guilt, upon whose verge he imminently teetered every hour;—then the utmost hate of Glen and Frederic were jubilantly welcome to him; and murder, done in the act of warding off their ignominious public blow, seemed the one only congenial sequel to such a desperate career.

3

As a statue, planted on a revolving pedestal, shows now this limb, now that; now front, now back, now side; continually changing, too, its general profile; so does the pivoted, statued soul of man, when turned by the hand of Truth. Lies only never vary; look for no invariableness in Pierre. Nor does any canting showman here stand by to announce his phases as he revolves. Catch his phases as your insight may.

Another day passed on; Glen and Frederic still absenting themselves, and Pierre and Isabel and Lucy all dwelling together. The domestic presence of Lucy had begun to produce a remarkable effect upon Pierre. Sometimes, to the covertly watchful eye of Isabel, he would seem to look upon Lucy with an expression ill befitting their singular and so-supposed merely cousinly relation; and yet again, with another expression still more unaccountable to her,—one of fear and awe, not unmixed with impatience. But his general detailed manner toward Lucy was that of the most delicate and affectionate considerateness —nothing more. He was never alone with her; though, as before, at times alone with Isabel.

Lucy seemed entirely undesirous of usurping any place about him; manifested not the slightest unwelcome curiosity as to Pierre, and no painful embarrassment as to Isabel. Nevertheless, more and more did she seem, hour by hour, to be somehow inexplicably sliding between them, without touching them. Pierre felt that some strange heavenly influence was near him, to keep him from some uttermost harm; Isabel was alive to some untraceable displacing agency. Though when all three were together, the marvelous serenity, and sweetness, and utter unsuspectingness of Lucy obviated anything like a common embarrassment: yet if there was any embarrassment at all beneath that roof, it was sometimes when Pierre was alone with Isabel, after Lucy would innocently quit them.

Meantime Pierre was still going on with his book; every moment becoming still the more sensible of the intensely inauspicious circumstances of all sorts under which that labor was

proceeding. And as the now advancing and concentering enterprise demanded more and more compacted vigor from him, he
felt that he was having less and less to bring to it. For not only
was it the signal misery of Pierre to be invisibly—though but
accidentally—goaded, in the hour of mental immaturity, to the
attempt at a mature work—a circumstance sufficiently lamentable in itself; but also, in the hour of his clamorous penniless-
ness, he was additionally goaded into an enterprise long and
protracted in the execution, and of all things least calculated
for pecuniary profit in the end.

At length, domestic matters—rent and bread—had come to
such a pass with him, that whether or no, the first pages must
go to the printer; and thus was added still another tribulation;
because the printed pages now dictated to the following manuscript, and said to all subsequent thoughts and inventions of
Pierre—*Thus and thus; so and so; else an ill match.* Therefore,
was his book already limited, bound over, and committed to
imperfection, even before it had come to any confirmed form
or conclusion at all. Oh, who shall reveal the horrors of poverty
in authorship that is high? While the silly Millthorpe was rail-
ing against his delay of a few weeks and months; how bitterly
did unreplying Pierre feel in his heart, that to most of the great
works of humanity, their authors had given, not weeks and
months, not years and years, but their wholly surrendered and
dedicated lives. On either hand clung to by a girl who would
have laid down her life for him; Pierre, nevertheless, in his
deepest, highest part, was utterly without sympathy from anything divine, human, brute, or vegetable. One in a city of hundreds of thousands of human beings, Pierre was solitary as at
the Pole.

And the great woe of all was this: that all these things were
unsuspected without, and undivulgible from within; the very
daggers that stabbed him were joked at by Imbecility, Ignorance, Blockheadedness, Self-Complacency, and the universal
Blearedness and Besottedness around him. Now he began to
feel that in him, the thews of a Titan were forestallingly cut by
the scissors of Fate. He felt as a moose, hamstrung. All things
that think, or move, or lie still, seemed as created to mock and

torment him. He seemed gifted with loftiness, merely that it might be dragged down to the mud. Still, the profound willfulness in him would not give up. Against the breaking heart, and the bursting head; against all the dismal lassitude, and deathful faintness and sleeplessness, and whirlingness, and craziness, still he like a demigod bore up. His soul's ship foresaw the inevitable rocks, but resolved to sail on, and make a courageous wreck. Now he gave jeer for jeer, and taunted the apes that jibed him. With the soul of an atheist, he wrote down the godliest things; with the feeling of death and misery in him, he created forms of gladness and life. For the pangs in his heart, he put down hoots on the paper. And everything else he disguised under the so conveniently adjustable drapery of all-stretchable Philosophy. For the more and the more that he wrote, and the deeper and the deeper that he dived, Pierre saw the everlasting elusiveness of Truth; the universal lurking insincerity of even the greatest and purest written thoughts. Like knavish cards, the leaves of all great books were covertly packed. He was but packing one set the more; and that a very poor jaded set and pack indeed. So that there was nothing he more spurned, than his own aspirations; nothing he more abhorred than the loftiest part of himself. The brightest success, now seemed intolerable to him, since he so plainly saw, that the brightest success could not be the sole offspring of Merit; but of Merit for the one thousandth part, and nine hundred and ninety-nine combining and dovetailing accidents for the rest. So beforehand he despised those laurels which in the very nature of things, can never be impartially bestowed. But while thus all the earth was depopulated of ambition for him; still circumstances had put him in the attitude of an eager contender for renown. So beforehand he felt the unrevealable sting of receiving either plaudits or censures, equally unsought and equally loathed ere given. So beforehand he felt the pyramidical scorn of the genuine loftiness for the whole infinite company of infinitesimal critics. His was the scorn which thinks it not worth the while to be scornful. Those he most scorned never knew it. In that lonely little closet of his, Pierre foretasted all that this world hath either of praise or dispraise; and thus foretasting both goblets, anticipatingly hurled them both in its teeth. All panegyric, all denunciation, all criticism of any sort, would come too late for Pierre.

But man does never give himself up thus, a doorless and shutterless house for the four loosened winds of heaven to howl through, without still additional dilapidations. Much oftener than before, Pierre laid back in his chair with the deadly feeling of faintness. Much oftener than before, came staggering home from his evening walk, and from sheer bodily exhaustion economized the breath that answered the anxious inquiries as to what might be done for him. And as if all the leagued spiritual inveteracies and malices, combined with his general bodily exhaustion, were not enough, a special corporeal affliction now descended like a sky hawk upon him. His incessant application told upon his eyes. They became so affected, that some days he wrote with the lids nearly closed, fearful of opening them wide to the light. Through the lashes he peered upon the paper, which so seemed fretted with wires. Sometimes he blindly wrote with his eyes turned away from the paper;—thus unconsciously symbolizing the hostile necessity and distaste, the former whereof made of him this most unwilling states-prisoner of letters.

As every evening, after his day's writing was done, the proofs of the beginning of his work came home for correction, Isabel would read them to him. They were replete with errors; but preoccupied by the thronging and undiluted, pure imaginings of things, he became impatient of such minute, gnat-like torments; he randomly corrected the worst, and let the rest go; jeering with himself at the rich harvest thus furnished to the entomological critics.

But at last he received a tremendous interior intimation, to hold off—to be still from his unnatural struggle.

In the earlier progress of his book, he had found some relief in making his regular evening walk through the greatest thoroughfare of the city; that so, the utter isolation of his soul, might feel itself the more intensely from the incessant jogglings of his body against the bodies of the hurrying thousands. Then he began to be sensible of more fancying stormy nights than pleasant ones; for then, the great thoroughfares were less thronged, and the innumerable shop awnings flapped and beat like schooners' broad sails in a gale, and the shutters banged like lashed bulwarks; and the slates fell hurtling like displaced ships' blocks from aloft. Stemming such tempests through the deserted streets, Pierre felt a dark, triumphant joy; that while others had crawled in fear to their kennels, he alone defied the storm admiral, whose most vindictive peltings of hailstones, striking his iron-framed fiery furnace of a body, melted into soft dew, and so, harmlessly trickled off him.

By and by, of such howling, pelting nights, he began to bend his steps down the dark, narrow side streets, in quest of the more secluded and mysterious taprooms. There he would feel a singular satisfaction, in sitting down all dripping in a chair, ordering his half pint of ale before him, and drawing over his cap to protect his eyes from the light, eye the varied faces of the social castaways, who here had their haunts from the bitterest midnights.

But at last he began to feel a distaste for even these; and now nothing but the utter night-desolation of the obscurest warehousing lanes would content him, or be at all sufferable to him. Among these he had now been accustomed to wind in and out every evening; till one night as he paused a moment previous to turning about for home, a sudden, unwonted, and all-pervading sensation seized him. He knew not where he was; he did not have any ordinary life-feeling at all. He could not see; though instinctively putting his hand to his eyes, he seemed to feel that the lids were open. Then he was sensible of a combined blindness, and vertigo, and staggering; before his eyes a million green meteors danced; he felt his foot tottering upon the curb, he put out his hands, and knew no more for the time. When he came to himself he found that he was lying crosswise in the gutter, dabbled with mud and slime. He raised himself to try whether he could stand; but the fit was entirely gone. Immediately he quickened his steps homeward, forbearing to rest or pause at all on the way, lest that rush of blood to his head, consequent upon his sudden cessation from walking, should again smite him down. This circumstance warned him away from

those desolate streets, lest the repetition of the fit should leave
him there to perish by night in unknown and unsuspected loneliness. But if that terrible vertigo had been also intended for
another and deeper warning, he regarded such added warning
not at all; but again plied heart and brain as before.

But now at last since the very blood in his body had in vain
rebelled against his Titanic soul; now the only visible outward
symbols of that soul—his eyes—did also turn downright traitors
to him, and with more success than the rebellious blood. He
had abused them so recklessly, that now they absolutely refused
to look on paper. He turned them on paper, and they blinked
and shut. The pupils of his eyes rolled away from him in their
own orbits. He put his hand up to them, and sat back in his
seat. Then, without saying one word, he continued there for his
usual term, suspended, motionless, blank.

But next morning—it was some few days after the arrival of
Lucy—still feeling that a certain downright infatuation, and no
less, is both unavoidable and indispensable in the composition
of any great, deep book, or even any wholly unsuccessful attempt at any great, deep book; next morning he returned to
the charge. But again the pupils of his eyes rolled away from him
in their orbits: and now a general and nameless torpor—some
horrible foretaste of death itself—seemed stealing upon him.

4

During this state of semi-unconsciousness, or rather trance, a
remarkable dream or vision came to him. The actual artificial
objects around him slid from him, and were replaced by a baseless yet most imposing spectacle of natural scenery. But though
a baseless vision in itself, this airy spectacle assumed very familiar features to Pierre. It was the phantasmagoria of the
Mount of the Titans, a singular height standing quite detached
in a wide solitude not far from the grand range of dark blue
hills encircling his ancestral manor.

Say what some poets will, Nature is not so much her own
ever-sweet interpreter, as the mere supplier of that cunning
alphabet, whereby selecting and combining as he pleases, each

man reads his own peculiar lesson according to his own peculiar
mind and mood. Thus a high-aspiring, but most moody, disappointed bard, chancing once to visit the Meadows and beholding that fine eminence, christened it by the name it ever after
bore; completely extinguishing its former title—The Delectable Mountain—one long ago bestowed by an old Baptist
farmer, a hereditary admirer of Bunyan and his most marvelous
book. From the spell of that name the mountain never afterward escaped; for now, gazing upon it by the light of those
suggestive syllables, no poetical observer could resist the apparent felicity of the title. For as if indeed the immemorial
mount would fain adapt itself to its so recent name, some people said that it had insensibly changed its pervading aspect
within a score or two of winters. Nor was this strange conceit
entirely without foundation, seeing that the annual displace-
ments of huge rocks and gigantic trees were continually modi-
fying its whole front and general contour.

On the north side, where it fronted the old manor house,
some fifteen miles distant, the height, viewed from the piazza of
a soft haze-canopied summer's noon, presented a long and beautiful, but not entirely inaccessible-looking purple precipice,
some two thousand feet in air, and on each hand sideways slop-
ing down to lofty terraces of pastures.

Those hillside pastures, be it said, were thickly sown with a
small white amaranthine flower, which, being irreconcilably dis-
tasteful to the cattle, and wholly rejected by them, and yet, continually multiplying on every hand, did by no means contribute
to the agricultural value of those elevated lands. Insomuch, that
for this cause, the disheartened dairy tenants of that part of the
manor, had petitioned their lady-landlord for some abatement
in their annual tribute of upland grasses, in the Junyload; rolls
of butter in the October crock; and steers and heifers on the
October hoof; with turkeys in the Christmas sleigh.

"The small white flower, it is our bane!" the imploring tenants cried. "The aspiring amaranth, every year it climbs and
adds new terraces to its sway! The immortal amaranth, it will
not die, but last year's flowers survive to this! The terraced
pastures grow glittering white, and in warm June still show like

banks of snow—fit token of the sterility the amaranth begets!
Then free us from the amaranth, good lady, or be pleased to
abate our rent!"

Now, on a somewhat nearer approach, the precipice did not
belie its purple promise from the manorial piazza—that sweet
imposing purple promise, which seemed fully to vindicate the
Bunyanish old title originally bestowed;—but showed the pro-
fuse aerial foliage of a hanging forest. Nevertheless, coming still
more nigh, long and frequent rents among the mass of leaves
revealed horrible glimpses of dark-dripping rocks, and mysterious mouths of wolfish caves. Struck by this most unanticipated
view, the tourist now quickened his impulsive steps to verify the
change by coming into direct contact with so chameleon a
height. As he would now speed on, the lower ground, which
from the manor house piazza seemed all a grassy level, suddenly merged into a very long and weary acclivity, slowly rising
close up to the precipice's base; so that the efflorescent grasses
rippled against it, as the efflorescent waves of some great swell
or long rolling billow ripple against the water line of a steep
gigantic warship on the sea. And, as among the rolling sealike
sands of Egypt, disordered rows of broken Sphinxes lead to the
Cheopian pyramid itself; so this long acclivity was thickly
strewn with enormous rocky masses, grotesque in shape, and
with wonderful features on them, which seemed to express
that slumbering intelligence visible in some recumbent beasts
—beasts whose intelligence seems struck dumb in them by
some sorrowful and inexplicable spell. Nevertheless, round and
round those still enchanted rocks, hard by their utmost rims,
and in among their cunning crevices, the misanthropic hill-
scaling goat nibbled his sweetest food; for the rocks, so barren
in themselves, distilled a subtle moisture, which fed with green-
ness all things that grew about their igneous marge.

Quitting those recumbent rocks, one still ascended toward
the hanging forest, and piercing within its lowermost fringe,
then suddenly one stood transfixed, as a marching soldier confounded at the sight of an impregnable redoubt, where he had
fancied it a practicable vault to his courageous thews. Cunningly masked hitherto, by the green tapestry of the interlacing

leaves, a terrific towering palisade of dark mossy massiness confronted one; and, trickling with unevaporable moisture, distilled upon one from its beetling brow slow thundershowers of
waterdrops, chill as the last dews of death. Now one stood and
shivered in that twilight, though it were high noon and burning August down the meads. All round and round, the grim
scarred rocks rallied and re-rallied themselves; shot up, pro-
truded, stretched, swelled, and eagerly reached forth; on every
side bristlingly radiating with a hideous repellency. Tossed,
and piled, and indiscriminate among these, like bridging rifts
of logs up-jammed in alluvial-rushing streams of far Arkansas:
or, like great masts and yards of overwhelmed fleets hurled high
and dashed amain, all splintering together, on hovering ridges
of the Atlantic sea,—you saw the melancholy trophies which
the North Wind, championing the unquenchable quarrel of
the Winter, had wrested from the forests, and dismembered
them on their own chosen battleground, in barbarous disdain.
'Mid this spectacle of wide and wanton spoil, insular noises of
falling rocks would boomingly explode upon the silence and
fright all the echoes, which ran shrieking in and out among the
caves, as wailing women and children in some assaulted town.

Stark desolation; ruin, merciless and ceaseless; chills and
gloom, all here lived a hidden life, curtained by that cunning
purpleness, which, from the piazza of the manor house, so beautifully invested the mountain once called Delectable, but now
styled Titanic.

Beaten off by such undreamed-of glooms and steeps, you now
sadly retraced your steps, and, mayhap, went skirting the inferior sideway terraces of pastures; where the multiple and
most sterile inodorous immortality of the small, white flower
furnished no ailment for the mild cow's meditative cud. But
here and there you still might smell from far the sweet aroma
of clumps of catnip, that dear farmhouse herb. Soon you would
see the modest verdure of the plant itself; and wheresoever you
saw that sight, old foundation stones and rotting timbers of log
houses long extinct would also meet your eye; their desolation
ill-hid by the green solicitudes of the unemigrating herb. Most
fitly named the catnip; since, like the unrenegade cat, though

all that's human forsake the place, that plant will long abide, long bask and bloom on the abandoned hearth. Ill-hid; for every spring the amaranthine and celestial flower gained on the mortal household herb; for every autumn the catnip died, but never an autumn made the amaranth to wane. The catnip and the amaranth!—man's earthly household peace, and the ever-encroaching appetite for God.

No more now you sideways followed the sad pasture's skirt, but took your way adown the long declivity, fronting the mystic height. In midfield again you paused among the recumbent sphinx-like shapes thrown off from the rocky steep. You paused; fixed by a form defiant, a form of awfulness. You saw Enceladus the Titan, the most potent of all the giants, writhing from out the imprisoning earth;—turbaned with upborne moss he writhed; still, though armless, resisting with his whole striving trunk, the Pelion and the Ossa hurled back at him;—turbaned with upborne moss he writhed; still turning his unconquerable front toward that majestic mount eternally in vain assailed by him, and which, when it had stormed him off, had heaved his undoffable incubus upon him, and deridingly left him there to bay out his ineffectual howl.

To Pierre this wondrous shape had always been a thing of interest, though hitherto all its latent significance had never fully and intelligibly smitten him. In his earlier boyhood a strolling company of young collegian pedestrians had chanced to light upon the rock; and, struck with its remarkableness, had brought a score of picks and spades, and dug round it to unearth it, and find whether indeed it were a demoniac freak of nature, or some stern thing of antediluvian art. Accompanying this eager party, Pierre first beheld that deathless son of Terra. At that time, in its untouched natural state, the statue presented nothing but the turbaned head of igneous rock rising from out the soil, with its unabasable face turned upward toward the mountain, and the bull-like neck clearly defined. With distorted features, scarred and broken, and a black brow mocked by the upborne moss, Enceladus there subterraneously stood, fast frozen into the earth at the junction of the neck. Spades and picks soon heaved part of his Ossa from him, till at last a circular well was opened round him to the depth of some thirteen feet. At that point the wearied young collegians gave over their enterprise in despair. With all their toil, they had not yet come to the girdle of Enceladus. But they had bared good part of his mighty chest, and exposed his mutilated shoulders, and the stumps of his once audacious arms. Thus far uncovering his shame, in that cruel plight they had abandoned him, leaving stark naked his in vain indignant chest to the defilements of the birds, which for untold ages had cast their foulness on his vanquished crest.

Not unworthy to be compared with that leaden Titan, where-with the art of Marsy and the broad-flung pride of Bourbon en-riched the enchanted gardens of Versailles—and from whose still twisted mouth for sixty feet the waters yet upgush, in ele-mental rivalry with those Etna flames, of old asserted to be the malicious breath of the borne-down giant—not unworthy to be compared with that leaden demigod—piled with costly rocks, and with one bent wrenching knee protruding from the broken bronze—not unworthy to be compared with that bold trophy of high art, this American Enceladus, wrought by the vigorous hand of Nature's self, it did go further than compare; it did far surpass that fine figure moulded by the inferior skill of man. Marsy gave arms to the eternally defenseless; but Nature, more truthful, performed an amputation, and left the impotent Titan without one serviceable ball-and-socket above the thigh.

Such was the wild scenery—the Mount of Titans, and the repulsed group of heaven-assaulters, with Enceladus in their midst shamefully recumbent at its base—such was the wild scen-ery, which now to Pierre, in his strange vision, displaced the four blank walls, the desk, and campbed, and domineered his trance. But no longer petrified in all their ignominious attitudes, the herded Titans now sprang to their feet; flung themselves up the slope; and anew battered at the precipice's unresounding wall. Foremost among them all, he saw a moss-tur-baned, armless giant, who despairing of any other mode of wreaking his immitigable hate, turned his vast trunk into a bat-tering-ram, and hurled his own arched-out ribs again and yet again against the invulnerable steep.

"Enceladus! it is Enceladus!" Pierre cried out in his sleep.

That moment the phantom faced him; and Pierre saw Enceladus no more; but on the Titan's armless trunk, his own dupli-
cate face and features magnifiedly gleamed upon him with pro-
phetic discomfiture and woe. With trembling frame he started
from his chair, and woke from that ideal horror to all his actual
grief.

5

Nor did Pierre's random knowledge of the ancient fables fail
still further to elucidate the vision which so strangely had sup-
plied a tongue to muteness. But that elucidation was most repul-
sively fateful and foreboding; possibly because Pierre did not
leap the final barrier of gloom; possibly because Pierre did not
willfully wrest some final comfort from the fable; did not flog
this stubborn rock as Moses his, and force even aridity itself to
quench his painful thirst.

Thus smitten, the Mount of Titans seems to yield this following stream:

Old Titan's self was the son of incestuous Coelus and Terra,
the son of incestuous Heaven and Earth. And Titan married his
mother Terra, another and accumulatively incestuous match.
And thereof Enceladus was one issue. So Enceladus was both
the son and grandson of an incest; and even thus, there had been
born from the organic blended heavenliness and earthliness of
Pierre, another mixed, uncertain, heaven-aspiring, but still not
wholly earth-emancipated mood; which again, by its terrestrial
taint held down to its terrestrial mother, generated there the
present doubly incestuous Enceladus within him; so that the
present mood of Pierre—that reckless sky-assaulting mood of
his, was nevertheless on one side the grandson of the sky. For it
is according to eternal fitness, that the precipitated Titan should
still seek to regain his paternal birthright even by fierce esca-
lade. Wherefore whoso storms the sky gives best proof he came
from thither! But whatso crawls contented in the moat before
that crystal fort, shows it was born within that slime, and there
forever will abide.

Recovered somewhat from the after-spell of this wild vision

folded in his trance, Pierre composed his front as best he might, and straightway left his fatal closet. Concentrating all the remaining stuff in him, he resolved by an entire and violent change, and by a willful act against his own most habitual inclinations, to wrestle with the strange malady of his eyes, this new death-fiend of the trance, and this Inferno of his Titanic vision.

And now, just as he crossed the threshold of the closet, he writhingly strove to assume an expression intended to be not uncheerful—though how indeed his countenance at all looked, he could not tell; for dreading some insupportable dark revealments in his glass, he had of late wholly abstained from appealing to it—and in his mind he rapidly conned over, what indifferent, disguising, or light-hearted gamesome things he should say, when proposing to his companions the little design he cherished.

And even so, to grim Enceladus, the world the gods had chained for a ball to drag at his o'erfreighted feet—even so that globe put forth a thousand flowers, whose fragile smiles disguised his ponderous load.

Book XXVI

1

"Come, Isabel, come, Lucy; we have not had a single walk together yet. It is cold, but clear; and once out of the city, we shall find it sunny. Come: get ready now, and away for a stroll down to the wharf, and then for some of the steamers on the bay. No doubt, Lucy, you will find in the bay scenery some hints for that secret sketch you are so busily occupied with—ere real living sitters do come—and which you so devotedly work at, all alone and behind closed doors."

Upon this, Lucy's original look of pale-rippling pleasantness and surprise—evoked by Pierre's unforeseen proposition to give himself some relaxation—changed into one of infinite, mute, but unrenderable meaning, while her swimming eyes gently, yet all-bewildered, fell to the floor.

"It is finished, then," cried Isabel, not unmindful of this by-scene, and passionately stepping forward so as to intercept Pierre's momentary rapt glance at the agitated Lucy, "That vile book, it is finished! Thank heaven!"

"Not so," said Pierre; and, displacing all disguisements, a hectic unsummoned expression suddenly came to his face, "but ere that vile book be finished, I must get on some other element than earth. I have sat on earth's saddle till I am weary; I must now vault over to the other saddle awhile. Oh, seems to me, there should be two ceaseless steeds for a bold man to ride—the Land and the Sea; and like circus men we should never dismount, but only be steadied and rested by leaping from one to the other, while still, side by side, they both race round the sun. I have been on the Land steed so long, oh I am dizzy!"

"Thou wilt never listen to me, Pierre," said Lucy lowly; "there is no need of this incessant straining. See, Isabel and I have both offered to be thy amanuenses—not in mere copying, but in the original writing; I am sure that would greatly assist thee."

"Impossible! I fight a duel in which all seconds are forbid."

"Ah Pierre! Pierre!" cried Lucy, dropping the shawl in her hand, and gazing at him with unspeakable longings of some unfathomable emotion.

Namelessly glancing at Lucy, Isabel slid near to him, seized his hand and spoke.

"I would go blind for thee, Pierre; here, take out these eyes, and use them for glasses." So saying, she looked with a strange momentary haughtiness and defiance at Lucy.

A general half-involuntary movement was now made, as if they were about to depart.

"Ye are ready; go ye before," said Lucy meekly; "I will follow."

"Nay, one on each arm," said Pierre, "come!"

As they passed through the low arched vestibule into the street, a cheek-burnt, gamesome sailor passing, exclaimed, "Steer small, my lad; 'tis a narrow strait thou art in!"

"What says he?" said Lucy gently. "Yes, it is a narrow strait of a street indeed."

But Pierre felt a sudden tremble transferred to him from Isabel, who whispered something inarticulate in his ear.

Gaining one of the thoroughfares, they drew near to a conspicuous placard over a door, announcing that abovestairs was a gallery of paintings, recently imported from Europe, and now on free exhibition preparatory to their sale by auction. Though this encounter had been entirely unforeseen by Pierre, yet yielding to the sudden impulse, he at once proposed their visiting the pictures. The girls assented, and they ascended the stairs.

In the anteroom, a catalog was put into his hand. He paused to give one hurried, comprehensive glance at it. Among long columns of such names as Rubens, Raphael Angelo, Domenichino, Da Vinci, all shamelessly prefaced with the words "undoubted," or "testified," Pierre met the following brief line:—
"No. 99. A stranger's head, by an unknown hand."

It seemed plain that the whole must be a collection of those wretched imported daubs, which with the incredible effrontery peculiar to some of the foreign picture dealers in America, were christened by the loftiest names known to art. But as the most mutilated torsos of the perfections of antiquity are not unworthy the student's attention, neither are the most bungling modern incompletenesses: for both are torsos; one of perished perfections in the past; the other, by anticipation, of yet unfulfilled perfections in the future. Still, as Pierre walked along by the thickly hung walls, and seemed to detect the infatuated vanity which must have prompted many of these utterly unknown artists in the attempted execution by feeble hand of vigorous themes; he could not repress the most melancholy foreboding concerning himself. All the walls of the world seemed thickly hung with the empty and impotent scope of pictures, grandly outlined, but miserably filled. The smaller and humbler pictures, representing little familiar things, were by far the best executed; but these, though touching him not unpleasingly, in one restricted sense, awoke no dormant majesties in his soul, and therefore, upon the whole, were contemptibly inadequate and unsatisfactory.

At last Pierre and Isabel came to that painting of which Pierre was capriciously in search—No. 99.

"My God! see! see!" cried Isabel, under strong excitment, "only my mirror has ever shown me that look before! See! see!"

By some mere hocus-pocus of chance, or subtly designing knavery, a real Italian gem of art had found its way into this most hybrid collection of impostures.

No one who has passed through the great galleries of Europe, unbewildered by their wonderful multitudinousness of surpassing excellence—a redundancy which neutralizes all discrimination or individualizing capacity in most ordinary minds—no calm, penetrative person can have victoriously run that painted gauntlet of the gods, without certain very special emotions, called forth by some one or more individual paintings, to which, however, both the catalogs and the criticisms of the greatest connoisseurs deny any all-transcending merit, at all answering to the effect thus casually produced. There is no time now to show fully how this is; suffice it, that in such instances, it is not the abstract excellence always, but often the accidental congeniality, which occasions this wonderful emotion. Still, the individual himself is apt to impute it to a different cause; hence, the headlong enthusiastic admiration of some one or two men for things not at all praised by—or at most, which are indifferent to—the rest of the world;—a matter so often considered inexplicable.

But in this Stranger's Head by the Unknown Hand, the abstract general excellence united with the all-surprising, accidental congeniality in producing an accumulated impression of power upon both Pierre and Isabel. Nor was the strangeness of this at all impaired by the apparent uninterestedness of Lucy concerning that very picture. Indeed, Lucy—who, owing to the occasional jolting of the crowd, had loosened her arm from Pierre's, and so, gradually, had gone on along the pictured hall in advance—Lucy had thus passed the strange painting, without the least special pause, and had now wandered round to the precisely opposite side of the hall; where, at this present time, she was standing motionless before a very tolerable copy (the only other good thing in the collection) of that sweetest, most touching, but most awful of all feminine heads—The Cenci of Guido.

The wonderfulness of which head consists chiefly, perhaps, in a striking, suggested contrast, half identical with, and half analogous to, that almost supernatural one—sometimes visible in the maidens of tropical nations—namely, soft and light blue eyes, with an extremely fair complexion, veiled by funereally jetty hair. But with blue eyes and fair complexion, the Cenci's hair is golden—physically, therefore, all is in strict, natural keeping; which, nevertheless, still the more intensifies the suggested fanciful anomaly of so sweetly and seraphically *blonde* a being, being double-hooded, as it were, by the black crape of the two most horrible crimes (of one of which she is the object, and of the other the agent) possible to civilized humanity—incest and parricide.

Now, this Cenci and "the Stranger" were hung at a good elevation in one of the upper tiers; and, from the opposite walls, exactly faced each other; so that in secret they seemed pantomimically talking over and across the heads of the living spectators below.

With the aspect of the Cenci everyone is familiar. "The Stranger" was a dark, comely, youthful man's head, portentously looking out of a dark, shaded ground, and ambiguously smiling. There was no discoverable drapery; the dark head, with its crisp, curly, jetty hair, seemed just disentangling itself from out of curtains and clouds. But to Isabel, in the eye and on the brow, were certain shadowy traces of her own unmistakable likeness; while to Pierre, this face was in part as the resurrection of the one he had burnt at the inn. Not that the separate features were the same; but the pervading look of it, the subtler interior keeping of the entirety, was almost identical; still, for all this, there was an unequivocal aspect of foreignness, of Europeanism, about both the face itself and the general painting.

"Is it? Is it? Can it be?" whispered Isabel, intensely.

Now, Isabel knew nothing of the painting which Pierre had destroyed. But she solely referred to the living being who—under the designation of her father—had visited her at the cheerful house to which she had been removed during childhood from the large and unnameable one by the pleasant woman in the coach. Without doubt—though indeed she might not have been at all conscious of it in her own mystic mind—she must have somehow vaguely fancied, that this being had always through life worn the same aspect to everybody else which he had to her, for so very brief an interval of his possible existence. Solely knowing him—or dreaming of him, it may have been—under that one aspect, she could not conceive of him under any other. Whether or not these considerations touching Isabel's ideas occurred to Pierre at this moment is very improbable. At any rate, he said nothing to her, either to deceive or undeceive, either to enlighten or obscure. For, indeed, he was too much riveted by his own far-interior emotions to analyze now the contemporary ones of Isabel. So that there came to pass a not unremarkable thing: for though both were intensely excited by one object, yet their two minds and memories were thereby directed to entirely different contemplations; while still each, for the time—however unreasonably—might have vaguely supposed the other occupied by one and the same contemplation. Pierre was thinking of the chair portrait: Isabel, of the living face. Yet Isabel's fervid exclamations having reference to the living face, were now, as it were, mechanically responded to by Pierre, in syllables having reference to the chair portrait. Nevertheless, so subtle and spontaneous was it all, that neither perhaps ever afterward discovered this contradiction; for, events whirled them so rapidly and peremptorily after this, that they had no time for those calm retrospective reveries indispensable perhaps to such a discovery.

"Is it? is it? can it be?" was the intense whisper of Isabel.

"No, it cannot be, it is not," replied Pierre; "one of the wonderful coincidences, nothing more."

"Oh, by that word, Pierre, we but vainly seek to explain the inexplicable. Tell me: it is! it must be! it is wonderful!"

"Let us begone; and let us keep eternal silence," said Pierre, quickly; and, seeking Lucy, they abruptly left the place; as before, Pierre, seemingly unwilling to be accosted by anyone he knew, or who knew his companions, unconsciously accelerated their steps while forced for a space to tread the thoroughfares.

2

As they hurried on, Pierre was silent; but wild thoughts were hurrying and shouting in his heart. The most tremendous displacing and revolutionizing thoughts were upheaving in him, with reference to Isabel; nor—though at the time he was hardly conscious of such a thing—were these thoughts wholly unwelcome to him.

How did he know that Isabel was his sister? Setting aside aunt Dorothea's nebulous legend, to which, in some shadowy points, here and there Isabel's still more nebulous story seemed to fit on,—though but uncertainly enough—and both of which thus blurredly conjoining narrations, regarded in the unscrupulous light of real naked reason, were anything but legitimately conclusive; and setting aside his own dim reminiscences of his wandering father's deathbed; (for though, in one point of view, those reminiscences might have afforded some degree of presumption as to his father's having been the parent of an unacknowledged daughter, yet were they entirely inconclusive as to that presumed daughter's identity; and the grand point now with Pierre was, not the general question whether his father had had a daughter, but whether, assuming that he had had, *Isabel,* rather than any other living being, *was that daughter;*) —and setting aside all his own manifold and inter-enfolding mystic and transcendental persuasions—originally born, as he now seemed to feel, purely of an intense procreative enthusiasm —an enthusiasm no longer so all-potential with him as of yore; setting all these aside, and coming to the plain, palpable facts, —how did he *know* that Isabel was his sister? Nothing that he saw in her face could he remember as having seen in his father's. The chair portrait, *that* was the entire sum and substance of all possible, rakable, downright presumptive evidence, which peculiarly appealed to his own separate self. Yet here was another portrait of a complete stranger—a European; a portrait imported from across the seas, and to be sold at public auction, which was just as strong an evidence as the other. Then, the original of this second portrait was as much the father of Isabel as the original of the chair portrait. But perhaps there was no original at all to this second portrait; it might have been a pure fancy piece; to which conceit, indeed, the uncharacterizing style of the filling-up seemed to furnish no small testimony.

With such bewildering meditations as these in him, running up like clasping waves upon the strand of the most latent secrecies of his soul, and with both Isabel and Lucy bodily touching his sides as he walked; the feelings of Pierre were entirely untranslatable into words.

Of late to Pierre, much more vividly than ever before, the whole story of Isabel had seemed an enigma, a mystery, an imaginative delirum; especially since he had got so deep into the inventional mysteries of his book. For he who is most practically and deeply conversant with mysticisms and mysteries; he who professionally deals in mysticisms and mysteries himself; often that man, more than anybody else, is disposed to regard such things in others as very deceptively bejuggling; and likewise is apt to be rather materialistic in all his own merely personal notions (as in their practical lives, with priests of Eleusinian religions), and more than any other man, is often inclined, at the bottom of his soul, to be uncompromisingly skeptical on all novel visionary hypotheses of any kind. It is only the no-mystics, or the half-mystics, who, properly speaking, are credulous. So that in Pierre was presented the apparent anomaly of a mind, which by becoming really profound in itself, grew skeptical of all tendered profundities; whereas the contrary is generally supposed.

By some strange arts, Isabel's wonderful story might have been, some way, and for some cause, forged for her, in her childhood, and craftily impressed upon her youthful mind; which so —like a slight mark in a young tree—had now enlargingly grown with her growth, till it had become this immense staring marvel. Tested by anything real, practical, and reasonable, what less probable, for instance, than that fancied crossing of the sea in her childhood, when upon Pierre's subsequent questioning of her, she did not even know that the sea was salt.

3

In the midst of all these mental confusions they arrived at the wharf; and selecting the most inviting of the various boats which lay about them in three or four adjacent ferry slips, and one which was bound for a half hour's sail across the wide beauty of that glorious bay; they soon found themselves afloat and in swift gliding motion.

They stood leaning on the rail of the guard, as the sharp craft darted out from among the lofty pine forests of ships' masts, and the tangled underbrush and cane-brakes of the dwarfed sticks of sloops and scows. Soon, the spires of stone on the land, blent with the masts of wood on the water; the crotch of the twin rivers pressed the great wedged city almost out of sight. They swept by two little islets distant from the shore; they wholly curved away from the domes of freestone and marble, and gained the great sublime dome of the bay's wide-open waters.

Small breeze had been felt in the pent city that day, but the fair breeze of naked nature now blew in their faces. The waves began to gather and roll; and just as they gained a point, where —still beyond—between high promontories of fortresses, the wide bay visibly sluiced into the Atlantic, Isabel convulsively grasped the arm of Pierre and convulsively spoke.

"I feel it! I feel it! It is! It is!"

"What feelest thou?—what is it?"

"The motion! the motion!"

"Dost thou not understand, Pierre?" said Lucy, eyeing with concern and wonder his pale, staring aspect—"The waves: it is the motion of the waves that Isabel speaks of. Look, they are rolling, direct from the sea now."

Again Pierre lapsed into a still stranger silence and reverie.

It was impossible altogether to resist the force of this striking corroboration of by far the most surprising and improbable thing in the whole surprising and improbable story of Isabel. Well did he remember her vague reminiscence of the teetering sea, that did not slope exactly as the floors of the unknown, abandoned, old house among the French-like mountains.

While plunged in these mutually neutralizing thoughts of the strange picture and the last exclamations of Isabel, the boat arrived at its destination—a little hamlet on the beach, not very far from the great blue sluiceway into the ocean, which was now yet more distinctly visible than before.

"Don't let us stop here," cried Isabel. "Look, let us go through there! 'Bel must go through there! See! see! out there upon the blue! yonder, yonder! far away—out, out!—far, far away, and away, and away, out there! where the two blues meet, and are nothing—'Bel must go!"

"Why, Isabel," murmured Lucy, "that would be to go to far England or France; thou wouldst find but few friends in far France, Isabel."

"Friends in far France? And what friends have I here?—Art thou my friend? In thy secret heart dost *thou* wish me well? And for thee, Pierre, what am I but a vile clog to thee; dragging thee back from all thy felicity? Yes, I will go yonder—yonder; out there! I will, I will! Unhand me! Let me plunge!"

For an instant, Lucy looked incoherently from one to the other. But both she and Pierre now mechanically again seized Isabel's frantic arms, as they were again thrown over the outer rail of the boat. They dragged her back; they spoke to her; they soothed her; but though less vehement, Isabel still looked deeply distrustfully at Lucy, and deeply reproachfully at Pierre.

They did not leave the boat as intended; too glad were they all, when it unloosed from its fastenings, and turned about upon the backward trip.

Stepping to shore, Pierre once more hurried his companions through the unavoidable publicity of the thoroughfares, but less rapidly proceeded, as soon as they gained the more secluded streets.

4

Gaining the Apostles', and leaving his two companions to the privacy of their chambers, Pierre sat silent and intent by the stove in the dining room for a time, and then was on the point of entering his closet from the corridor, when Delly, suddenly following him, said to him, that she had forgotten to mention it before, but he would find two letters in his room, which had been separately left at the door during the absence of the party.

He passed into the closet, and slowly shooting the bolt—which, for want of something better, happened to be an old blunted dagger—walked, with his cap yet unmoved, slowly up to the table, and beheld the letters. They were lying with their sealed sides up; one in either hand, he lifted them; and held them straight out sideways from him.

"I see not the writing; know not yet, by mine own eye, that they are meant for me; yet, in these hands I feel that I now hold the final poniards that shall stab me; and by stabbing me, make *me* too a most swift stabber in the recoil. Which point first?—this!"

He tore open the left-hand letter:

SIR: You are a swindler. Upon the pretense of writing a popular novel for us, you have been receiving cash advances from us, while passing through our press the sheets of a blasphemous rhapsody, filched from the vile Atheists, Lucian and Voltaire. Our great press of publication has hitherto prevented our slightest inspection of our reader's proofs of your book. Send not another sheet to us. Our bill for printing thus far, and also for our cash advances, swindled out of us by you, is now in the hands of our lawyer, who is instructed to proceed with instant rigor.

(*Signed*)   Steel, Flint & Asbestos

He folded the left-hand letter, and put it beneath his left heel, and stood upon it so; and then opened the right-hand letter.

Thou, Pierre Glendinning, art a villainous and perjured liar. It is the sole object of this letter imprintedly to convey the point-blank lie to thee; that taken in at thy heart, it may be thence pulsed with thy blood, throughout thy system. We have let some interval pass inactive, to confirm and solidify our hate. Separately, and to-gether, we brand thee, in thy every lung cell, a liar—liar, because

that is the scornfullest and loathesomest title for a man; which in
itself is the compend of all infamous things.

   (*Signed*)   Glendinning Stanly,
                                        Frederic Tartan.

He folded the right-hand letter, and put it beneath his right
heel; then folding his two arms, stood upon both letters.

"These are most small circumstances; but happening just now
to me, become indices to all immensities. For now am I hate-
shod! On these I will skate to my acquittal! No longer do I hold
terms with aught. World's bread of life, and world's breath of
honor, both are snatched from me; but I defy all world's bread
and breath. Here I step out before the drawn-up worlds in wid-
est space, and challenge one and all of them to battle! Oh, Glen!
oh, Fred! most fraternally do I leap to your rib-crushing hugs!
Oh, how I love ye two, that yet can make me lively hate, in a
world which elsewise only merits stagnant scorn! Now, then,
where is this swindler's, this coiner's book? Here, on this vile
counter, over which the coiner thought to pass it to the world,
here will I nail it fast, for a detected cheat! And thus nailed fast
now, do I spit upon it, and so get the start of the wise world's
worst abuse of it! Now I go out to meet my fate, walking toward
me in the street."

As with hat on, and Glen and Frederic's letter invisibly crumpled in his hand, he—as it were somnambulously—passed into
the room of Isabel, she gave loose to a thin, long shriek, at his
wondrous white and haggard plight; and then, without the
power to stir toward him, sat petrified in her chair, as one em-
balmed and glazed with icy varnish.

He heeded her not, but passed straight on through both intervening rooms, and without a knock unpremeditatedly entered
Lucy's chamber. He would have passed out of that, also, into the
corridor, without one word; but something stayed him.

The marble girl sat before her easel; a small box of pointed
charcoal, and some pencils by her side; her painter's wand held
out against the frame; the charcoal-pencil suspended in two fingers, while with the same hand, holding a crust of bread, she

was lightly brushing the portrait-paper, to efface some ill-con-
sidered stroke. The floor was scattered with the bread crumbs
and charcoal dust; he looked behind the easel, and saw his own
portrait, in the skeleton.

At the first glimpse of him, Lucy started not, nor stirred; but
as if her own wand had there enchanted her, sat tranced.

"Dead embers of departed fires lie by thee, thou pale girl;
with dead embers thou seekest to relume the flame of all extinguished love! Waste not so that bread; eat it—in bitterness!"

He turned, and entered the corridor, and then, with outstretched arms, paused between the two outer doors of Isabel
and Lucy.

"For ye two, my most undiluted prayer is now, that from your
here unseen and frozen chairs ye may never stir alive; the fool of
Truth, the fool of Virtue, the fool of Fate, now quits ye forever!"

As he now sped down the long winding passage, someone
eagerly hailed him from a stair.

"What, what, my boy? where now in such a squally hurry?
Hallo, I say!"

But without heeding him at all, Pierre drove on. Millthorpe
looked anxiously and alarmedly after him a moment, then made
a movement in pursuit, but paused again.

"There was ever a black vein in this Glendinning; and now
that vein is swelled, as if it were just one peg above a tourniquet
drawn overtight. I scarce dare dog him now; yet my heart mis-
gives me that I should. Shall I go to his rooms and ask what
black thing this is that hath befallen him? No; not yet; might be
thought officious—they say I'm given to that. I'll wait; something may turn up soon. I'll into the front street, and saunter
some; and then—we'll see."

5

Pierre passed on to a remote quarter of the building, and
abruptly entered the room of one of the Apostles whom he knew.
There was no one in it. He hesitated an instant; then walked up
to a bookcase, with a chest of drawers in the lower part.

"Here I saw him put them—this, no—here—ay—we'll try this."

Wrenching open the locked drawer, a brace of pistols, a powder flask, a bullet bag, and a round green box of percussion caps lay before him.

"Ha! what wondrous tools Prometheus used, who knows? But more wondrous these, that in an instant, can unmake the topmost three-score-years-and-ten of all Prometheus' makings. Come: here's two tubes that'll outroar the thousand pipes of Harlem. Is the music in 'em? No? Well, then, here's powder for the shrill treble; and wadding for the tenor; and a lead bullet for the concluding bass! And—and—and—ay, for the top-wadding, I'll send 'em back their lie, and plant it scorching in their brains!"

He tore off that part of Glen and Fred's letter, which more particularly gave the lie; and halving it, rammed it home upon the bullets.

He thrust a pistol into either breast of his coat; and taking the rearward passages, went down into the back street; directing his rapid steps toward the grand central thoroughfare of the city.

It was a cold, but clear, quiet, and slantingly sunny day; it was between four and five of the afternoon; that hour, when the great glaring avenue was most thronged with haughty rolling carriages, and proud rustling promenaders, both men and women. But these last were mostly confined to the one wide pavement to the west; the other pavement was well-nigh deserted, save by porters, waiters, and parcel carriers of the shops. On the west pave, up and down, for three long miles, two streams of glossy, shawled, or broadcloth life unceasingly brushed by each other, as long, resplendent, drooping trains of rival peacocks brush.

Mixing with neither of these, Pierre stalked midway between. From his wild and fatal aspect, one way the people took the wall, the other way they took the curb. Unentangledly Pierre threaded all their host, though in its inmost heart. Bent he was, on a straightforward, mathematical intent. His eyes were all about him as he went; especially he glanced over to the deserted pavement opposite; for that emptiness did not deceive him; he

himself had often walked that side, the better to scan the pouring throng upon the other.

Just as he gained a large, open, triangular space, built round
with the stateliest public erections—the very proscenium of
the town;—he saw Glen and Fred advancing, in the distance, on
the other side. He continued on; and soon he saw them crossing
over to him obliquely, so as to take him face-and-face. He continued on; when suddenly running ahead of Fred, who now
chafingly stood still (because Fred would not make two, in the
direct personal assault upon one), and shouting "Liar! Villain!"
Glen leaped toward Pierre from front, and with such lightning-
like ferocity, that the simultaneous blow of his cowhide smote
Pierre across the cheek, and left a half-livid and half-bloody
brand.

For that one moment, the people fell back on all sides from
them; and left them—momentarily recoiled from each other—
in a ring of panics.

But clapping both hands to his two breasts, Pierre, on both
sides shaking off the sudden white grasp of two rushing girls,
tore out both pistols, and rushed headlong upon Glen.

"For thy one blow, take here two deaths! 'Tis speechless
sweet to murder thee!"

Spatterings of his own kindred blood were upon the pavement; his own hand had extinguished his house in slaughtering
the only unoutlawed human being by the name of Glendinning;
—and Pierre was seized by a hundred contending hands.

6

That sundown, Pierre stood solitary in a low dungeon of the
city prison. The cumbersome stone ceiling almost rested on his
brow; so that the long tiers of massive cell-galleries above
seemed partly piled on him. His immortal, immovable, bleached
cheek was dry; but the stone cheeks of the walls were trickling.
The pent twilight of the contracted yard, coming through the
barred arrow-slit, fell in dim bars upon the granite floor.

"Here, then, is the untimely, timely end;—Life's last chapter
well stitched into the middle! Nor book, nor author of the book,

hath any sequel, though each hath its last lettering!—It is ambiguous still. Had I been heartless now, disowned, and spurningly portioned off the girl at Saddle Meadows, then had I been
happy through a long life on earth, and perchance through a
long eternity in heaven! Now, 'tis merely hell in both worlds.
Well, be it hell. I will mould a trumpet of the flames, and, with
my breath of flame, breathe back my defiance! But give me first
another body! I long and long to die, to be rid of this dishonored cheek. *Hung by the neck till thou be dead.*—Not if I forestall you, though!—Oh now to live is death, and now to die is
life; now, to my soul, were a sword my midwife!—Hark!—the
hangman?—who comes?"

"Thy wife and cousin—so they say; hope they may be; they
may stay till twelve," wheezingly answered a turnkey, pushing
the tottering girls into the cell, and locking the door upon them.

"Ye two pale ghosts, were this the other world, ye were not
welcome. Away!—Good Angel and Bad Angel both!—For Pierre
is neuter now!"

"Oh, ye stony roofs, and seven-fold stony skies!—not thou art
the murderer, but thy sister hath murdered thee, my brother,
oh my brother!"

At these wailed words from Isabel, Lucy shrank up like a
scroll, and noiselessly fell at the feet of Pierre.

He touched her heart. "Dead! Girl! wife or sister, saint or
fiend!" seizing Isabel in his grasp, "in thy breasts, life for infants lodgeth not, but death-milk for thee and me! The drug!"
and tearing her bosom loose, he seized the secret vial nestling
there.

7

At night the squat-framed, asthmatic turnkey tramped the
dim-lit iron gallery before one of the long honey-combed rows of
cells.

"Mighty still there, in that hole, them two mice I let in—
humph!"

Suddenly, at the further end of the gallery, he discerned a
shadowy figure emerging from the archway there, and running

on before an officer, and impetuously approaching where the turnkey stood.

"More relations coming. These wind-broken chaps are always in before the second death, seeing they always miss the first. Humph! What a froth the fellow's in? Wheezes worse than me!"

"Where is she?" cried Fred Tartan, fiercely, to him; "she's not at the murderer's rooms! I sought the sweet girl there, instant upon the blow; but the lone dumb thing I found there only wrung her speechless hands and pointed to the door;—both birds were flown! Where is she, turnkey? I've searched all lengths and breadths but this. Hath any angel swept adown and lighted in your granite hell?"

"Broken his wind, and broken loose, too, ain't he?" wheezed the turnkey to the officer who now came up.

"This gentleman seeks a young lady, his sister, some way innocently connected with the prisoner last brought in. Have any females been here to see him?"

"Oh, ay, two of 'em in there now," jerking his stumped thumb behind him.

Fred darted toward the designated cell.

"Oh, easy, easy, young gentleman"—jingling at his huge bunch of keys—"easy, easy, till I get the picks—I'm housewife here. Hallo, here comes another."

Hurrying through the same archway toward them, there now rapidly advanced a second impetuous figure, running on in advance of a second officer.

"Where is the cell?" demanded Millthorpe.

"He seeks an interview with the last prisoner," explained the second officer.

"Kill 'em both with one stone, then," wheezed the turnkey, gratingly throwing open the door of the cell. "There's his pretty parlor, gentlemen; step in. Reg'lar mouse-hole, arn't it? Might hear a rabbit burrow on the world's t'other side; are they all 'sleep?"

"I stumble!" cried Fred, from within; "Lucy! A light! a light!—Lucy!" And he wildly groped about the cell, and blindly caught Millthorpe, who was also wildly groping.

"Blister me not! take off thy bloody touch!—Ho, ho, the light!—Lucy! Lucy!—she's fainted!"

Then both stumbled again, and fell from each other in the cell: and for a moment all seemed still, as though all breaths were held.

As the light was now thrust in, Fred was seen on the floor holding his sister in his arms; and Millthorpe kneeling by the side of Pierre, the unresponsive hand in his; while Isabel, feebly moving, reclined between, against the wall.

"Yes! Yes! Dead! Dead! Dead!—without one visible wound— her sweet plumage hides it. Thou hellish carrion, this is thy hellish work! Thy juggler's rifle brought down this heavenly bird! Oh, my God, my God! Thou scalpest me with this sight!"

"The dark vein's burst, and here's the deluge-wreck—all stranded here! Ah, Pierre! my old companion, Pierre—school-mate—play-mate—friend! Our sweet boys' walks within the woods! Oh, I would have rallied thee, and banteringly warned thee from thy too moody ways, but thou wouldst never heed! What scornful innocence rests on thy lips, my friend! Hand scorched with murderer's powder, yet how woman-soft! By heaven, these fingers move!—one speechless clasp! all's o'er!"

"All's o'er, and ye know him not!" came gasping from the wall; and from the fingers of Isabel dropped an empty vial—as it had been a run-out sand-glass—and shivered upon the floor; and her whole form sloped sideways, and she fell upon Pierre's heart, and her long hair ran over him, and arbored him in ebon vines.

Marquis de Sade

EUGÉNIE DE FRANVAL [*Excerpt*]

MARQUIS DE SADE (1740-1814), born in France, had a stormy life, a large part of which was spent in prisons. He left a large and imposing literary legacy, some of which has been lost, perhaps destroyed, and other parts ignored. His fame, or perhaps his notoriety, today rests almost exclusively on the fact that a brutal and terrifying word in many languages has been coined from his name. "His books take hold of us," writes Simone de Beauvoir, "as soon as we become aware that for all their repetitiousness, their platitudes and clumsiness, he is trying to communicate an experience whose distinguishing characteristic is, nevertheless, its will to remain incommunicable." The first of the two selections used here is taken from *Eugénie de Franval*, the second from *La Philosophie dans le Boudoir*.

1

When Eugénie reached the age of seven, Franval took her to his wife. This affectionate parent, who had not seen her own child since she brought it into the world, was unable to caress her enough; she held her two hours tightly to her bosom and covered her with kisses and tears. She wanted to know what little talents she had; but Eugénie had only those of reading fluently, enjoying the most vigorous health, and being as beautiful as an angel. Madame de Franval's despair was renewed when she realized that it was only too true that her daughter was ignorant of even the first principles of religion.

"What, sir," she said to her husband, "are you bringing her up for in this world? Have you not stopped to consider that she may not live in it more than a moment? Like us, she will plunge into fatal eternity, if you deprive her of something that will allow her to enjoy a happy fate at the feet of the Being to whom she owes her life."

"Madame," replied Franval, "if Eugénie knows nothing, if these maxims have been carefully kept from her, she cannot be unhappy. For if they are true, the Supreme Being is too just to punish her for her ignorance, and if they are false, what need is there to talk to her of them? As for other cares of her education, I beg you to trust me; as from today I am her teacher, and I declare that in a few years, your daughter will surpass every child of her own age."

Madame de Franval wanted to stand her ground, calling on the eloquence of the heart to support that of reason, and a few tears appeared to aid her. But Franval, who was not softened by them, did not even seem to notice. He had Eugénie taken away, saying to his wife that if she had it in her mind to thwart in any way whatsoever the education he aspired to give his daughter, or if she suggested principles other than those he was going to nourish her on, she would deprive herself of the pleasure of seeing her, for he would place his daughter in one of his châteaux. Madame de Franval yielded and was silent. She implored her husband not to separate her from so dear a possession, and tearfully promised to disturb no single part of the education that was being planned.

From now on, Mademoiselle de Franval was boarded in a very fine apartment next to her father's, with a most intelligent governess, an undergoverness, a chambermaid, and two girls of her own age to play with. She had writing masters and tutors in drawing, poetry, natural history, elocution, geography, astronomy, anatomy, Greek, English, German, Italian, fencing, dancing, riding, and music. Every day Eugénie rose at seven, whatever the time of year. Running out into the garden, she went to eat a large portion of rye loaf, which was her entire breakfast. She returned at eight, and spent a few moments in her father's room, while he frolicked with her or taught her parlor games. She got ready for her exercises until nine when the first master arrived; she received five before two o'clock. Dinner was served apart with her two playmates and the first governess; it consisted of vegetables, fish, pastries, and fruit—never of any meat, soup, wine, liqueurs, or coffee. From three to four, Eugénie went back to the garden to play for an hour with her young friends; and they practiced tennis, playing at ball, skittles, and kites, or running marked distances. They made themselves comfortable according to the season; here there was no constricting the waist; they were never imprisoned in those ridiculous whalebones, as dangerous to the stomach as to the chest, and which, by hindering a young person's breathing, inevitably attack the lungs. From four to six, Mademoiselle de Franval received new teachers, and as all were unable to appear the same day, more came the day after. Three times a week, Eugénie went to the theater with her father, in a little railed box hired for her by the year. At nine she returned to supper. Only vegetables and fruit were served. Four times a week, from ten to eleven, Eugénie played with the women, read a few novels, and then went straight to bed. The other three days, when Franval was not supping out, she went alone to her father's apartment, and this time was employed in what Franval called "her lectures." There he instilled into his daughter his maxims on morality and religion; on the one hand, he presented her with what certain men thought on these matters, and on the other, he established what he himself believed.

With great spirit, wide knowledge, a keen mind, and passions already aflame, the progress of Eugénie's soul under such methods may be readily believed; but as the outrageous Franval was not content with improving the mind, his lectures rarely came to an end without exciting the heart, and this horrid man had so exactly hit on the means of pleasing his daughter, he instigated her with such art, he made himself so essential to her education and her pleasures, he so enthusiastically whirled ahead of all that she might like, that Eugénie, even surrounded by the most brilliant company, found nothing so likable as her father. Even before she had explained his conduct, the innocent and yielding creature had gathered in her young heart all the feelings of friendship, gratitude, and tenderness that cannot fail to lead to burning love, and for him. In society she saw only Franval; he alone was distinct; and she fought against the very idea of anything that could have separated her from him. She would have lavished on him, not her honor, not her charms, for all these sacrifices would have seemed too slight for the tender object of her idolatry, but her blood, her very life, if this dear companion of her soul had asked it.

The impulse of Mademoiselle de Franval's heart was by no means the same toward her respectable and unfortunate mother. The father, by shrewdly informing his daughter that Madame de Franval, being his wife, demanded attentions from him that often prevented his doing all for his dear Eugénie that his heart dictated, had found the secret of putting far more of hatred and jealousy in this young person's soul than the tender and considerate feelings that should have awakened there for such a mother.

"My friend, my brother," Eugénie would say sometimes to Franval, who would have his daughter use no other expressions with him, "this woman you call yours, this creature who, as you say, brought me into the world, is indeed very demanding, since by wanting you always by her side she is depriving me of the happiness of spending my life with you. I see very well that you prefer her to your Eugénie. I, I shall never love what takes your heart away from me."

"My dear," replied Franval, "no, no being in the whole universe shall gain as powerful a right as yours. The ties between this woman and your best friend are the fruits of custom and social convention, and since I view them philosophically, they shall never sway those that bind us. . . . You will always be my favorite, Eugénie; you shall be the angel, the light of my days, the home of my soul, and the power behind my existence."

"Oh, how tender your words are!" replied Eugénie. "Tell me often, my friend. . . . If only you knew how these words of love charm me!"

And taking Franval's hand she placed it on her heart. . . . "Here, I feel them all here," she went on.

"How your soft caresses reassure me," replied Franval, taking her into his arms . . . and so the treacherous man, with no trace of remorse, brought about the seduction of this unhappy girl.

2

In the meantime Eugénie had reached her fourteenth year, and here was the age at which Franval wanted to consummate his crime. Tremble! . . . For he did.

The day she came to this age, or rather when this course of time was run, as both of them were in the country, without relations or any embarrassments, the Count, after first decking his daughter that day like virgins that in ancient times were dedicated in the temple of Venus, had her appear in a luxurious drawing-room, towards ten o'clock in the morning. The lighting was softened by gauze, and the furniture was strewn with flowers. A throne of roses stood out in the center. Franval led his daughter to it.

"Eugénie," he said, seating himself, "today—be the queen of my heart, and let me adore you on bended knees."

"You, my brother, adore me, when it is I who owe you everything, when you made me, formed me . . . oh, rather let me fall at your feet, it is my only place, the only one I aspire to with you."

"O my dear Eugénie," said the Count, drawing near her on these flowered seats that were to assist his triumph, "if you truly owe me something, if the feelings you show me are as sincere as you say, do you know the way to convince me?"

"And what is it, my brother, tell me quickly, that I may grasp it with all my heart?"

"Eugénie, all those charms Nature has lavished upon you, all the attractions she has beautified you with, you must sacrifice to me at once."

"But why are you asking me? Are you not the master of all; doesn't what you made belong to you; can another enjoy your handiwork?"

"But you know the prejudices men have."

"You have never hidden them from me."

"I do not wish to transgress them without your consent."

"Do you not despise them as I do?"

"Yes, but I do not wish to be your tyrant, even less so your seducer. The blessings I ask for I want only out of love. You know the world, and I have never concealed its attractions from you, never kept men from your eyes; not to let you see anything but me would have been a deceit unworthy of me. If there is a being in the world you prefer to me, name him at once, and I will go to the ends of the earth to find him and fetch him at once into your arms. In a word, it is your happiness, my angel, that I want, yours much more than mine. These pleasures, then, that you can give me would be nothing to me, if they were not the reward of your love. Decide then, Eugénie; you are near to being immolated, as you must be; but name the sacrificer yourself. I renounce the pleasures that title secures me if they do not come from your soul and are unworthy of your heart. If it is not me you prefer, at least by bringing you someone you can cherish I shall have deserved your affection. If I have been unable to capture your heart, I shall be Eugénie's friend, having failed to be her lover."

"You shall be all, my brother, you shall be all," Eugénie said, burning with love and desire. "To whom would you have me sacrifice myself, if not to the only one I adore. What being in the world can be more worthy than you of the feeble charms you desire . . . and that your feverish hands search for so fervently already. Can you not see by the fire that consumes me that I am as eager as you to know the pleasure you talk of? Ah, take me, dear brother, best of friends, make your Eugénie your victim; sacrificed by your dear hands, she will ever be exultant!"

Our passionate Franval, who, conforming to the character we know him to have, had only paraded such tact the more shrewdly to seduce, soon took advantage of his daughter's credulity; and once all obstacles were set aside, he made his wicked conquest as much by the principles he had nourished in this impressionable soul as by the art he used to capture it at this late moment. He became with impunity the destroyer of a virginity that both Nature and his capacity had confided to him to defend. Several days went by in mutual ecstasy. Eugénie was of an age to know the pleasures of love and, encouraged by his methods, applied herself unreservedly; and Franval taught her all the secrets, showed her every way. As his homage grew, his captive was more closely bound; she would have him pay respects in a thousand temples at once; she charged her friend's imagination with not being sufficiently perverse; it seemed to her that he concealed something; she blamed her age and her ingenuousness that perhaps did not make her seductive enough. If she wished to be more knowledgeable, it was only so that no means of exciting her lover should remain unknown to her.

They returned to Paris. But the criminal pleasures this perverse man had reveled in had been so exquisite a flattery to his moral and physical talents that the unfaithfulness that usually broke up all his other intrigues could not sever the knots of this one. He fell desperately in love, and from that dangerous passion the inevitable result was his most heartless neglect of his wife. . . .

3

"Well, Eugénie," Franval said to his daughter that evening, "as you can see, they want to make us part. Shall they succeed, my child? Will they manage to break the sweetest bonds of my life?"

"Never, never! Oh, my dearest friend, do not fear. These bonds you delight in are as precious to me as to you. You did not deceive me; I see by making them how far they outrage our customs; and being so little afraid of transgressing habits that vary from clime to clime and can have nothing sacred about them, I wanted these bonds; I have forged them without any regrets. Do not fear that I will break them."

"Alas, who knows? Colunce is younger than I am. He has everything to captivate you; pay no heed, Eugénie, to the last throes of a madness that doubtless blinds you. Age and the light of reason, by dispelling the glamor, will soon cause regrets which you will lay in my heart, and I shall never forgive myself for being their begetter!"

"No," Eugénie replied firmly, "no, I have decided to love you alone. I should think myself the unhappiest of women if I had to take a husband. . . .

"I," she continued warmly, "I, to be joined to a stranger who, not having like you twin reasons for loving me, would make his desires the very limit of his feelings . . . abandoned, despised by him, what would become of me afterwards? Should I be

prude, saint, or whore? No, no—I would rather be your mistress, my friend, a hundred times so than be reduced to playing
one of these infamous roles in society. . . .

"But what is the cause of all this?" she went on bitterly. "Do
you know it? Do you know her? Your wife? She, only she, and
her implacable jealousy; there, without doubt, is the true cause
of the misfortunes that threaten us. Oh, but I do not blame her;
it is all too easy and understandable when it is a matter of keeping you. What would I not do in her place, if someone wanted to
steal your heart?"

Franval was amazingly moved, and embraced his daughter a
thousand times. She, further encouraged by these criminal caresses and fostering her evil soul with even more energy, went so
far as to suggest to her father, with unforgivable effrontery, that
the only way of being less observed was to procure a lover for
her mother. This plan amused Franval; but being even more
wicked than his daughter, and wishing to prepare this young
heart imperceptibly for all the brands of hatred against his wife
that he wished to impress on it, he replied that this seemed too
lenient a revenge, and that there were many other means of
making a woman unhappy when she put her husband on his
mettle.

4

Madame de Franval bribed one of Eugénie's women; a pension, good prospects, the semblance of a worthy act, all this determined the creature, and she promised, as from the following
night, to put Madame de Franval in the way of confirming her
misfortunes.

The moment came. The wretched mother was shown into a
room next to the apartment where her falsehearted husband
outraged all heaven and his bonds of marriage every night. Eugénie was with her father; several candles were still alight in a
corner to illuminate the crime . . . the altar was ready, and the
victim took her place . . . the sacrificer followed. . . . Madame de Franval . . . broke the doors that held her back and

threw herself into the room; there, falling tearfully on her knees at the feet of the incestuous pair. . . .

"You," she cried at Franval, "the despair of my life, from whom I have not deserved such treatment; you whom I still worship despite the wrongs I receive from you, witness my tears, and do not spurn me. . . ."

Marquis de Sade

PHILOSOPHY IN THE BOUDOIR [*Excerpt*]

Eugénie. Tell me, my dear, who was the happy man you made master of your virginity?

Madame de Saint-Age. My brother. He had worshiped me from childhood, and from our youngest days we had often amused one another without reaching the end. I promised him I would surrender myself to him as soon as I was married. I kept my word, and as my husband had fortunately done no damage, he gathered all. We continued to indulge in this intrigue, but without putting either of us to a disadvantage; we nonetheless plunged, each on his own, into the divine welter of lewdness. We even did each other services: I procured him women, he introduced me to men.

Eugénie. What a delightful arrangement! But is not incest a crime?

Madame de Saint-Age. Can the sweetest liaisons Nature knows be so regarded, those she lays down for us, those she most advises! Let us reason for a moment, Eugénie: how, after the vast misfortunes our earth has undergone, could the human species reproduce itself other than by incest? Do we not find both example and proof in books honored by Christianity? The families of Adam and Noah—could they perpetuate themselves other than by this means? Search, examine the ways of the universe: you will see incest permitted everywhere, and regarded as a wise rule made to cement family ties. In a word, if love is born of affinity, where could it be more perfect than between brother and sister, between father and daughter? Mistaken politics, the product of fearing to make certain families too powerful, forbids it in our moral code; but let us not delude ourselves to such an extent that we take the law away from Nature, which would be following the dictates of self-interest or ambition; rather let us sound our hearts, to which I always refer our moral pedants; let us enquire of this sacred organ, and we will realize that there is nothing more refined than the carnal liaison of families. Let us stop blinding ourselves to the feelings of a brother for his sister, or a father for his daughter. One and the other are vainly disguised beneath the veil of legitimate fondness; the most violent love is the only feeling that kindles in them, for that is the only one Nature has put in our hearts. So let us double and triple these delightful incests and fear nothing, and believe that the closer the object of our desires, the more charms we shall enjoy in it.

Un de mes amis vit habituellement avec la fille qu'il a eue de sa propre mère; il n'y a pas huit jours qu'il dépucela un garçon de treize ans, fruit de son commerce avec cette fille; dans quelques années ce même jeune homme épousera sa mere. Such are my friend's wishes, and he has in store a fate for them similar to that of his other projects; his intentions, as I know, are to enjoy still more fruits that shall be born of this wedding; he is young and has reason to hope. You see, dearest Eugénie, with what a heap of incests and crimes this good friend of mine would defile himself if there were any truth in the prejudice that makes us see evil in these liaisons. In a word, in such matters I always have one principle as starting point: if Nature forbade sodomitic indulgences, incestuous practices, pollutions, and so on, would she allow us to find so much pleasure in them? It is impossible that she would tolerate what really outrages her.

Eugénie. Oh, heavenly teachers, how well I see that according to your principles, there are very few crimes on earth, and that we can peacefully abandon ourselves to all our desires, however strange they may appear to the fools who, taking offense and alarm at all things, are stupid enough to mistake social institutions for the divine laws of Nature.

Leonhard Frank

BROTHER AND SISTER [*Condensed*]

LEONHARD FRANK, born in Germany in 1882, attracted considerable attention from the time that his first works were published in 1914. He was a pacifist during World War I, and expressed this pacifism in his literary works. Frank was deeply interested in psychoanalysis, and attempted to use its techniques and understanding in his works. He exiled himself from Germany after the rise to power of Hitler, continued to write, and returned to Germany again in 1951. *Brother and Sister* was written in his middle years, and was widely read and discussed at the time of its publication.

1

One rainy afternoon, in the autumn of 1906, Mr. and Mrs. Schmitt, whose marriage had been dissolved a few days previously, were sitting in the office of Mr. Schmitt's solicitor, making the financial rearrangements which had now become necessary. Mrs. Schmitt's legal adviser was also present.

The two lawyers had neither to contend nor to negotiate; they had merely to draft, to their mutual satisfaction, the legal form of contract for dictation to the typist. Shortly after their marriage, husband and wife had found cause for violent quarrels in almost every word that was spoken, often merely in what they considered the offensive intonation of a word, in a glance, an open or closed door, the merest trifles, such as occur daily; yet now they made no sort of difficulties over money matters, despite the fact that a great fortune was being finally disposed of.

Mr. Schmitt, director and chief European agent of the largest American company for the manufacture of agricultural machines, was a rich man. He was a German-American, Mrs. Schmitt a Russian.

When they came to points of specially far-reaching importance, the solicitors asked the divorced couple once again whether they were fully satisfied; and always they were told to proceed according to the proposals of Mr. Schmitt, or to follow the wishes of Mrs. Schmitt. They could not quite conceal their astonishment at this extraordinary unanimity in a matter which led as a rule to the wildest orgies of acquisitiveness.

At sight of their surprise the divorced couple exchanged an occasional glance, accompanied on both sides by a faint, resigned smile, which expressed their mutual acknowledgment of the fact that each had been tormented beyond endurance for nine years by a person of blameless character.

"Really very sensible! In spite of this—generosity—very sensible indeed!" whispered the astonished solicitor, when he had read through the final form of agreement to his colleague, who nodded assent. He handed the document portentously to Mrs. Schmitt, whose glance, inquiring whether she must read it, wandered past her former husband. Mrs. Schmitt could be characterized by three numbers: she was thirty, looked twenty, and took threes in shoes. In every circumstance of life, there had always been someone to relieve her of all care and responsibility.

Mr. Schmitt signed the counterpart of the agreement, inquiring at the same time whether he might add a clause respecting the children. They had agreed in the divorce court that the father should have the custody of Constantine, aged eight, and the mother that of Lydia, aged three; and now Mr. Schmitt wished her to promise not to interfere in any way with the boy's upbringing; for nothing but harm could result if a child were advised by two persons of equal authority who were so antipathetic to each other, and whose opinions, particularly in matters of education, were so diametrically opposed.

"So you don't care whether Lydia is brought up wrongly or not! That is a matter of indifference to you—Disgraceful!"

"Not at all. But you certainly will not want to part with Lydia too?"

"What a suggestion!"

He made no answer to this. He said, "Besides, you are convinced that your methods of training are right and good."

"But you believe the contrary."

Old bitterness, deposited in thousandfold strata, made him smile resignedly; he reflected that she had never admitted him to be right in anything.

They stared past each other bitterly.

The lawyers understood better now; they quickly formulated the additional clause concerning the children, and Mrs. Schmitt, who had never yet acted independently in anything, turned her helpless, childish eyes inquiringly on her former husband: "Here?"

"No, here."

But still she signed in the wrong place.

At that moment the old nurse, an East Prussian, with a huge, bulbous nose and small shrewd eyes, who had watched over Mrs. Schmitt's own childhood, was putting little Lydia to bed. The child was already in her long nightgown, which was tied round the waist with a gold thread. She would not sleep without this gold thread.

Her hair was black, like the silk fringe of a black shawl, and her large diamond eyes were deep blue with a shimmer of bottle-green. Her little mouth was thoughtful.

She stretched out one tiny hand for the kneeling nurse to wash, at the same time looking across serenely, and yet with the liveliest interest, at Constantine, who was drawing a face with bright colored chalks.

On her way to fetch the towel, the nurse looked over the boy's shoulder and recognized the huge nose, with the two small points to left and right of it, as a portrait of herself. "You cheeky little imp!"

Nature had designed the eight-year-old boy, like his little sister Lydia, as a serious human being. This was shown in the build of his head, the modeling of his face and the thoughtful look in his eyes. Now a feeling of hilarity rose irresistibly from the depths of his being; he could not suppress his triumph at her recognition of the portrait.

Lydia looked across at him without blinking, still holding out her hand, though the washing operations were now over. Her brother's triumph and hilarity leapt over to her so immediately that a faint, jubilant sound slipped suddenly from her smiling, firmly closed lips. At once the white face, with its plump cheeks framed by the black, silken fringe, became grave again.

Lying in bed, unnoticed by her brother, she kept completely still, watching side-eyed till he looked up. Then her eyelids fluttered enticingly, coquettishly. The nurse was in the kitchen.

After a while Constantine held the paper triumphantly above his head for Lydia to see the drawing. Without showing the faintest interest, she closed her eyes contentedly to sleep. It was as though she hid her delight at the attention he had paid her.

Next morning Mr. Schmitt took his son away. He went first to England—where he arranged for Constantine to be sent to Eton—then to New York for a week to attend a shareholders' meeting, and finally to Russia, where he expected to stay for the next ten years. He had transferred the chief European agency to St. Petersburg, in order to open up the Russian and East Asiatic markets.

Faithful to the agreement made in the Berlin solicitor's office, Mrs. Schmitt wrote to her son only once a year, on his birthday. For the first few years Constantine replied with short reports of his progress in football and boxing. He used technical terms which even the nurse, when her advice was sought, failed to understand. Afterwards he did not answer at all.

Seven years later, Mrs. Schmitt, who retained the image of the eight-year-old boy as she had seen him last, was still asking him in her birthday letter to be careful not to soil his handkerchiefs with those stupid colored chalks, and not to swallow cherry stones. By this time Constantine was a grave adolescent, hardened by sport, engaged in comparing the philosophies of Hume and Nietzsche. His tutor answered this letter, telling her that Constantine Schmitt had left the school, having been summoned to Russia by his father.

That was in 1914. Mr. Schmitt had sent for his son between two operations. He made use of the interval to bring Constantine in touch with an old and tried friend, who had agreed to adopt the boy if the second operation ended disastrously.

Constantine's father died shortly before the outbreak of war. And the boy of sixteen, who had passed eight decisive years of his development completely shut off from the influences of early childhood, who had almost forgotten the existence of his mother and had never acquired a son's feelings for his absent father, was conscious of no grief, that bright sunny day, as he walked behind the coffin into the cemetery.

At his adoption, Constantine's identification papers were called in by the authorities. From now on his surname was Berant. And after spending a few weeks in the lively, cheerful company of his adoptive parents, Constantine had more sense of kinship, of belonging to someone, than he had ever had before in his life.

Constantine was rich. From his sick-bed Mr. Schmitt had sold his securities, his shares in the business and all his American holdings in real estate, for the management of them would have been too much for Constantine's adoptive father. A huge fortune in cash was deposited in American banks.

Mrs. Schmitt had heard no more of her former husband since that afternoon in the solicitor's office. The separation was complete. She did not know of his death, and there was no means of finding out—the war had come; in one day life had rolled over on to the other side, and the fates of hundreds of millions of people were changed.

Even after the end of the war, all investigation would have been useless owing to the Russian revolution. But Mrs. Schmitt had not the courage to touch that deep wound in her life. Only once did Lydia inquire after her father and brother, and then she stood confounded at her mother's sudden collapse. Never again did the precocious child attempt to touch on the past.

Lydia's mother had resumed her maiden name of Leskov. They lived in seclusion. Zurich, the quiet home of old-established craftsmen, hotel-keepers and gulls, became, in the second year of the war, a haunt of swindlers, political refugees, deserters, *agents provocateurs* and spies from every country of Europe.

On windless nights, when the life of the town had subsided, when the gulls had gone to rest and the white mountain peaks stood out vast and tranquil, Lydia heard from far away the urgent thunder of the guns: it was so faint as to be scarcely perceptible, and yet monstrous and horrible.

Constantine Berant, whose adoptive father had been killed in the war, was studying economics in Petrograd, and continued his work even during the years of revolutionary upheaval. When he left Russia in 1920, he bore in his eyes the incorruptible knowledge that is born of experience, the knowledge of a man who has seen at close quarters the prodigious sufferings, conflicts and convulsions, the darkness, the madness, the willing self-immolation of a people building a new story on the edifice of human history.

In 1921 Constantine came back from America. The fortune he had inherited had so multiplied in the meanwhile that it would have been impossible for him, even by the most spendthrift habits, to dispose of a substantial portion of his yearly income.

The distinguished stranger who disembarked at Havre was confronted for the first time since early youth with the opportunity of enjoying the other and more generous side of existence. He was free, inwardly and outwardly, untouched in soul and body, with a mind deeply chastened by the great historical events through which he had lived.

Constantine Berant had no personal ties of any sort. The wife of his adoptive father had died of typhus. He was traveling alone. He was twenty-three and had no plans. He followed his momentary impulse, went first to Paris, then to Vienna, from Vienna to Switzerland, and finally decided, when in Zurich, to set out on a carefully-planned world tour, which was to occupy three years.

Constantine Berant came out of the travel agency. The gulls screamed as they glided past above him, out over the smooth, sunny lake; the water smelled fresh, and the distant mountain peaks, calm and white, seemed to have moved nearer, so dear and beautiful was the day.

He turned into the Bahnhofstrasse, which is lined with smart shops; but that morning a vegetable market was being held there, as though Zurich were a little country town. All down the street were rows of baskets, and round them a crowd of housewives, examining the goods, bargaining and buying.

Madame Leskov, who could not distinguish raw spinach from lettuce, and yet had fought all her life for the reputation of an efficient housewife, never failed to attend the market in person. The cook had gone home with a net bag full of vegetables. Madame Leskov and Lydia were walking slowly down the street, looking in at the shop windows.

In 1906, the woman of thirty had looked like a young girl, now at forty-five she looked ten years older than her age: a woman excessively frail and aged prematurely by severe illness.

When Lydia looked at her unobserved, she always held ready a careless smile to cover her great anxiety. She was eighteen, and bore in her face the signs of untouched youth, great beauty and inborn seriousness, poignantly mingled.

Mother and daughter and brother, separated only by the purchasers of vegetables, had come within a few paces of one another, when a hurrying newsboy on the further side of the street called out the latest midday edition. Constantine turned his head, crossed the road and walked on slowly down the further pavement, reading the paper he had bought.

If the newsboy had come but two seconds later, Constantine would have seen his mother. The sight would have had no significance for him—he would just have passed a distinguished old lady.

But he would have seen Lydia.

The same evening he set out on his world tour, which kept him far away from Central Europe for three years.

2

Thick fog in London, reported the ship's wireless. Constantine Berant, his world tour completed, was bound for London from the tropics. There he intended to write a great work on economics. On the spur of the moment he decided to land at Trieste and spend a few days in Berlin, where he would feel the change of climate less acutely.

On that same day Lydia Leskov, whose trunks were already packed, received news which caused her to change her plans: she remained in Berlin. To spare Lydia anxiety, her mother would have written from her death-bed that she was feeling particularly well; but she was ill, and lest Lydia should discover the fact, she had asked her urgently to postpone her return to Zurich. The decorators, she said, were still at work in Lydia's rooms.

Constantine left his hotel intending to take a car and drive out into the country; but with his foot on the running board, he glanced up at the cloud-covered sky and decided to have tea in a hotel in Unter den Linden.

While Lydia was putting on her hat and applying the rouge to lips so smooth and red and bright, against the blinding whiteness of her cheeks, that the smear of artificial crimson was scarcely perceptible, Constantine was crossing the lounge of the hotel on his way to the glass-roofed courtyard. This courtyard gave on an open room where a jazz band was seated beside a shining parquet floor. Every movement of his trained, well-proportioned body was controlled, and as he walked across the court to inquire silently of a waiter, with a scarcely noticeable gesture, whether a little table was free, he gave the impression of a man whom no one could approach. From his face, sharp, unwrinkled, rather thin, and browned by the tropics, came a look that seemed to set him apart from others. The sun had bleached his brown hair on the crown to a lighter shade. Constantine was twenty-six; the seriousness of his nature made him look older.

Lydia came down the main staircase, walking in the middle. Every motion of her spirit found its immediate expression in her gait. By the leisurely way she raised her knee and placed her foot one could tell that she had nothing definite in view; the afternoon had been fixed for her departure; now it belonged to chance.

She wore a black silk dress. The top of her underskirt was visible about half way up her bosom, and above this the blinding white of her breasts shone through the thin net.

For a second she stood in the lounge of the hotel, listening to the jarring tones of the jazz band that came from the courtyard far behind her. She had never had tea in the court. Everything was different today. She walked towards the noise of the band.

Not the faultless beauty of her legs, whose lines flowed down, as though finished at white heat, from the knee to the slenderly modeled foot, not this was significant, but the fact that when these legs were in motion Lydia's inmost being was poignantly expressed in them. Her legs ran down so straight that when she walked there was an eighth of an inch between her knees, and on the inner side, from the calf to the hollow of the knee, rose the line of her womanhood.

Constantine, looking down at the floor in front of him, thinking of his work, saw nothing at first but this exciting flow of legs from the knee downward.

"The progressive unification of the means of production within the capitalist system"—this, a title he had just thought out for his coming book, vanished from his mind. His eyes rose from the burnished legs, past the knees, to the thigh, whose roundness was revealed beneath the black silk; thence to the bosom, firm and motionless under the thin net. He saw the tall column of her neck, and then that head, that face, poignantly animated like her walk and her knees, matte-white, seeming to receive its last inner gleam of beauty from the black wings of the tragedy of human existence.

Only beneath the unexpected blue of her eye was a faint shimmer of brown. Her brows were black as silk.

Constantine's first sensation was that of a violent pain in the neighborhood of his heart, then a hot stream poured through him, down neck and back, through shoulders and arms to the tips of his fingers. He looked slowly away and lowered his eyes to the ground again. For some time he did not look up. The wave of impatience, because this woman was still a stranger to him, sank back upon itself.

In the first vitally decisive minute, as he looked in front of him with averted head, the image of her being formed itself in his soul, immovably and for ever.

He needed only to raise his head and he could compare the burning image inside him with her.

He did not raise it.

She had taken a seat at the edge of the crowd, at one of the little tables reserved for guests in the hotel. She had entered quietly, unnoticed by the rest; but now she was sitting there, impossible to ignore. As she came in, she had noticed only Constantine's outward appearance, his bearing, his rather severe profile.

They sat by the wall scarcely two yards apart, Lydia facing the lounge of the hotel, he with his eyes on her if he chose to raise them. There was no table between.

Of their own accord Constantine's hands spread the toast on both sides with butter. Quite unintentionally, as though returning to life from a dream, with a knowledge deeply emotional, yet sharp and bright, that in Lydia the meaning of life would be fulfilled for him, he slowly raised his head.

In that look was the plan and nature of the man, his whole identity, his devotion and his desire, strong and vital; Lydia received it like a seed in her unguarded heart. It was he who first lowered his eyes, but not till he had fired that shot into her soul.

Under the smooth surface of her life a perturbing unrest had arisen, transforming the features of her existence, the features of her face, as a coming earthquake affects the smooth surface of the sea, before its power has been upthrown.

She could look at him: he was sitting with averted head. She could not resist comparing the harmony of the masculine lines of his face with the glance he had given her. She felt, as he sat there, that she was in him, she felt her triumphant power, and at the same time the irresistible, deeply agitating, blissful help-lessness of a woman who has been stricken.

Constantine knew that she would get up at once and go, and he did not raise his eyes again to her. He saw only the slenderly modeled foot, the close play of the legs. Not till she had crossed

the court and reached the lounge did he look up; then he saw
that she walked with bent head.

The sight tore him out of himself. He was overcome by a
dread of letting her out of his sight. Berlin was large.

One minute later he knew she was staying in the hotel, knew
the number of her room. He knew her favorite flower. It was
not till he had called at three shops that he found the Marechal
Niel roses. He sent the bouquet without a card. Then he drove
to his own hotel and packed; some minutes later his trunks
were standing in the suite next to hers.

Lydia had passed through the dusk of the lounge as far as the
doorway; there she had looked out into the sunshine, turned
back and, with quivering unrest in her heart, climbed the staircase, slowly, her hand on the rail. She felt what had happened
in the hollows of her knees. Suddenly she saw her white face
in a mirror on the staircase, and in her face the light of triumph
and a woman's helplessness. Happiness. Under her own eyes she
tried to regain her self-control.

There was a knock on the door of the outer room. She heard
the voice of her maid. It was all quite natural: that he should
send her flowers, and that he knew her favorites. She accepted
the bunch of roses as though she had ordered it herself.

Her eyes felt hot and red. If only she could be quite alone
with him! She told the maid to go. With weak hands she took
the three Marechal Niel roses that stood on her toilet table and
put them with his.

She took off her hat as though life were just beginning. Her
silky black hair slipped down over her small ear. Then she sat
down at the mirror, to see whether she was beautiful. And
there, before the mirror, the woman in her regained her self-
control.

Without a second's hesitation, Constantine took the risk of
seeming to act indelicately: that same evening he drew a circle
of spies round Lydia, from the porter to the chambermaid. She
could not take a step now without his knowledge, so deep was
the dread in his heart. Restlessly he walked up and down the
big room.

His secretary, a doctor of philosophy, who had dragged an extensive reference library all round the world, possessed vast knowledge but could not put the smallest idea on paper. He arranged Constantine's closely-written notebooks, his pamphlets and statistical reference works, on the inadequate writing table, and set out pen and ink and fresh sheets of foolscap.

"That'll never come to anything."

The secretary, who was very clever, but sometimes could look very stupid, made a dumb, astonished inquiry. In doing so he lifted the tip of his thick nose. His gold spectacles had grown into his plump face.

"No time! Not now! And I don't know when I shall have!"

At that the secretary could only pull down the creases in his waistcoat, as he always did when disconcerted. At last, he inquired: "But when are we going to London?"

"London? I don't know where she's going."

He could not understand that; the tip of his thick tongue appeared between his thick lips. Now he looked stupid.

"The suite next door was occupied half an hour ago," said Lydia's maid, as she took Lydia's evening frock out of the wardrobe.

Lydia knew immediately that he was on the further side of the wall. Her hand to her throat, she listened, and caught his restless step.

"I think he must be an Englishman or an American. His secretary looks like a cold dumpling."

Lydia asked abruptly: "Don't you ever intend to marry?"

"Not before you, at any rate!" This girl, twenty-five, well-grown, rosy cheeked and pretty, accepted all the affairs of life in a simple, practical way. It was hard to disturb her equanimity.

"There's no particular need to marry, Miss Lydia; you can manage as you are, nowadays. I'd rather you told me whether we're to dine downstairs this evening."

"No. I'm going to the opera." She had only thought of that a moment before.

It was seven o'clock. Marie, whom nothing surprised, asked calmly: "Which frock?" She chose suitable stockings and shoes and an evening bag, and went down to the porter to book seats in a box.

Two minutes later, the porter knocked at Constantine's door. "The lady from number seventeen is going to the opera in half an hour. 'The Marriage of Figaro.' I've booked another seat in the same box." He neither whispered nor smiled discreetly; his voice and manner were quite businesslike. Constantine had given him a hundred marks.

Constantine's brow grew hot. I wonder if she'll resent all this spying? "Not in the same box—of course not! A stall—but not far away!"

"The lady was going to leave at midday today I forgot to tell you. But she's staying for the present. Those were her words: 'For the present.' "

The porter had a considerable knowledge of human nature, but he would never have thought it possible for this self-assured young stranger, who never spoke a word more than was necessary, to stare in front of him so completely at a loss.

Marie always dressed in black and wore a gold cross on a chain round her neck. She was in the box with Lydia. "There he comes, our neighbor from the hotel, but without the dumpling."

Under his close-fitting dress coat, Constantine's well-knit body, his broad shoulders and small hips, his taut but effortless bearing, the tropic brown of his face, showed up to still greater advantage.

Lydia had not the power to look at him. In her right temple, which was towards him, she felt where he was sitting: he was in the second row, close to her box, which was rather nearer the stage.

The blood still throbbed in her right temple. Her first thought—a hot emotion—was that she was too exposed—throat, arms, shoulders—too terribly exposed.

What remained was swathed in pale yellow tulle.

Not till the house was in darkness did he turn his head. He did not look away again. Even now, in the warm darkness of the box, she shone, dazzlingly white.

Neither of them heard anything. Surrounded by the upward

rush of notes, aspiring ever higher, wherein heavenly choirs sang jubilant, they heard only the dark beat of the blood in their ear drums.

Then the light burst down again from the candelabra. The audience pushed their way out amid a hubbub of talk. It was the interval. Constantine found himself standing, surrounded by richly-dressed people, in the brightly-lighted foyer with its marble columns.

There went Lydia, enchantingly bright, and beside her the black shadow with the gold cross. He saw the innocence of her breast and, when she had passed, all her living body under the pale yellow tulle.

Now she was standing by a pillar, with her white bewitching face, looking into his heart.

He could go to her, go to her now, take her hand, say nothing or say everything.

A long-drawn shrilling of bells. He heard nothing. When he came to the surface again, and looked up, she had vanished: the foyer was disenchanted. Now that she had gone, he went up, as though under compulsion, to the shining, yellow column of marble. The air that she had breathed must still be there. It must be here. "Here, just where she was standing."

It was very late that night when Constantine came back to the hotel.

He had spent some time in a West End champagne-restaurant, where the bald-headed conductor shouted the words to the jazz-time, and chubby, attractive page boys, scarcely more than three feet tall, sold colored paper streamers which, thrown to and fro amidst the crush of the dancers, linked up cocottes with corpulent gentlemen. But he had found himself very far removed from this kind of life.

He stood in his bedroom, listening, separated only by a thin wall from Lydia, who lay wide awake in bed, less exposed in her cream-colored nightdress than she had been at the opera. On both sides of the wall a heart was beating in the pitch darkness.

Awakening early, Constantine said: "It can't go on like this." As a man after a long spell of sloth sets out his writing mate-

rials on his desk with exaggerated energy, noise and vigor, determined from now on to turn over a new leaf, Constantine resolved to put an end to vacillation and sprang energetically out
of bed.

When his secretary came in, carrying a book, Constantine
was standing stark naked in his room, his muscle developers
vigorously extended across his chest. Every part of his broad-
shouldered, well-trained body was as brown as his face, and at
their largest point his thighs, swelling with muscle, were a fraction of an inch broader than his hips.

He knew what time Lydia left her room in the morning. In
ten minutes he had taken a cold shower, shaved, put on a dark
blue shirt and belted trousers, and found himself with a full
hour in front of him and absolutely nothing to do.

Whenever Constantine was faced by an enterprise of particular difficulty, he reached a point at last where his vigorous self-
assurance overcame all hesitation. Thus as he strode down Unter den Linden behind Lydia, he slapped his thigh softly with
his gloves and threw an occasional glance at the silky blue of
the sky, for the day was warm and bright. No finer hindrance
to traffic could be conceived, he thought, as he saw an omnibus,
a traveling house, squeeze with difficulty through the Branden-
burger Tor.

The Tiergarten, a vast park in the midst of a vast city where
every square yard of ground costs gold, the most precious legacy left by the forefathers of Berlin to their successors of the
twentieth century—who have no time for it—lay spread out in
its quiet splendor, old and ever new, traversed by backwaters
which mirrored the dazzling sun, and poured forth a freshness
on that spring day that was entirely at one with Constantine's
frame of mind.

In front of him walked Lydia, holding her head a little bent,
in a manner so individual that she seemed to be wrapped in
her beauty. He saw by her back that she felt how near he was.

Then he was walking at her side. "I beg your pardon. My
name is Constantine Berant." Anyone might have said that.

She raised her eyes for a brief moment to his. "How sun-

burnt you are! Have you been in the tropics? I thought so
yesterday."

And she says that to me! What a wonderful confession! A
shudder of joy quivered down his back. "Yes, I've been traveling about the world for three years." As he said the words, he
thought: If flowers could produce sounds, her voice would be
like the ringing of a large heavy-scented, white blossom.

He looked at her small ear as he spoke, which lay pressed
close to the silky, black hair, and was incredibly white in its
mysterious convolutions: "You are only here for a short time?
You wanted to leave yesterday. I made inquiries and found that
out—please forgive me!—and much more. All about you! I
made up my mind to confess at once."

And as though everything were now in order: "You are incredibly beautiful."

"You mustn't speak like that." With a short glance that told
him that he might.

Every step they took led them deeper into the mysterious
glen where flowers bend before the feet of lovers and the thorn-
bush waits. Happiness.

"Please, say that again. 'I thought so yesterday.' "

And when she remained silent, he repeated with upflashing
glance:

"Please say it again." His heart was listening.

And Lydia, who knew that these words would be a confession of her fondness, said as though to herself: "I thought so
yesterday."

Then she gave him a direct look, gave him the whole of her
proud face.

For a second he kept hold on himself, then joy opened his
lips: "We ought to be married in London. Everything can be
arranged there much quicker and more simply than in Germany. No formalities . . . Obviously!" He cried in high spirits,
for her shoulders were shaking with noiseless, irresistible laughter.

She was not surprised. He had to be like that. It was all natural and right.

Suddenly Lydia stopped and laid her hand on Constantine's

arm. "Look!" Seven grey ducklings no bigger than sparrows
sailed softly whispering out of the shadow of the trees, across
the backwater, followed and guarded by the two old birds,
which, with head and neck drawn well back, cackled to each
other proudly and contentedly.

At sight of this family, Lydia said what every young girl or
young woman would have said: "Look, how sweet!"

But he stood beneath the intense effect of the hand that still
rested in self-forgetfulness upon his arm, a hand blue-white and
so slender that it seemed incredible that five fingers could find
room there. The rosy nails were rounded almost to a semi-circle,
like tiny arched gateways.

It was only just nine o'clock and there was no one to be seen.
A short time before, he had thought: How touchingly naive the
way she carries her splendid breast, a delicious gift for anyone,
for casual passers-by! In this sudden, overflowing desire he took
Lydia to himself. He took her with too great urgency and felt
her resistance; he loosened his arms, and then, as her resistance
died softly upon itself, lips found lips in a harmony of desire.

Lydia had known no other kiss than her mother's. When
they had walked some way in silence, the wonderful, unfamiliar
feeling that had destroyed her equanimity was still rising
from her knees and the hollows of her knees. "I'm afraid of
you."

None the less, in that same second she wanted to touch the
spot behind his ear with her lips, the spot where the line of the
hair ran down in a sweeping curve to his neck. And this craving
came from a different source, from deeper down, where love's
give and take, and love itself, is born.

"You are not afraid." Suddenly he saw her rise from the
tea table and cross the courtyard. Her legs are that famous fraction of an inch too long, he thought enraptured, and again he
was striding under a blood-red dome.

The joy of life was pulsing in her, and a new lighthearted-
ness, that musically permeated the gravity of her nature. This
showed itself at once in the prickling fluidity of her legs and in
her mouth, set like a miracle, clear and red, in her matte-white
face.

Her eyes flashed deeper as, with her rapid glance, she said challengingly: "Anyone as irresistible as you has no need to make such elaborate inquiries."

"Especially now that I know all about you. Everything! But the fear that you might leave without my knowing! That terrible fear! What would have happened if you had left Berlin yesterday evening?"

"Why, nothing," she said; and thought: What would have happened to me? Zurich, mother, and his picture in my heart! She saw the gulls flying, in the sun and beneath grey skies, saw herself standing under the verandah. That is what would have happened to me!

But when she heard the cheerful tones of his voice again, the veil fell from her eyes.

"As it was, I knew you were going to the opera a minute after you knew yourself." Delighted with the completeness with which he had hemmed her in, he was about to slap his thigh with his gloves, but he arrested the half-completed movement at sight of Lydia standing by the marble column. "You looked inexpressibly beautiful."

Lydia grew silent; everything within her grew silent. Her matte-white face could not flush; only her ears grew hot, and they remained white.

Then he wanted to speak her name, and thought with a shock how wonderful it would be to hear it from her own lips. He stopped.

In that pause she answered: "Lydia."

Suddenly he let his hands and arms fall to his sides. "Kiss me once more. Once more, Lydia!"

Tears stood in her eyes unawares and yet her lips were smiling. He drank her leisureliness blissfully to the last drop, as she stepped up close, coming to one side and a little behind him, took his head in both hands and lightly touched the spot behind his ear with her lips. He did not move.

It was Lydia who brought a sudden strangeness between them, an inner distance, as though their proximity had been much too close for her. She spoke of casual matters in a tone she might have used to a chance companion, and yet the change was so naturally graduated that he could make no objection to it.

When they reached the hotel, Constantine had a desolating sense of being further away from Lydia than he had been one minute after their meeting on the previous day.

Before lunch—Constantine had been sitting waiting for hours in the lounge—the porter came up to him officiously. Constantine took the words out of his mouth. "Thank you, there's no need to do any more." With that he put an end to the whole system of espionage.

Now she could go away. He would do nothing to stop her. Even if the very heart sprang out of his breast. The nearness she had experienced laid an obligation on her too. After what had happened she owed him as much as he owed her. He will never forget those last horrible four hours of uncertainty; he hopes never to experience such torment again.

When Constantine clenched his teeth, his eyes grew bigger. Did she not want him? Had it been merely a caprice? A fleeting response? He knew all about her. He had seen her, seen her in that first moment. They belonged to each other. That was fate. But what if he had seen her wrongly? Was that possible? Then, of course, he would really know nothing about her. All or nothing!

What had the hall porter wanted to tell him? What had happened? Where was Lydia? Perhaps she had received a telegram and been forced to leave. He put the pen down again. Unconsciously he slipped his coat on and went out.

There were only a few guests sitting in the lounge. Nearly everyone was in the restaurant. The porter was standing in front of his key rack. Two strangers came in through the revolving doors. An old lady with a limp gave in her key. A telegraph boy arrived.

That telegram might be for Lydia. What had the porter wanted to tell him? He cursed his former precipitancy. Should he go up and ask him? "I mustn't do that."

She came down the stairs with complete serenity. He saw

her first; saw her knees and their rhythmic motion. All feeling died out of him, everything grew white and cold.

She was on her way to ask the porter to send for Constantine, when she saw him sitting there. With incomparable ease and naturalness she went up to him, gave him her hand as he sprang in confusion from his chair, pressed it perceptibly with her finger tips, and said with a tender smile: "I've sent Marie over to you twice." (With one giant leap he came out of his confusion and reached himself again, and all so quickly that she noticed nothing.) "But you weren't there. Please come with me, I want to do some shopping." She was wearing three of his roses high up on her shoulder. Everything was soft and warm, fluid and marvelously natural. Thus they looked at each other. A dark promise lay behind her glance. And the certitude struck him: If I were in her room now, at this minute, she would melt in my arms.

Lydia raised no obstacle to his wish to leave as soon as possible for London so that they could be married. He asked whether they ought not first to visit her mother, and after a moment's reflection, she said with a gentle and thoughtful smile: "Mother would be less able to deal with the situation than a lost child in a city crowd. She would find fault with it somehow or other. She would never give her consent."

Fear took hold of him: "Why not?"

"Because she's like that. She can't agree to anything. Even when I want to buy some plums she's against it. She's just against things. You must try to understand. She has such an odd sort of ambition. You could win her over if you told her at the right moment she was a wonderful housewife, or understood a lot about sport." Lydia's eyes sparkled with tender amusement.

Her good humor communicated itself immediately to him. "Then let's buy the plums without asking."

"That's what I've always done."

They took a car back to the hotel. When she stepped out, Lydia was changed. She gave him her hand in the lounge, stiffly, withdrew it at once, withdrawing at the same time into herself, and went up the stairs. But this time he kept his head.

:

The large room was dimly lighted and the corners were in darkness. Only the subdued light of a six-foot standard lamp, whose hemispherical shade of yellow silk was closed in beneath with the same material, fell on Lydia's figure on the ottoman.

At Constantine's entrance Lydia opened the bottom of the shade, and stretched out her arm in a sudden flood of light. As her hand fell back and he lifted his head, there was between them that tension, fraught with mystery, that arises between lovers when they are alone for the first time in a room, whose four walls exact and facilitate intimacy.

The rug had slipped from her knees. The sleeveless white silk frock was so short that her knee was visible, and even the beginning of the line that curved up from it, though she was lying stretched out straight on her back.

"Will you smoke? I've put things ready for you."

Sweets, newspapers, cigarettes, lay beside the liqueur bottles on a little table by the ottoman.

He said only two simple words: "Thank you." But each word and gesture of Constantine and Lydia gained a deeper significance, hiding but scantily the tension that might burst next second into a flame that would engulf them both.

"You can move your chair a little nearer . . . Here!" She smiled, but there was in her eyes the dark questioning of a woman to whom the man is still unknown, and with it the fine pride that was part of her character, that would cause her to yield unreservedly to her passion, if she yielded at all.

Constantine was a man; his eyes saw the matte-white shoulders; the arms were bare; his senses were eyes that saw what was hidden, and when he bent forward in his chair only half an inch separated him from Lydia's soft, clear lips; a single unguarded heart beat could bridge that little space. "White suits you."

At these poor words, Lydia felt she could no longer withhold the glance which would have allowed him everything. She closed her eyes.

He stood up.

In his arms her last faint resistance would perhaps have given way completely. But there must be nothing, nothing, for her to overcome. He did not think that out with his head; it came from his deep tenderness.

Constantine walked to and fro, pausing when he spoke. She sat up, to be nearer him, and her open heart followed him.

"I love you, Lydia, so much that I shall never, never, find a way to tell you of it." He stood some distance away from her. He could speak now; he stood bent forward a little and kept his hands hidden behind his back. Oh, he had no need of hands or arms!

"How much do you love me?"

Heavens, how she said that! He leaned against the wall opposite her; the room was large. "But it's impossible. Impossible!"

"How much?"

"When you stand near me, quite close to me, the top of your head just reaches to my lips; I will watch over you like that, every second . . . May I say something?"

"You can say everything now."

"If you went blind, if a disease destroyed your beauty, disfigured you altogether, if only the pressure of your hand was left to me—"

"Would you still love me then?"

"It would be as though nothing had happened . . . Now do you understand me, Lydia?" He began walking to and fro again and her eyes followed him. Did his heart belong to her so utterly?

Lydia, lying outstretched on her back, floated in the air above the ottoman, horizontal. She floated. Ecstasy in her heart, she shut her eyes and tasted in a swoon this weightless, hitherto unknown sweetness. Her mouth opened soft to his firm lips; they slipped down into the chasm of her wild and fainting surrender, which inflamed him ever afresh to the verge of madness.

It was nearly morning when he tore himself away and stole from the bedroom. She lay on the low bed, in the light from a reading lamp on the bedside table, as he had left her. Her breasts were full and firm. She laid her hands sideways upon them, and lay motionless. The lower part of her body had a faint brown shimmer like that beneath her eyes. She had refused him nothing; in overcoming her shame she had done and given the uttermost. In the singing of her blood she fell asleep.

Marie crept through the door. Lydia's finger tips guarded her breasts. Marie had never seen her thus. Touched by the mystery, she placed the coverlet with reverent care over the immaculate body, whose breath came deep and rhythmic, and put out the light.

That day Lydia remained in her rooms; he did not see her, and when on the day following he passed through the lounge, the porter came up to him and said: "The lady from number seventeen has gone."

3

His face, burned by the tropic sun, could not grow pale; the lips only were white as he asked: "Where?"

"The lady didn't give her destination, and the maid spoke quietly to the chauffeur, apparently so that I shouldn't hear."

As he stood there in the lounge and saw the coming and going, without seeing anything, he was like the man in the fable who stood by the edge of the desert and was to die unless he found a particular grain of sand. His mind was numbed, and it seemed impossible ever to find Lydia again.

A woman, sitting near the lift, had fixed her eyes on Constantine with an expression so devoted and so forlorn that it seemed as if she had renounced from the beginning the faintest hope of ever being able to approach him.

This woman, who came of a wealthy, aristocratic family in Dresden, had spent the preceding year in Turkey with her husband, a former secretary to the Turkish Embassy in Berlin, and had met Constantine at the Hotel Tokatlian in Constantinople. Every day for weeks she had frequented the hotel-restaurant with her unsuspecting husband, and had spent hours looking at Constantine, without excitement, as though in a state of hypnosis, doing will-lessly what she had to do.

This woman, who bought her clothes at the most expensive

shops, and always looked ill-dressed because she did not know how to wear them, crossed the lounge, without emotion, as though this too had been preordained for her in the scheme of things, and went up to Constantine; she raised to his face her lusterless blue eyes, and said in a voice as colorless as her ash-blonde hair: "The lady booked two tickets for Frankfort-on-Main."

As calmly as she had come to him, in obedience to the command of her poor heart, she turned, recrossed the lounge as far as the lift, her gait strangely lifeless, as though even in walking she made no movement, and ascended to one of the upper floors.

Once in her room, she began immediately to pack, changed her clothes, and sent the chambermaid to the porter for a first-class ticket to Frankfort-on-Main, all without agitation, as though in hypnosis, with tragic inevitability.

"Why?" asked Constantine, who was standing by a window in the corridor of the Frankfort express. The man in him knew very well why Lydia had gone. The man in him had lived through the burning convulsions of that night, had seen Lydia's pride broken and submerged in her wild and boundless passion.

She gave me her pride, and now she has taken it back. The lady from number seventeen has gone. Constantine was calm. The world was very small and love all-powerful. What was there stronger in the world? Not even death! That night Lydia had whispered her love into his ear.

The wife of the Turkish diplomat stepped back into her sleeping compartment. She did not want him to see her. She was traveling in the same train with him; that was enough.

Constantine found out by telephone the hotel where Lydia was staying. He did not take a taxicab: it was nine o'clock, Lydia's time, and he might meet her. He walked watchfully down the main street, and saw more friendly, laughing faces in five minutes than he had seen in five days in Berlin.

Lydia had gone to Frankfort because it was on her way to Zurich. She had been sitting in the writing room for an hour, but had not yet succeeded in writing to her mother. Since she awoke from that night of love, she had not been able to free herself from a choking sense that she was locked up in a narrow, airless cell. Her mother's nerves would feel in every word that something had happened.

What had happened? What had she done? At once the images swarmed round her like wild beasts. How hard it was to breathe!

The contest was too terrific between her clear, fine pride and her wild, insensate surrender. Even the greatest and strongest of us must go on growing as we live; Lydia, who had known neither herself nor Constantine, had to learn in the school of love to find a place in her pride for her loveliest faculty, that of belonging to her lover with complete self-surrender. That was hard.

She stiffened to a life-sized figure of thin glass which the merest touch would shatter.

"Please don't pursue me."

"Lydia, what are you doing?"

"Please leave me at once."

"What are you doing to me, Lydia? You have no right now to send me away. Not now!"

He should not have said that. There was cold madness in her eyes. "I don't want to know you any more."

He turned round and went out.

At that she started up in horror, both hands to her face, and stared at Marie, who was entering the room.

"What's the matter, Miss Lydia?"

"He's gone."

"He told me he would be back immediately. He's only gone to fetch the roses. But you must get into bed now, and all will be well."

Lydia placed her forefinger warningly on her lips: "Ssh!" Constantine stole towards her on tiptoe, as she lay on the bed. "My beloved!"

But Marie entered the bedroom behind him; she was wearing her black dress. "Miss Lydia, you must get up now. It's three o'clock. You've been sleeping for five hours."

Lydia woke up with the words: "But I've only just lain down." She saw him immediately, standing before her in the writing room. "I don't want to know you any more." She saw his face grow thin at her words, saw his lips blanch till they were nothing but a white line.

That white line in his brown face was terrible; her heart ached with tenderness. Why had she done that to him? Why? She was so happy! Oh, beloved! Her whole life belonged to him. He must come to her, come at once. "Marie, dearest Marie, go down to the porter and tell him to ask Mr. Berant to wait for me in the lounge."

Then she was sitting at her toilet table, examining her bright eyes, her serene face. In the mirror she saw her own happiness. He would be angry. She was a little afraid of him. But even her fear was sweet. She was no longer proud. She would stroke his face, stroke his lips with the tips of her fingers, very gently —till they grew red again.

"The porter says there is no one named Berant staying here."

Her heart gave a little throb and was shut; the great fear could not enter. It was not so bad as all that; he was staying at some other hotel. He would come back.

The scene in the writing room came into focus again. He would not come back. He was gone. Constantine would never come back.

A great fear came over her. Nothing mattered to her now. There was no such thing as shame before Constantine or Marie. "Please make inquiries in the hotels, in all the hotels—go quickly, my dear Marie, take a taxi. Go everywhere!"

While Marie was driving from hotel to hotel, Constantine was walking through the streets, enduring the fate of one who, when he held his beloved in his arms, knew with iron certainty that she was his for life, and now staggers under the annihilating knowledge that he has lost her for ever.

"I don't want to know you any more." These words went with him.

In Frankfort-on-Main every pedestrian arrives inevitably at the Hauptwache, just as in the west of Berlin one arrives at the Gedachniskirche. For the third time he came on the little old cafe, standing in the middle of a square, surrounded by a row of tiny tables at which the guests sat close together in the sunshine. Seven streets and lanes opened on to the square; an old church, cottages centuries old, palatial modern shops and offices, announced in like manner the spirit of their own times and of the town. Here tradition, modern enterprise and the tempo of the twentieth century are vitally mingled in the people and in the outward appearance of the place.

He walked aimlessly down a broad street. The newsboys came running out of a huge newspaper building. Constantine's mind was divided; he turned his head as before at the newsboys' cry, and simultaneously he was in Lydia's bedroom in Unter den Linden.

"Please don't pursue me." No, no, that was not what he was doing. He could not do that; but what could he do? What could he do in Frankfort-on-Main?

There is something in every man that seeks salvation at all costs. So first he must go back to Berlin. And then to London to write his book?

He had taken a room in the first hotel he saw. The place stood in a side street and catered for travelers passing through Frankfort. His trunk was still unpacked.

"You'll have to take a taxi. The train goes in eight minutes. You'll just do it. But you must pay for the room."

While he was paying the five marks, the boots brought down his trunk, the page fetched a taxicab and, with one single beat, his heart won back the whole fullness of life, for Lydia came into the lounge.

When a mother has lost her child in a crowded city street and suddenly finds it again, her happiness is too great. She needs a few minutes to recover. The joy sticks in her breast and cannot get out. Tears are still nearer than gladness.

The page was standing on the running board of the approaching car, the chauffeur's good-humored eyes turned inquiringly over his shoulder.

"Out into the country! Whichever way you like."

They did not speak; they did not look at each other; her

head lay beside him so that the crown touched his lips; he held
her tightly clasped, and thus they went, taking no heed of the
men and women in the crowded street.

Some time later—they had driven a considerable way along
the river bank, through woodlands and fields, back through the
wood, and had reached the river again—the chauffeur asked,
without turning his head, whether he should drive back.

"Go on!"

A word had been spoken, and the little movement, closer to
him, had to be made afresh. A tender kiss on the crown of her
head brought them back at once to the center of quietude.

The sturdy young chauffeur, who came from a little town not
far from Frankfort, whistled two soft notes under his breath; an
artful look came into his eyes, and he took the road for home,
where his sweetheart was. If only those two behind him would
remain a little longer as they were, he could carry out his cunning plan. He accelerated imperceptibly.

The car sped through a village that had lain all day under
the sun and now was resting in the evening shadows—dashed
past a red sandstone quarry. That was a sign of home for the
chauffeur. Half his native town was built of red sandstone.
Everything grew noticeably redder, the ground and the rubble
in the valleys that ran down to the road, where thin waterfalls
shone like silver.

"Say that you love me."

He said it through her open lips into her heart, and Lydia's
entranced eyes closed with the kiss.

The fiery disc was already touching the edge of the distant
chain of hills, the river was of gold, the light flamed back from
tiny windows, the whole valley was aglow, and up here the fields
and woods stood in the sunless, dark-green peace of evening.

Afraid of endangering his plan, the chauffeur slackened
speed. As he looked forward towards his goal he whistled from
time to time those two artful notes. Now he only needed to say
that it would be better to drive on into the town. He had constructed the right sentence, and could read it, as it were, from
the steering wheel in front of him, which for his sweetheart's
sake he was holding very firmly in his hands. But no one asked

him to turn back. Happiness does not ask where it is going.

Suddenly the sound of the engine stopped; the car slid down a hill into a valley, calmed, as though its goal were close at hand and glided along the river bank, through alternate stretches of shade and red, evening sunshine. The chauffeur pushed back his cap from his moist forehead and smiled cheerfully, one hand resting lightly on the steering wheel.

They overtook peasants trudging home from the fields. Constantine and Lydia sat still, each in a corner, on their best behavior. Throughout the journey they had seen nothing but each other, even when their eyes were shut; but now their senses took in the vital peace of their entry into the town.

A girl with blooming cheeks, who was carrying a rake on her shoulder, stopped and stood transfixed. The chauffeur winked his left eye. He would explain to her later on exactly how he had managed it.

The car reached the market square. Patrician houses, fresh, high-gabled, beautiful, the church, the town hall and the Black Eagle Inn, baroque buildings, pure and harmonious in style, surrounded the open space. In the center was a tall fountain with ten jets; and the rays of water rising in noble curves mingled with the last rays of the sun. The hostess of the Eagle, in a black dress, looking as Lydia's maid would look in thirty years' time, took off her apron as she came out to the car.

Constantine could hardly suppress his delight—his eyes sparkled despite his efforts to appear matter-of-fact—as he allowed Lydia to assume towards the landlady the role of a wife, whose duty it was to discuss and arrange matters for herself and her husband. She did it nobly, with incomparable naturalness.

One of the two available rooms was small and contained two narrow beds, and the "best room" was so large that the dark brown, polished baroque furniture—a huge brass-mounted wardrobe, carefully preserved armchairs and a four-poster bed nearly seven feet wide—left space enough for dancing. All along the wall by the window was a polished frame on which lay last year's apples. The curtains had been taken down, for the room was seldom used. She took both.

Meanwhile Constantine was bargaining with the chauffeur.

It seemed to have grown a little too late for them to return that day.

"Can't help it, Sir."

"We must have been nearly an hour."

The chauffeur whistled his two soft notes, but this time inwardly: "An hour? Exactly three and a half!"

Constantine was surprised that so many people greeted them. Even the women nodded as they passed, and then smiled with downcast eyes. A few bare-footed boys moved cautiously forward in a wide semi-circle, a step at a time, with wide-open eyes, and whispered from a discreet distance: "Hans!"

"You see, I come from here." In doubt as to the effect of these words, he blinked up at Constantine, who was studying the harmonious beauty of the square, the river, the chain of hills—now blue—and thinking: Anyone who grew up here has something to take with him all his life.

The night was very mild, for all day long the earth had breathed deep and undisturbed beneath the sun. Brother and sister, born of the same womb, walked with the tingling sense that the night belonged to them. Their blood, the same in each, uttered no warning; it had spoken for union and their hearts had merely followed its word. The blood knows nothing of the laws of men; it is subject only to the pure law of nature, whose dearest sister is consummating love.

They walked along the river bank. The foot of the line of hills, soft as though covered in dark velvet, quivered under the clear, starry tent, and the soft voice of the river carried on its eternal conversation with the night.

Constantine took what she had given him in the car; and she gave him her mouth and her craving body. The deep song of their blood joined in the speech of night and river.

"Now I'll give you back my property for a while; I'll lend it you, Lydia, only lend it you. Take care of it for me."

"Shall I give you the rest too? Everything, my beloved? . . . Everything belongs to you!"

She listened. "The water has just called our names. Listen, the water says: 'Constantine and Lydia.' Hark!"

On the little chests on each side of the bed were wooden

candlesticks with thick candles that gave a big, steady flame. Constantine was sitting in the smaller room; he could hear Lydia undressing. His trunk had been left behind in Frankfort. He tore off his clothes and listened. The gate of happiness stood open. He went in, and Lydia saw how beautiful he was.

His entrance came a second too early. She too was almost naked; the pale blue silk chemise, thin and short as those in the shop window that he had taken for children's, could not protect from his eyes the beauty that shimmered through it.

At sight of him she forgot her desire to close the window and arrested her movement towards it; she stood in front of him in the soft light of the candle flames, with legs and bare feet pressed together. She was more than naked. Slowly she raised one hand only: it was too small to guard her breast.

Only certain sensitive young souls, too delicate to preserve their sanity in this world, only these and lovers know the tactful sympathy that can build a bridge whereby a person too vulnerably exposed can pass from helpless shame to the calm, blissful certainty that the other's rich, sensitive spirit will not harm him.

That was done by the worship in his face, so that she too could take a step towards him and look in his eyes as they embraced.

Both sank together to their knees, and in their drunken glances was the innocent delight of children at play. For a long time they had to look at each other and smile, look at each other for a whole lifteime and say little silly words, followed by quick short kisses on the cheeks.

Constantine had not yet seen her climb into bed. As she placed her foot on the mattress, the narrow chemise grew taut midway between her precious knee and hip; the other knee also had to bend a little; her finger tips were planted on the bed.

His senses held fast that pose for all time. In it the lines and contours of her body raised a new monument of feminine beauty. Then she let herself sink down, turning to him in the flowing grace of the movement, and as she did so, he was lying beside her.

:

"I've had two letters sent on to me today, one from my mother, the other from a friend." They were climbing up between two vineyards, by the side of a narrow fissure in the rock, through which a trout stream gushed down.

So now he had a mother. That was good; he could do with a mother. Yes, he needed a mother badly, he told Lydia and explained to her, briefly, why.

On his arrival in Berlin, Constantine had applied to the municipal enquiry office in an attempt to discover his mother's whereabouts. There were a great many women in Berlin named Schmitt. Either they were young or very old, small shopkeepers or workmen's widows. Constantine's parents, in their estrangement, had always addressed each other formally, and, since he had heard his mother's Christian name so seldom, he could not remember it; moreover, he knew neither her maiden name nor the date of her birth, so that for the time being his researches had been in vain.

"And who is this friend of yours?"

"His letter contains a proposal of marriage, but he's been in love with me for a long while."

His inside was suddenly filled full of cement; nothing could move; only his head remained clear. "How do you know that?"

"A woman notices such things. Mr. Elliot is an English professor of zoology, but he is working in Italy. In the hot summer months he stays next door to our villa in Zurich, and in the winter too. And he comes in to see us every day."

With the same suddenness everything began to move again and he could joke: "You can give him a new wig for a wedding present."

"Oh, Mr. Elliot is not much older than you. Perhaps thirty-three. . . ."

"I'm twenty-six. But that may be a disadvantage."

"Oh, he's a very good-looking man," she concluded, and stopped. She kissed Constantine's two eyes and, with an outburst of high spirits, kissed him quickly on the mouth and the tip of his nose.

On the third night they left the little town. The car climbed

the hill to the plateau, above which the full disc of the moon
was hanging clear. Woods and fields were of shimmering velvet;
the river flashed in silver from the dreaming valley; the car,
moving silently, was part of the dream; Lydia's head was resting again beside him, the crown touching his lips.

In 1924 everyone traveling in Europe carried all his identification papers with him. The journey to London, the preliminary visit to the registry office, the actual marriage—the fair-
haired official was surprisingly young for his serious calling,
for his lips showed not the faintest trace of down—and the return crossing over the Channel to France, occupied only four
days. They went to Zurich to their mother.

4

In the garden of the Hotel Baur au Lac, an old lady,
wrapped up to the chin in woolen rugs, was lying motionless in
an invalid chair. Her whole face was of a lemon-yellow color,
and her hair had been so thinned by the disease that it scarcely
covered her scalp.

Constantine and Lydia, who had found out where the mother
was staying when they arrived at the villa, had already walked
past her, when the invalid sat up with comparative ease and
cried in a frightened voice: "Lydia!"

Even when she came up to her, Lydia could scarcely recognize her mother. Both were shocked to the marrow, and both
smiled and spoke as though there were no reason to be shocked
at all.

Lydia learned that her mother had suddenly been taken ill
with jaundice six weeks before. "The doctors say I shall be well
again in a week. Quite well! It's not dangerous. You would only
have worried about me unnecessarily."

"Of course it's not dangerous! But you must, you must—"
She could maintain her smile no longer.

"And meanwhile I've had the whole house done up."

She had to introduce Constantine. She had to say something

about him. But not that he was her husband! That was impossible now. He was standing there. What was he thinking of?

"Mr. Constantine Berant. We met in Berlin."

Madame Leskov's womanliness came back to her from far away. "You mustn't look at me while I'm like this. This illness has disfigured me so." She covered her left cheek, which was yellower than the right, with her hand.

"That will go as suddenly as it came," he said, with forced lightness, as though he knew all about it.

Mother and son looked at each other with a smile, and neither felt the slightest twinge of recognition. Eighteen years and colossal changes lay between that glance and the last, when the boy of eight, eager for the journey, had been sitting beside his father in the car.

Lydia was seated two short steps away, learning her care free smile. Constantine looked straight into her eyes. For a few seconds all three were silent. The nurse approached the fateful triangle.

With sudden hot pleasure, which produced a look of fright in her face, Lydia noticed that her mother raised herself unaided, and that her bearing as she sat there was not the bearing of an invalid. The disease was already conquered; the organism was already invigorated.

"But what about us? What are we to do?" They were sitting in the lounge. They had not yet taken rooms.

They decided to remain unmarried even to the hotel staff, to live on different floors, and, on the day they initiated Madame Leskov into the secret, to move to another hotel . . . so that no one here would afterwards discover the true position.

The nurse appeared and asked Lydia to go to her mother.

The inhibitions that sometimes affect the members of a family, who love each other and are yet unable to exchange caresses, were unknown to Lydia and her mother. They kissed each other long and tenderly.

"Who is he? Tell me!"

"Do you like him?"

"You've always thought me stupid, my dear."

"How can you say that?"

"But I'm a woman and have good eyesight."

Lydia saw that there was not a glimmer of fear behind her mother's knowing smile, and proceeded after all according to her well-proven method. The moment was favorable. "I know very well, mother dear, that nothing escapes you. But that— that's impossible."

"How he looked at you just now in the garden! I watched him."

"Mother, we were married yesterday." She snatched at her hand.

The little, self-centered ambition was submerged beneath a great shock. "So suddenly?" she whispered. "So suddenly? . . . And what about me? What about me?"

Under the wild, imploring caresses of Lydia's hands, the look of a timid child dawned on her mother's shocked and frightened face. "He'll love you, dearest, because you bore me! He said so—because you bore me. Oh, how I love him!"

And now it was the mother's turn to stroke Lydia's head, comfortingly, soothingly.

Minutes passed—the nurse had come and gone again—and at last the mother said in quite a satisfied tone: "You're a bad girl. . . . Give me my medicine."

He knew by Lydia's glance and bearing, as she came towards him, that she had told her mother everything. As they walked on she took his arm, and still she said nothing. But her whole body was full of music. Constantine did not ask. His state of mind was that of the lucky man who takes success for granted.

The villa was a long building with eight rooms looking directly towards the lake and the rising sun—four on the mezzanine floor and four on the first floor, where Constantine and Lydia were accommodated—even from the windows at the end of the house the whole length of the lake could be seen, to a point where the shore merged, for the onlooker, into the lower slope of the foothills.

For the first few days Madame Leskov did not leave her room, and Constantine's visits never lasted more than a minute or so, for the convalescent wished to show herself as little as possible on account of her disfigurement.

When, at their first meeting in the hotel garden, Lydia had introduced him by the name of "Constantine," a pale recollection of her little son had arisen in Madame Leskov's mind. At the same moment she had seen a cork go bobbing down a stream, and disappear.

Every time she heard the name "Constantine" from Lydia's lips, she saw this disappearing cork, and gradually her feeling connected it equally with her little son and her son-in-law. The sensation she experienced was slight, insubstantial, with a trace of sadness, and it occupied only a tiny space in her present happiness.

Every morning at seven o'clock, Constantine and Lydia bathed together in the lake. Sometimes Lydia was sitting at a still earlier hour on the diving board, feeding the gulls; and it happened that when Constantine appeared she had swum far out, and he had to bid her good morning in the water. They occupied separate bedrooms.

Marie was serving breakfast on the sunny verandah. Stephan was down below in the garden, standing quite still among the bushes, at his side a young, brown dachshund, the grandchild of the first.

"I must tell you that we have a mole in the garden, and your Herr Stephan has made friends with it. Every morning he takes down some bread. He's a queer fellow! Moles never eat bread, and besides he always takes the dog with him; so you can be quite sure that the mole will not come out for a walk with Herr Stephan!"

They already felt that this man, who combined the staunchness of a true friend with the sensitiveness of a diffident girl, had enriched the happiness of the household with a calm radiance all his own.

Madame Leskov went up to Stephan and picked from his coat a few bits of dandelion fluff that the wind had dropped. "How can you be so untidy?" The two had already made friends. "And I can't allow you to spoil that dog of mine. He'll end by eating himself to death."

The dachshund, standing motionless on its straddling legs, obviously sided with Stephan.

This was the first time that Madame Leskov had come to breakfast on the verandah or shown herself for any considerable time. The yellowness had nearly gone from her skin and her eyes were clear. Constantine had drawn up a chair for her. The lake lay bright under the sun; a strong scent of jasmine came from the garden; not a leaf moved; nothing disturbed the serenity of that morning hour. Lydia was wearing a light, sleeveless dress of flowered silk muslin that lay as light as perfume over her breast and legs.

Her mother had never spoken of her marriage, of her husband and son, and Lydia had never again dared to inquire, after the violent agitation that had seized her mother on the first occasion.

If there was a report in the newspaper of a divorce case, Madame Leskov read it with her eyes, but her consciousness refused to take in anything of the meaning; she might just as well have been holding the paper upside down, with such art did she avoid any subject that might remind her of that break in her life.

It was she who asked Constantine to tell them about his family.

"I can't tell you much that's good," he began. "My father died eleven years ago. My parents were divorced."

Lydia knew that distraught look in her mother's eyes; it could be compared only with that of a young, unfledged bird that has fallen from the nest and cannot save itself from cats or human beings.

And as he thoughtfully went on, telling them that his life would probably have shaped itself quite differently if his parents had not been separated, the mother, though she heard nothing but the words, and did not permit their meaning to enter her mind, became so violently agitated that flecks of color appeared suddenly in her face, and Lydia had lightly to intervene with: "I'd rather you told us about your world tour." A quick glance made the position clear to him.

Madame Leskov did not dream that her weakness of character, which prevented her from squarely facing her misfortune, had saved her that moment from a mortal blow.

Professor Elliot had promised to come to tea at five o'clock. He had only returned a day or so before from Italy, and knew nothing of Lydia's marriage. A tall, fair-haired man with the face of a handsome boy, which yet contained clear traces both of experience and of a hunger for life, he jumped neatly over the box hedge that separated the two gardens.

Lydia introduced them. Laying her hand on Constantine's shoulder, she added lightly and with a smile: "We've been married a week!" Her tone of voice was intended to make it possible for Elliot to preserve his self-possession.

Only by Constantine's tranquil look did he realize that Lydia was not joking. The pleasure of seeing her again died from his face. The blow came so unexpectedly that his eyes and his suddenly lipless mouth failed for a second to hide his jealousy and hate.

But at once he had himself under control again, offered congratulations, smiled, and explained he had come only to tell them that—unfortunately—he could not stay to tea. Lydia accompanied him to the garden gate. He did not speak a word.

And Constantine, who had only that moment realized how certain Elliot had been of winning her love, fingered reflectively the lobe of his ear, a habit of his when a word eluded him at his work.

"He was not quite self-possessed enough," he said, "to go back the way he came—over the hedge." As Lydia returned, he looked inquiringly at her.

"And I might actually have married him. Think of that—I might actually have married him."

"Did you ever promise?"

"Not in words." She regretted the phrase as soon as she had said it, and at the same time she felt in every nerve the joy of triumph at his jealousy.

Elliot ordered his servant to bring a bottle of brandy. The skin of his face, even that of his ears, forehead, and neck, was always of a uniform reddish color, and had that peculiar smoothness one finds in elderly women who are massaged daily. His blue eyes were a little too small, and his handsome mouth,

as he poured out the first glass of cognac, was like that of a boy
who has been unjustly treated.

With dangerous calm he poured out glass after glass, standing
in the middle of the room behind the table, like a barman
consuming his own drinks.

He remained standing for a minute longer, the empty bottle
in his hand, then, holding himself upright by main force,
walked to his bed, let himself fall and was immediately asleep.

Looking out of his window Constantine saw a vermilion
point far away on the lake. That was Lydia's bathing cap. He
had been swimming for some minutes before he reached her,
and then Elliot's wet, fair head bobbed up behind her. Now it
was Constantine's turn to preserve his self-possession, an easier
matter in the lake than on the lawn. At any rate he could swim
further out.

The three of them remained where they were, standing upright and treading water. The whole of Lydia's back was bare,
and the narrow strip in front did not cover her breasts. Thus
she bobbed vertically up and down with a more vigorous movement than was necessary, shining with freshness, and listening
to the formal remarks of the two men. In the water Lydia was
never more than eleven years old.

"Good morning!" Constantine threw himself on his side and
swam further out. She reached him again close to the last buoy,
almost in the middle of the lake. Stephan's hairy body, surprisingly powerful of build—he was swimming back shoreward,
his hands reaching out into space—appeared near the buoy.

He tried to kiss Lydia's hand, but blushed and sank. Stephan
made use of this mishap to come up about ten yards away, and
then disappear again.

"Is this to happen every morning, Lydia?"

"But my dear, we've bathed together for years."

"You're mad. He can see everything, and he loves you."

"That doesn't enter my head, dearest."

"Innocence has its own coquetry, and it's the most dangerous
and provoking."

They were swimming towards the shore, Lydia on her back,

he on his breast, close together, his head level with hers. Like a flash she slipped under him and thus, face to face, they let themselves sink, deep down. The loveliest death! thought Constantine, and held his love embraced under the water.

After lunch Elliot came to drink black coffee on the verandah. And, now that Lydia was dressed, it seemed incredible to Constantine that she had allowed Elliot to see her in her bathing suit. He saw in that fresh-colored, handsome, boyish face the traits of experienced manhood. There was irrepressible passion in the quick glances he gave her, as he thanked her for sugar and cognac, and Constantine's torment was intensified by the gracious manner in which Lydia played the hostess. Evidently she felt very much at ease in that dangerous atmosphere of tension. In honor of the guest they spoke English.

Elliot praised Constantine's command of the language, and forced himself to look appreciatively into his eyes as he did so.

"I was educated in England, at Eton."

The mother's face suddenly changed, as though from far away a hand had passed over it.

For a few seconds Elliot forgot all else in the pleasure of reminiscence. He, too, had been five years at Eton, but probably before Constantine's time. Had little Crook still been a master there? "Every day he used to spend an hour juggling with an empty whisky bottle before he uncorked a second."

"In my time he used to juggle with two empty bottles. . . . But he was the only one we really learnt anything from."

With a practiced movement Elliot emptied his cognac glass. "He's probably juggling with half a dozen empty bottles by now. When Crook gets the sack from Eton, he'll be able to go on the halls."

Madame Leskov, master of the art of forgetting, joined with relief in the laughter.

Stephan came up, with a closely-written sheet of paper in his hand, and asked Constantine to explain a paragraph he could not read. It's not so serious after all, thought Constantine, as he returned to the table and saw that Lydia and Elliot were in the room that opened from the verandah, dancing to the jarring tones of a gramophone.

And how she dances! As though there were nothing in the world more delightful. He thought of those terrible years in Russia. No one had danced there. And even he himself seemed mentally some hundredweights too heavy for it.

Suddenly Lydia stopped. He saw her push the Englishman indignantly from her, saw his distorted face. She went to the gramophone and occupied herself with it till the record was finished.

This is the feeling a man has before he commits murder, thought Constantine, ice cold with fury. Elliot followed Lydia slowly to the table.

Constantine's expression was that of a man prepared for anything, who has thrown off excitement and is calm again. He would not pretend he had not seen what had happened, and Lydia's face concealed nothing. He had never seen her more beautiful.

In her mother's presence, she threw herself, as soon as Elliot had gone, into Constantine's arms, took his head in her two hands and looked into his eyes without speaking.

She never told him what had happened. She bathed no longer in the lake when there was any possibility of meeting Elliot.

Every afternoon between three and half-past four it was Constantine's habit to sit in a cafe on the Limmat and look through a couple of dozen newspapers. And every afternoon the wife of the Turkish diplomat was seated at the table farthest away from him.

She never touched her coffee, never relaxed, never looked at a newspaper or the other visitors: she was aware of nothing but Constantine's presence, and paid for this satisfaction with all the rest of her existence. If his eyes happened to meet hers, she felt constrained to get up and go immediately, lest she should in any way incommode him.

She carried his look, the gift and booty of the day, back through the streets to her hotel, up to her room under the roof, whence she could see the villa in which he lived. Once when she was watching him from a distance, she had seen a street photographer take a snapshot of him as he walked past among other pedestrians. She had purchased the photograph and had it enlarged. There were three framed prints in her room.

Constantine went home through the gardens by the lake. The day was blossoming. A flight of gulls circled inaudibly in front of him. Not a cry. He overtook Madame Leskov. In a sudden flood of tenderness, he put his arm under hers: "Mums!"

That had been his pet name for his mother when he was a boy of eight. "Feeling well?"

Yes, she was feeling well again. The blow, quick and bright as lightning, had struck through the center of her consciousness and was gone as though it had never been. Had he bought the car yet? Not till Constantine had begun to tell her the virtues of the new car he was to try out on the morrow did she feel the pressure that still remained in her breast.

A little later, Madame Leskov was sitting alone on the terrace. The copper beech in the garden stood out black against the evening sky; a last gleam of day still lingered on bush and lake; a bird in the jasmine bush, dazed with scent and sleep, twittered a single note and went on dreaming; the dachshund sat by Madame Leskov, sometimes turning its head to right and left, watching everything intently.

It was one of those soft summer evenings, full of deep self-content, that help men to make their peace with life and with the long path of suffering that lies behind them. She caught sight of Constantine and Lydia in the garden, felt the fulfillment of their happiness as the fulfillment of her own life, and suddenly was able to think this simple thought: My son, too, is a man now.

With gentle, painless melancholy she tried to imagine him as a grown man. She could not; she saw him as a boy of eight. "I wonder where he is now?"

A sense of disquietude forced its way up from unknown depths. She had overrated her strength. And she could not immediately close her inner eye as she had done hitherto, for she had tried for the first time after many years to be reconciled with the past.

The same evening she sent off a cable to the firm her husband

had been connected with in America, to find out his whereabouts and, through him, Constantine's.

The following morning she received an answer. Mr. Schmitt
had died eleven years before. After a few minutes she put
down the telegram with the feelings of a person who enters the
dining room expecting to find on the table the soiled dishes,
glasses, plates and silver, all the disorder of a meal, and is surprised to find a smooth, blank table.

Before the first shock had subsided, the question arose of how
she was to find her son. She had not the smallest clue to work
on; she knew of no living person whom she could ask. Everything was blank, disquietingly blank.

Lydia had difficulty in concealing her surprise at the unac-
customed candor with which her mother informed her of the
contents of the cable; she went on to speak of the past, and to
explain calmly why it seemed almost impossible to discover
Constantine's whereabouts.

The road to disaster was open.

Only a few minutes later Madame Leskov had to take the
first step. Constantine hurried past with a page of manuscript in
his hand: "Good morning, Mums!"

For the fraction of a second—far too long, an eternity too
long—the mother's consciousness was off its guard. This time a
diamond had scratched the word "Mums" on her brain, inefface-
ably. That fraction of time had been long enough for her lips to
open in bewildered astonishment.

A change had come about in Madame Leskov. Her eyes saw
Constantine more sharply, as though the optician had found the
right glasses for her. The little idiosyncracies that cling from
childhood throughout life no longer escaped her. Several times
she caught herself watching him, observing his movements at
meal times, and how he walked and spoke. These observations
were accompanied by remembered details that flashd up from
the distant past, and yet had no connection with the present.

"Tell me, when did Constantine's mother die?" she asked
Stephan in the hall. They had just passed each other. Both
stopped with one foot forward and head and shoulders turned
back.

"She's not dead, Madame. That is to say, we don't know that she is. Most probably Mrs. Schmitt is still living, but hitherto we have failed to discover her whereabouts."

"Schmitt?" she asked of the wall that suddenly rose in front of her. "Schmitt, did you say?"

"Yes. But Constantine doesn't know the date of his mother's birth. In fact he knows nothing about her, he's never seen her since he was a child, and there are so many people called Schmitt in the world. That's the difficulty. But she doesn't seem to be still living in Berlin. Constantine has employed an inquiry agent."

"And she lived in Berlin? In Berlin?" she asked, speaking into the hot darkness within her, and reeled into Stephan's quickly extended arms.

He helped her to a cane chair on the verandah. "That will soon pass in the fresh air." And ran for water.

"And educated at Eton College." Suddenly she thought she saw a mouse flit past, and started up in alarm. The first dark suspicion had quivered through her and was gone again. For a few seconds she completely lost her memory. Not till she saw Constantine embrace Lydia on the stroke of five did she remember her talk with Stephan, and everything came back to her.

Pervaded by a sudden, unaccountable repugnance for Constantine, she stared down at the embraced lovers. The dog raced up to her; she did not notice him; he trotted away again and barked angrily towards the sky.

Constantine and Lydia passed, and called out to her that they were going to fetch the new car. All feeling ebbed out of her; she was not conscious of distress, nor anxiety, nor repugnance; everything in her was lifeless. Thus she sat, her glance resting vacantly where it happened to fall. Gulls were in flight, the clatter of the typewriter came down softly from above, and in the intervals her ear caught the buzzing of flies.

When the car stopped outside the villa, Madam Leskov was still sitting in the cane chair on the glass-roofed verandah. Her attitude was unchanged, her eyes were still fixed on the jasmine bushes, as they had been an hour before.

An alien will raised her from the chair and led her into the room where her husband's letters and the photographs of Constantine as a child were lying in the bureau. It was many years since she had opened that drawer. Resistance was impossible. The same alien will unfastened the blue ribbon. She looked at the childish face, read the few letters the boy had written her from England. Her paralysis was dissolved in tears.

Stephan hurried down the stairs. She heard the car drive off with its three occupants.

"There are so many people called Schmitt in the world." Coincidence! All coincidence! Hope gave her new strength. Life came back to her; she could think again.

She only needed to look up the date of his birth. The sixth of February, 1898. . . . "My papers are upstairs in my writing desk," he had said, when he had to register himself with the authorities, and he had gone up to his study. She could see him going up. She must do that too. She must go up.

On the stairs she was overwhelmed by terror lest she should find proof; she felt the fear of death rise to her heart, and it stopped.

It took her some minutes to reach the study. Then everything happened in a whirl of sudden, wild excitement. Her heart was racing. At last she found the switch, wrenched out the drawer, tore out the writing-case, snatched the papers from it, many papers and letters, but found no birth certificate. Tears of renewed hope burst forth, because there was no birth certificate; then a single, wordless cry rang through the house.

While she screamed, her eyes read: ". . . mind you don't dirty your handkerchief with those silly colored chalks."

It was her own writing. She drew breath and screamed again with all the strength of her lungs. Her mouth was wrenched wide open. The scream broke off; her breath was not exhausted; her eyes stared to right and left: no one was there; her ear listened and caught the sound of the gramophone. In those few seconds she lived only with her head.

With insane cunning she put everything in order, flitted over to the switch, looked once more round the room like a murderess, and switched off the light.

Only to get away! Away! Down the stairs, out of the house with flying haste, on to the road. She dropped down in the grass on the bank of the lake and lay there in a heap. At her side the water was lapping.

The car with Constantine and Lydia glided noiselessly past.

5

That night, long before daybreak, they left for the mountains, taking with them Stephan and a portable typewriter.

Lydia had crept into the dark bedroom; her mother had stared towards her and closed her eyes again, before Lydia reached the bed.

She had to pretend to be asleep; she had to wrest from her mortal anguish one second of simulation; she dared not move nor cry, else with a word she would have slain her child. She dared not tremble.

The car drove off.

Her hand turned the switch: the lamp beside her bed illumined the wreckage of a human face, a gaping mouth, that had been wrenched open by that heavy blow of fate, and could not close again.

Suddenly all her breath was gone; the look in her eyes was no longer human—she saw something incredibly hideous:

A man was leading Lydia up a dirty stone stairway to a room in an infamous hotel. Lydia undressed—she did it like an unsuspecting child. He threw her on the bed.

Suddenly Constantine also was lying in the soiled bed, demanding something of Lydia with a vicious gesture. The other man laughed and his eyes inquired which she preferred, himself or Constantine.

"Not Constantine! Not Constantine!" screamed the mother, and saw, as she lost consciousness, that Lydia did what Constantine demanded.

It was as still as death in the house. The light from the bedside lamp fell on the unconscious woman's lifeless face. Her eyelids lifted; memory tore open her mouth again. She stared at the tangled heap of the two men in the bed. Of her violated child she could see only the white face and the look in her eyes.

The wall beside the bed was covered with filthy stains. A lighted candle stood on the corner of the table. Human limbs were moving fearfully in the bed. Only Lydia did not move; she let it happen; her deathly glance was fixed unflinchingly on her mother, without accusation. For Lydia was already dead; she lived, suffered everything, and was already dead.

The bodies grew rigid and remained immobile, like living statuary in a theatre. The candle lighted up their intertwined limbs. A creature half a yard long, a thick worm with many feet, crawled from between those lewd, embraced bodies, reached the edge of the bed, reared up its head and forelegs into the air, exposing its whitish belly, took hold on the floor and drew its body sinuously after it. The creature left on the bed linen a damp, iridescent track.

Ice crystals formed in the mother's spine. With a cry, choked by her hand's firm pressure on her mouth, she sprang out of bed and flew to the switch. The room grew as bright as day.

On the bedside table were still lying the photographs of Constantine and the letters he had written her from England.

What if Lydia had seen them! Lydia must never know that Constantine is her brother! Her brother! Her brother! Never! She must not! She must not! The mother alone knew it. No one else in the world. She must die; she must die that very day. At once! Then Lydia could never know; she could live and be happy—her innocent, proud child!—always be happy.

There was a glass of water on the table. In the drawer was a little glass tube containing a powerful remedy for insomnia.

There were only two left. That was not enough. Her face grew burning hot. It was not unpleasant. There were flames before her eyes. Then a cool sense of relief rose up her spine to the base of her brain. It is hard to die.

Madame Leskov did not go to the chemist's. She was ready for death, and many ways led to it. The lake was deep—filled with tablets to the brim.

Out of her great readiness for death, out of the quietude of the beyond, which had so completely absorbed all the forces of her life that she seemed to be drawn thither by some alien power, arose the question: What will happen to Lydia when I am gone?

She must tell Lydia. Lydia would die of it. She had to kill her child. For that polluted happiness was worse than death. Then, not till then, would she kill herself, and that man, that accursed stranger, could go on living.

Like a woman who has lost her child, and now, rigid with grief, orders the coffin and the wreath and decides the hour of burial, Madame Leskov forced herself to consider how she could best inform Lydia, how she could best murder her child. There were many possible ways. Hours passed before she went to the telephone.

When the manager of the hotel in Sils-Maria told her that the lady and the two gentlemen had gone out for a walk and would not be back before lunch, she remained sitting motionless for long, dark hours before the telephone, hours that belonged to death and yet had to be lived.

It was a wonderful summer morning, not a blade of grass was stirring and the sunshine lay radiant on the mountains in their remote tranquility. As Constantine and Lydia walked through the scented pine forests, they had a feeling of standing on the highest point of the earth, and were completely sure of their happiness.

Their skin prickled as they came back to lunch; the strong air had made them ravenously hungry. It was natural that Lydia should go up at once to change her dress, and so Constantine went to the telephone in her place.

"Is that you, Lydia?"

He knew by the intonation that something extraordinary had happened. It was the voice of one who had sustained a heavy blow and was speaking for the first time after hours of silence; it came hoarsely out of the throat.

The mother gave no explanation of why Lydia was to return immediately; she answered Constantine's question with a sinister, threatening cry: "At once!" And rang off.

That was not Lydia's mother as he knew her. Something had happened to change her, fundamentally.

Constantine had known for a long time that if anything serious ever happened to Madame Leskov the mutual pathologically exaggerated affection of mother and daughter would produce the greatest danger for Lydia.

And now it had come: the mother had hitherto concealed from her daughter every trouble and illness; now she had dropped all consideration and demanded Lydia's immediate return.

Just as once, in the hotel in Unter den Linden, he had drawn a close circle of spies round Lydia, so now he bound the telephonist, the page and the manager to secrecy and silence, asked Stephan to take to his bed on the pretense of illness and lied to Lydia. He told her that unfortunately he would have to go back himself to obtain one or two indispensable reference books from the university library.

In the train he asked himself which doctors he should summon, from Zurich, Berlin, Paris, and how he could raise Lydia above the disaster that certainly lay before them. He arrived in Zurich with every nerve taut and, suspecting nothing, sent in his name to the mother. The waves of catastrophe closed over him.

She was sitting in the little Louis-Seize boudoir. There were three chairs, an armchair and a little corner cabinet. The curtains were drawn across the window that faced over the flood of sunshine on the lake. The electric light had been switched on since the previous night.

As usual, Madame Leskov was wearing a black dress. Her face was yellowish-white, sunken and yet tense. Her mouth and general expression were changed; her eyes were greatly enlarged.

She had expected Lydia. She had been prepared to meet her. The few words that had to be spoken to Lydia were graven unalterably on what remained of her emotional life, as on a gramophone record.

The inner life of a dying man or woman moves slowly.

Now she would have to live another day and speak first to this detested man.

Constantine entered. A wave of relief shot through him. She was not in bed. She could not be seriously ill. Had she lost all her money? That was nothing: he was rich. He would invent the most beautiful and least transparent of deceptions, say that by skillful manipulation he had retrieved her lost fortune, even increased it. Increased it! "Good afternoon, Mums!"

"Sit down." Only a mortal enemy who has brought innocent souls to ruin would be received with such coldness and contempt.

Without emphasis, as though she were merely carrying out a formality: "You lived on the Lutzowufer in Berlin till you were eight. Before your adoption, your name was Schmitt. My name was Schmitt, too, by marriage, but after the divorce I took my maiden name again. My husband was a German-American. Your father was a German-American. You had a sister six years younger than yourself."

"Yes. But, Mums, why are you talking to me like this?"

She had no energy left for hatred or disgust; she needed her strength to die and to take Lydia with her to her death.

"You told us yourself that you were educated in England from the age of nine to fourteen, at Eton, and then went to Russia to your father."

"My father died on the seventeenth of July, 1914," he said, in the tone of an innocent man who is willing to give all the information he has.

"I know." She pointed to the table: "There are the letters you wrote to your mother from England."

Still he suspected nothing. How could he? How could he see in the withered hand of his companion the knife that was about to cut his throat?

"Those letters were written to me."

Perhaps as his heart stopped, the blood stopped flowing in the arteries of his brain. He saw a phantom of mist.

With the same deadly calm as before: "Lydia is your sister."

It came from too far away, came from beyond the conceivable limits of the world. It took time.

Constantine laid his hand on his heart. His brain grew freer, regained the power of thinking and sent the first thought into his consciousness.

He clung to a hope that was a hope no longer. He asked:

"When you came into the nursery . . ." —It was no longer Constantine's voice— ". . . on the right . . . was Lydia's bed in the corner? . . . With a blue quilt?"

Not even the eyelids quivered above the fixed, staring eyes of the mother.

"And was my bed on the left, by the window? . . . My paint brushes in the cloisonné vase on the table? . . . Answer me! . . . Did little Lydia always have a gold thread before she went to sleep, tied round over her nightdress?"

The eyelids moved now; the head nodded.

"Because she wouldn't sleep without it." Even now a feeling of tenderness shot through him for his beloved. "We used to call her Schönchen. Well . . . is that true?"

"It is true."

His body drooped forward very slowly.

When the mother looked up, to say that Lydia must return at once, Constantine was no longer in the room.

He had no recollection of how and when he had left the room and descended the stairs. That was unpleasant. He had certainly been upstairs in the little Louis-Seize boudoir, and now he was standing on the glass-roofed verandah! In front of him the garden and the lake; church spires in the distance. How had he got down here on the verandah? Puzzling! It was as though he had ceased for a few minutes to exist!

As though walking in a dream, he entered the drawing room. Then it came back to him with the speed of lightning: the instant he saw the cloisonné vase beside Lydia's photograph on the table, the vase he had used seventeen years before to stand his paint brushes in, his memory returned with terrific force. From that time there was no possibility of eluding it.

"Sister?" He could take no account of that. He could not, even if he would. It was utterly beyond his power. Die?—Yes. But live?—Only with her!

At first it was only his head that made the decision.

Constantine was young, clean and courageous, and he wanted to live.

He must fight. His love for Lydia could not die. He saw her before him in all her splendor. She walked triumphantly into his open heart.

And into the broad, deep stream of his love for Lydia, there trickled unaware and uncontrolled a thin, new, perilously sweet feeling towards the sister and wife.

Here were the two of them, and there was the world. As years ago! Now they must fight for their happiness, which had been perhaps too great and too easily won.

Constantine asked himself immediately who in the world there was who could find out that he and Lydia were brother and sister. Only their mother knew. And danger could only come from the agency he had commissioned to search for his mother and sister. He wrote to the agent at once, telling him to stop his investigations, saying he had received official information that both had perished in the revolutionary upheavals shortly after the end of the war. He went hot and cold as he wrote it though he was not superstitious.

He left the house to post the letter. Now there were no foes to be vanquished but internal foes, in his mother and in Lydia. In himself also? Nothing could stop him going through life as before, with Lydia. Nothing on earth!

At the station, Constantine telephoned to the villa and left a message for his mother that he was returning to Sils-Maria. He boarded the train with the knowledge that he was going to the fight of his life, a fight that must be won, either at the first blow or after years of struggle. Everything was at stake.

Madame Leskov made no answer to Constantine's message. The idea had occurred to her, coming as it were from her former life, that she should telephone to Lydia and tell her everything before Constantine arrived. She did not do it; there could be no question here of forestalling, of tactics; one does not set an avalanche in motion by talking on the telephone; it comes down in obedience to its own law and sweeps all things with it.

Constantine's thoughts were also of a high order that excluded tactics, but they sprang from the contrary pole: his goal was life.

He must be calm. Before he arrived, he must absorb the fact that Lydia was his sister into the quiet stream of his emotional life, so that he could freely control it in his resolute fight for happiness.

Thus steadied, he drove from the station to the hotel, calm in the strength of his soul. When he reached his room fear leapt up in his throat. He sat down at the table before Lydia's photograph. Her grave beauty, that yet knew how to smile, her nobility entered into his heart. He sent word to Lydia that he was there.

She came out on to the balcony that connected her room with his, and looked in at him through the open window. She had stood there many times during their brief separation, listening motionless to the throbbing desire of her heart. The room had been empty.

Now he was sitting at the table, his head in his hands, looking intently at her picture. Never had her emotion, her joy over a proof of love, been greater than in this gratuitous moment, when the rapt lover believed himself unseen.

She used a word that women often use without thought or feeling, she whispered: "My husband." And again: "My husband."

Now Lydia's eyes grew black and that unfulfillable request arose in them. "Tell me how I am to tell you. My Constantine, how am I to tell you?"

Her expectant eyes were sunk in his as she placed her thin middle finger to her breast, where the explosive pressure was contained. "How?"

Constantine knew that gesture. He made a helpless effort to find relief for himself and her; he said what all lovers say: "More than everything in the world, more than my life!"

She slowly repeated his words, listening greedily to herself: "More than everything in the world, Constantine; I love you more than my life. . . ."

"But that's not enough, my Constantine, that's not enough,"

she said, and again tapped with outstretched middle finger on her breast. "In there! How shall I tell you?"

A breath of subtle guile slipped out between her parted teeth to the corners of her mouth. For now he must not only find for her the magic phrase she would have to repeat, but simultaneously he must tell her how much he loved her. And she could never tire of hearing it.

But he could not find the words no lover on earth has ever found. He said: "I need my whole life to show you how much I love you."

Her face grew soft and contourless: "I will be shameless, if you want that as a proof. What shall I do? For you?"

That—yes, from her that would be the greatest proof of love. She waited.

Then he asked something; he said it quite slowly.

Even as he spoke her feminine pride crumpled. Then her high spirit, the limitlessness of her love, had conquered. She did it for him; she did what he had asked, exposed to his eyes.

As she reeled abashed into his arms, seeking safety on his breast, he was seized with pity. Constantine was modest, like all real men and women, and proud to be the object of her great love.

At the caressing touch of his hand, she felt his emotion and his happiness. Gladdened by the knowledge that she could trust him, whatever she might do, she retrieved from his quiet eyes the pride she had offered up to him.

But she had been picked out by chance and fate, he thought, to give another, final, unique proof of her love. What will happen when I tell her? Will her love die in hatred and disgust, will it change into horror, or will it stand firm and enter into the infinite? Is her love stronger than all else on earth? What will happen to my Lydia? What would happen to her if I told her now that she's my sister? His feelings posed the question, still under the impress of what she had done for him a minute before, done in defiance of all shame.

Hitherto he had been convinced that he knew Lydia as he knew himself. He had always known, even in the strangest and rarest situations, what she would do; he had often amused himself and her by anticipating her answers before she could open her lips, giving them word for word and with the most delicate intonations of her voice; and now he did not know whether she would say at once: Brother and sister? What is that to me? Those are words, a mere nothing compared with my love. Or whether, stricken to death like her mother, she would sink, immediately and unresistingly, into the black, engulfing swamp?

Perhaps he ought to prepare her carefully weeks ahead, test her, and find out what opinions she had about the love of brother and sister, without letting her know that she was personally involved. Should he tell her some fictitious story and ask what she would do in the woman's place? . . . In any case he needed time. He had to be alone with her, quite alone! Safe from discovery! Their mother might telephone again at any moment, or tomorrow she might walk into the room.

Lydia turned round to him: "All this time I've been wondering why you are so quiet, and I can't find the reason. How strange!"

"I have a proposal to make."

"We'll do it," she said eagerly, with light hands placing the waves of her hair in position.

"We'll go on a motoring tour and spend the nights wherever it happens to suit us."

"That will be splendid. . . . We'll spend the nights, you and I—Constantine, don't you think that things are going a bit too well with us? . . . You are very happy too! I know it."

"Because I have you, Lydia, you!"

"Is it always like this, do you think?—Oh, Constantine!"

He sent Stephan back to Zurich with instructions to spend the next few weeks collecting data for his second volume.

Perhaps it would never be written. The struggle might end fatally. For Constantine there were only two alternatives: to live with Lydia as before, or to die with her.

6

They were independent of time and space. The direction
and goal of each day's journey were decided entirely by the
state of the roads. Only the European motoring handbook,
which gives the best roads of the continent, knew where they
were at any given time. No news could reach them. The whole
of Europe had become Robinson Crusoe's Island. They were
untraceable.

They sped past the great, luxurious hotels. Lydia was amazed
at Constantine's appetite for romance. At sunset he was drawn
to lonely farmsteads, or he managed to find a mill in a remote
forest vale, where there was no telephone and the hand-woven
linen in the beds, compared with Lydia's smooth, silken skin,
was as rough as a file.

"Better than sleeping in the woods," said Lydia, with well-
acted reluctance, when the farmer confessed he had only one
spare bed.

Every day she sent several cards to Zurich; they flew into the
hands of her mother like bright, strange birds. The mother saw
by the postmarks where Lydia had been a day before, and she
knew from the few written words that her child was still happy,
still unsuspecting.

This pile of picture postcards contained the record of Lydia's
wifely happiness, which for her mother was naked horror. She
lived in a pit, full of ghastly thoughts, from which she could not
escape for a second either by day or during the long, long
nights.

She was powerless. She could live no longer and she could not
yet die.

The fear of dying before she had enlightened her daughter
caused her now and then to choke down a scrap of food, but it
changed into a worm and crawled back up her throat. For her,
the physical union of those two signified the most dreadful and
irreparable violation of Lydia that was possible on earth.

The weeks flew past in an intoxication of love. Constantine's
position was like that of a poor man who, by a caprice of fate, is

allowed to live for a short time as a spendthrift millionaire, and greedily takes from life whatever he can grasp, before the hand of poverty seizes him again. That was a dangerous condition, and Constantine knew it.

He intended, when they reached Trieste, to put into execution his last and most dangerous plan for the preparation of Lydia. In half an hour they would be there. He had invented a fictitious report of the proceedings in a criminal prosecution and had had it distributed to the Trieste newspapers by a news agency, ostensibly as an actual record of fact.

"This time I should like to go to the best hotel. I want a good wide bed and a porcelain bath. Perhaps we shall stay a day or two in Trieste, then at last I shall be able to write mother a long letter, and we can wait for her answer. I want to know how she's getting on. I shan't trouble to telegraph; she's had enough telegrams lately."

He straightened himself and diminished the speed of the car. "Good! We'll stay in Trieste till you get an answer from your mother!"

The car took the last rise and reached the heights above the town. He switched off his headlights. The thousand points of light that lay below in the clear blue of the night were the town and the sea. They could not tell where the houses ended and the sea and the harbor began, with the lights of ships: a glittering gem on blue velvet.

"Beautiful!" said Lydia. "There are stars down there. Like the sky on the earth."

"Very beautiful!" . . . Down there it would happen to her. Strange how cool he felt! And yet his heart was so heavy!

Presently Lydia said to herself with gentle melancholy: "My ship is gliding into a valley and there I must be alone."

He caught her words above the noise of the car. He was entirely absorbed in what he had to say to her and, in sympathy with her mood, which coincided exactly with his own and was clearly expressed in the tone of her voice, he suddenly thought she suspected what lay before her. "You must be alone?"

"Alone for a long time!" Lydia felt that she was a mother; she had conceived in that first night of love.

"Why alone, my Lydia, why?"

"I can't tell you."

There was nothing to be seen as yet, and Lydia had wrested from herself the decision not to allow him to see her when she began to lose her figure. Before that he should know nothing.

The car had nearly stopped. "Is there something you can't tell me, Lydia? Can't you tell me?" At that she looked at him calmly; her look was detached from her secret, though it completely filled her. The first time she had not been with him entirely.

An hour later they were sitting in the open air, bathed and changed, drinking coffee. A band was playing in the square and crowds of people were abroad. The smell of the sea filled the warm air.

A newsboy came; many people purchased his papers, and Constantine also placed a coin on the table. He was as calm as though a beloved hand was laid upon his eyes.

An old Italian woman went past among the dapper officers and the dark-skinned girls. On her arm her grandchild was sitting up straight of its own accord, cheerfully waving its hands, and yet was no bigger than an infant at the breast.

Lydia held her breath in sudden fear. "How small the child is, how terribly small!"

"The Italians are small as a race," said Constantine. He was a practiced reader of newspapers; at the first glance he had found his fictitious story. Calmly he handed Lydia the law reports, and began to read the stock markets.

LET HIM THAT IS WITHOUT SIN AMONG YOU—

A young workman and his sister appeared in Court yesterday, at the little German town of Merzburg, on a charge of incestuous intercourse. During the hearing of the case the following facts came to light: The mother, a domestic servant, was compelled to put out her illegitimate son to nurse immediately after his birth, and for years was unable to take care of the child. After her marriage to the child's father—she had meanwhile borne a second child, a girl—she brought back the son to live with them. The two children were inseparable from the beginning, and grew up together in the deepest affection.

Later their love assumed an erotic form, and when this came to the notice of the father, he turned the son out of the house. As these two could not bear to separate and saw no possibility of ever again living together, they resolved to take their lives in a wood outside the town. The revolver failed to act. They returned to the town and bought another revolver. Meanwhile the girl's flight had been discovered, the police searched the wood and were in time to prevent the deed by force.

The Judge was so impressed by the simplicity with which the two accused spoke of their love that he reduced the penalty to the legal minimum, and sentenced them only to two months' imprisonment.

"How sad that is! Have you read it?" She handed him the paper.

"Yes." His heart was beating faster now.

"Do you believe it really happened?"

"At least it might have happened. Sexual relations between brothers and sisters are much more frequent than people think. But generally they are very unpleasant cases, purely physical, caused by external conditions, excessive poverty and overcrowding."

"But it seems to be very different with these two people. For many years there was a deep, spiritual bond between them, a deep and tender love such as there should always be between the children of the same parents, though that seldom happens, and the physical desire grew up on that foundation. That seems really quite simple, quite natural . . . But perhaps there are other, unknown elements—strange and dreadful things—"

That was the truth as Lydia felt it. He could see it in her face. It was true that a dark residue remained unsolved. But perhaps with his help she could overcome it, when all their happiness was at stake. Now that the terrific tension had suddenly relaxed, and hope came mightily back to him, he felt the load he had been carrying in the last few weeks.

"What will this brother and sister do when they come out of prison?"

Lydia answered immediately and without reflection: "They must go abroad, to some place where no one knows them."

"Yes, and then? What then?" He looked at her.

". . . I don't know. They are brother and sister. . . . But they wanted to die! And therefore I think—I think they should be allowed to live together!" And as if in defense of her opinion, she added quickly: "For this girl, her brother is the dearest of men, the only man in the world. And she is the same for him. They love each other. . . . I am sorry for those two. What are they to do?"

He was satisfied with the turn Lydia had given to the conversation. She would remember those poor folk, for their fate had touched her heart; she was no longer quite unprepared. He did not dare to say more that evening.

But on the following morning, shortly before seven o'clock, the chambermaid rushed, without knocking, into Constantine's room, which was separated by the bathroom from Lydia's suite. Madame had fainted; she was lying on the carpet.

The evening before, Lydia had been alone for a few moments while she was changing her frock, and had dictated on the telephone a telegram to her mother, giving the name of the hotel at which they were staying. This was contrary to her previous intention. That morning, about a quarter to seven, she had received almost simultaneously a telegraphic reply and a telephone call from Zurich.

Constantine knew both these facts the moment he entered. The telegram lay half under the bed, the telephone receiver was dangling by the cord and still gently swaying.

Lydia was lying half naked. He drew her dressing gown across her, shyly and carefully as though he were a stranger, and stood up. He did not touch her again; he did not disturb the benefaction of unconsciousness.

She would wake, and then destruction would spread of itself, or a new life.

A heavy calm was within him: a still, ripe preparedness for death; nothing else could possibly conquer fate.

Her eyelids lifted as though she were awaking from sleep. There was no other movement. Her eyes, fixed upon him, were rigid and strange as though she looked out of another life.

Then consciousness struck down to her emotions, with tremendous force. In a flash she started up to a sitting posture, her hands planted on the floor behind her, unbounded horror in her eyes. Groping backward in the same attitude, she moved away from him with convulsive spasms that ran through her whole body; her horrified retreating glance was fixed unwaveringly on him, and she screamed, screamed with all the force of her lungs.

He understood: "Go, go!"

Suddenly she leapt to her feet and fled down the length of the room. Pressed into a corner, both hands thrown up to her face: "Go!" Her voice broke.

Confronted with this last degree of horror, he had nothing to say. His head sank down and he went slowly, with bent back, towards the door.

Reeling, Lydia collapsed, dropped on her knees and toppled forward unconscious. Her forehead struck hard against the floor.

Now it was possible: he could go and pick her up, lay her on the bed, a wet towel round her brows—no, first stroke back the hair from her forehead, then the wet towel—and sit down. His actions followed his thoughts automatically.

She opened her eyes again and saw him, but did nothing and spoke not a word. He moved further away, so that she could not see him, and watched her.

Nothing happened. The minutes passed, inserted between death and life, minutes in which fate took possession of their existence.

He saw that she was not thinking or feeling or suffering. Her eyes were open. She turned to the wall like someone who is alone in a room.

He remained crouching there.

Her body moved a little sometimes. She was unaware of it.

Nothing was in the room, nothing moved there. Stillness of death. No living thing. There was no will in the room.

Lydia was as though torn in two by exhaustion. Nothing mattered—less than that: she could not even feel that nothing mattered. A brown buzzing!

But her body was young and healthy; it emerged victorious

from the conflict between itself and the exhausted mind; it began to negotiate with her. The brown buzzing stopped.

One black, silky lock hung over the middle of her forehead, curled round the bridge of her nose and down to the corner of her mouth. The shining, finely-curled tip moved with her breathing.

Her hand stroked back the lock of hair; as it did so her eyelids fluttered, she took a deeper breath, her tongue moistened her lips, her hand passed with a stroking movement down her cheek, and dropped on the bed. With this series of connected movements she took a step back into life.

Lydia let herself sink slowly down on to the pillow—the movement was evidently quite conscious—and looked at the ceiling. She did not hide her bare arms; she only drew the lace edge of her nightdress over her slightly exposed breast. She would have done the same even if Constantine had still been her lover.

Can a deep and true love fade in a quarter of an hour, die, be cauterized out of the heart? What joy if she would only despise him! Then he could fight; his love would give him words. But Lydia left no loophole open for him; she did not oppose him.

Man grows greater by his fate, even if it kills him, and still greater when he endures it. Constantine took leave of happiness. Something crystallized in his breast, a feeling subject to laws of its own, beyond all hope and speculation. He would wait, unswerving, joyless, hopeless, yet ever prepared. Even if he had to wait for years and years! That was to be his life.

Compassion seized him for his exhausted love, for he saw her black eyelashes sink and nestle softly into the dark-brown half circles beneath her eyes. Her lids still quivered as the sleep of exhaustion drew near. He breathed in rhythm with her breathing, so that no contrary motion should hinder the approach of sleep.

And when he had thus breathed her to sleep, and the shadow of dream passed over her brow, he no longer allowed himself to sit by the bed, looking at the absent one. He assumed no rights that he did not possess.

Hours passed. The events of the last few weeks, from the moment when his mother had told him everything, circled round him, first as an inextricable chaos of images. Gradually they cleared, to reveal the fact, which had to be faced and accepted, that Lydia had no longer the faintest interest in him. He stared numbly at the white wall.

When the first sound reached his ears, he got up. But as he entered the room, he found Lydia already dressed and with her hair done. Even the coverlet of the bed had been smoothed. She must have been up at least half an hour. So deep had been his absorption.

Her glance brushed past him. She looked away immediately and began to put her toilet table in order, obviously without thinking, merely to collect herself. Once more a glance of the deepest bewilderment fell on him. But this was no longer the Lydia who had lain on the bed exhausted and indifferent. With the vitality that time and sleep had given her, the woman had arisen within her, the woman who loved—more than anything in the world, more than her own life—her husband, who was her brother.

That morning she had been vanquished by a surprise attack of fate, and had paid the penalty with exhaustion to the point of swooning, and with a mental derangement that had lasted for minutes.

But now the fight began, violent, agonizing, heart-oppressive, the fight in which she might prove that her love was stronger than fate—the very proof she had longed for the night before.

He saw all this at once by the line of her back, her bearing, the way she stood before the dressing table, inactive, her head bent a little to one side. This time his tears burst through the dam that he had built against their sudden pressure.

Hope and gladness overwhelmed him. He was in the position of a man surprised by joy, who had thought his beloved dead and finds her alive. This apparently impossible turn of events filled him with such tempestous hope that for a moment he thought he had already won the battle that was only just beginning.

That sudden resurgence of hope carried him too far forward.

He said, in the tone that had formerly so deeply enraptured her: "Lydia! My Lydia!"

That was enough to revive with terrible force the conflict of feelings within her. She turned round, again with that helpless inner recoil, and had to support herself with her hands on the edge of the table. A look, a facial expression, say more than words can say.

"Back! Back!" he whispered to himself, and instinctively retreated across the room. Then, as he approached her again and placed a chair for her, to step back immediately to the further wall, it was clear that the act was not one of intimacy but of common consideration, such as anyone may pay to another. Nevertheless, she took another chair.

She was not accusing him, he could see that. There was no hatred and no reproach. She held to the kernel of the matter. While she was dressing she had thought it all out and, like a good doctor who wants to be on the safe side, she had first excluded everything that could be excluded.

For her, love contained no inhibitions of a moral nature; for her the law that forbids and penalizes incest did not exist. But if it had come to that—what happiness it would have been to lie in prison and to be at one in heart with her lover, like the couple she had read of in the newspaper! Those were not the obstacles she would have had to remove.

Lydia did not know, did not know what it was: it was there inside her, possessed of exceeding great power, and she had no access to it. The idea of giving herself to her brother, bodily, was inconceivably repulsive, and the idea of never again giving herself to her lover was unthinkable, it was death. The two powers stood arrayed against each other, equipped with the same power and strength.

"Everything is the same for us, Lydia—just the same. You are a woman and I am your lover . . . Lydia, come to yourself again! It is nothing."

But his words did not reach her.

Despair gave him an idea. "We could begin again from the beginning. Let us do it. We've just arrived here and only got to know each other on the way. We've just found out who we are.

We have meals and go for walks together. I accompany you when you go shopping. Perhaps we take a steamer trip. We talk of all sorts of things. Gradually we get to know each other better. Of course we'd be nothing more than friends—the rest generally takes time. And of course I make love to you a little, look at you sometimes. Perhaps that's not unwelcome, later, when you're better acquainted with me and know what sort of man I am. Time can do so much. Perhaps you take me as your lover, perhaps! . . . But that would be all in the future, far ahead! We've only just made each other's acquaintance."

It was his despair and helplessness that made him hope this proposal was practicable.

Lydia heard every word. Her ear heard. An extraordinary idea had entered her mind: You can't moor a steamship to a cork bobbing on the waves.

And yet, in the hours that followed, as they did not separate, their companionship had to take on the outer form of his proposal. Two strangers, well-dressed and distinguished, walked through the streets of Trieste, sat down in a café, did not touch what the waiter brought, and scarcely ever spoke. It was hard to come nearer to a woman, when one can say everything to her but this: You are beautiful.

It was the first time they had been for a walk as brother and sister. And it differed from their previous walks, when the happiness of each had communicated itself to the other as a constant flashing movement to and fro, like the invisible shuttle of a sewing machine that provides the thread and fastens stuff to stuff. Neither was it the sort of walk a man takes, when he has met a pretty woman on a journey and, arrived at their destination, strolls through the streets with her, courting her favors— as Constantine, in his helplessness, had proposed.

Later, Lydia remembered exactly and in the smallest detail the street corner where she resolved to escape from him in secret, so that she could be alone with her inevitable fate: the three little scratched tables on the pavement, and the waiter just lifting a blue siphon, with his thumb on the lever. The same second that the thirsty customer raised his glass to the siphon, the fact became clear in her mind that it would be senseless and impossible to stay with Constantine any longer. She must go away, secretly, and remain in hiding, if she were to gain the only boon that still remained open to her: indifference to everything.

Back in the hotel, it was he who brought the soporific that should send her to sleep. In his presence, she put it in her mouth, but did not swallow it. She lay down and he went to his room. The bathroom was between them. She got up at once—in a few minutes her cabin-trunk was packed—bought a ticket for Berlin at the travel bureau in the hotel, and twenty minutes later was sitting in the moving train.

She was correct in assuming that Constantine would have no difficulty in finding out her destination at the hotel. The next train for Berlin left in the evening. She traveled only as far as the frontier and then changed into a train that was returning to Trieste.

In Trieste she went straight from the train to the boat, and so to an island in the Adriatic.

7

Without a word of preparation, her mother had told Lydia everything by telephone, through the noises of the world's life, in a tone of voice as though both had been swallowed up by an earthquake and were buried so deep that nothing but death was possible.

Sitting at the telephone in Zurich, she had heard the effect her words had produced in Trieste, up to Lydia's scream before she fainted. Her last duty was done. Lydia would die. Perhaps she was already dead. The mother was old. She had not been united with Constantine in happy love. Death for her was a matter of course.

Her suicide ended a life of painful unrest, of continual waiting for a happiness that was always in the future. The moment one of her hopes was realized, its reality was of no value to her, and it was immediately superseded by a new hope that lay in the future. She had never possessed the present. She had never been happy and content. Happiness is a quality of the mind.

Lydia owned the fact that she had not been caught and destroyed by this constantly grinding mill of needless suffering entirely to the rare strength of her spirit, which alone had enabled her, as a girl of eleven, to see the lights and shades of life, to keep them apart, and with delicately tactful superiority to play the mother to her mother.

Everyone dies as he has lived. The mother, who could not distinguish spinach from lettuce and yet wished to be a good cook and even believed she was one; this woman, who all her life had left her real and valuable qualities unused, who had always forgotten in the trivial cares of the hour the things of incomparably greater moment, was capable, just before she died, of forgetting even death itself, in her vain efforts to get the tablets out of the tube.

She could not remove the wad of cotton wool; the idea of using a matchstick or a hairpin did not occur to her; she could not reach it with her fingernail. She looked round for some hard object with which to break the glass, and when she succeeded in smashing it with a flower vase, she forgot all else in a feeling of satisfaction. She died as she had lived.

At the same time Constantine was arriving in Berlin. When he left the station and entered the busy square outside, to drive to his hotel, he felt that Lydia was not in Berlin. He felt it. And three days later he knew it, for he had inquired in vain at every police station where the registration forms of travelers are sent on their arrival.

If Constantine had left Berlin to the north or south, to the east or west, his prospect of success would have been just as great and just as little. Not knowing what to do, he went to Zurich, though he knew he was less likely to discover anything there of Lydia's whereabouts than in any other town in the world. For she, too, would know that he would go to Zurich to try to find out where she was. But there he could visit places pregnant with memories, places where he had been with Lydia. He found a corpse.

When he came back from the funeral, he wandered through the orphaned rooms, aimlessly, to and fro; sat down in a chair, stared in front of him, full of bitterness because he had broken

into that house as a destroyer, a messenger of fate, driven the
mother to her death and Lydia to a gulf of suffering that was
somewhere in the world, but undiscoverable. And it became
clear to him that nothing but the love that bound him and
Lydia together, that eternal, inscrutable mystery of the heart,
could stand in opposition to fate in their struggle for life and
happiness. He himself could do nothing more, nothing! He
could only wait to see whether love would conquer in Lydia too.
He would wait. Even if he had to wait a lifetime!

And yet he could not wait a minute. Restlessness drove him
day and night, drove him out of the house and away from
Zurich, through the health resorts of Europe, where at least a
millionth chance might aid him in his search for her.

It happened that he met people in Egypt whom he had met
weeks before in Nice. In Ostend he saw the wife of the Turkish
diplomat. The headwaiter told him, unasked, that she had an
affair with a professional dancing partner at the hotel. There
was nothing unusual in that; but it was remarkable for a
woman of such unusual beauty and charm, who obviously
belonged to the best society, to show it so openly, before all the
guests in the hotel. The manager would give the dancer notice.
He was there for all the ladies.

That was the last meeting of Constantine and the woman
from Saxony. He never saw her again.

Once more his consuming restlessness drove him forth
through the winter resorts of Europe. He came back crushed,
with broken nerves. On the bedside table lay a revolver.

One evening, a few minutes after the letters had come, Lydia's maid asked if she might go home for a week to St. Gallen.
When he nodded, she packed a weekend case, according to
Lydia's instructions, and half an hour later bought a ticket and
booked a place in the sleeping car. She traveled to Trieste, and
thence by steamer to the island in the Adriatic.

The letter to her maid had been handed by Lydia to the
captain of a ship bound for Shanghai, with the request that
he post it when he got there. As a further safeguard, she had
written that her peace of mind depended on Marie's silence.

She relied on the fact that her maid was a woman and would take the woman's part, though, in fact, Marie could scarcely bring herself to leave Constantine to his poisonous impotence.

The image of the tortured man still pursued her in her sleep: She was standing behind the counter of a baker's shop, between mountains of fresh bread. He came in, thin, with sunken cheeks, on the verge of starvation, and, with his lipless mouth bitten tight, asked for a loaf. She refused him without a word. But when he raised his revolver to his wasted brow, she gave him a loaf. The loaf changed into Lydia's letter, and she shouted quickly: "Eat it! It's still warm!" But he fired.

She started up and listened, terrified, to an abruptly ending report: the train had passed over a railway bridge.

She could sleep no longer. Marie was a courageous girl, unprejudiced, and the necessary things of life arranged themselves simply and clearly in her mind and heart. But she, too, knew the anxiety and excess of Lydia's love for her mother. With the sympathy of her loyal heart, she asked herself in what way she could break to Lydia the news of her mother's death. She could not find an answer. Ten times she experienced Lydia's wild sorrow in advance. So the night passed.

Marie and the servants did not know that Madame Leskov had taken her life. "A stroke"—that is what Stephan and the doctor had agreed to say, so that Lydia should have no grounds for self-reproach, for thinking that her mother had committed suicide in a deep fit of depression over their long separation.

Only members of that cosmopolitan class who, despite their wealth, have still retained some feeling for harmony and quietude, visited this island. Marie was met by an Italian girl of ten, who led her far away from the hotel to the only private villa in the island, which stood on the farther side, hidden behind a little forest of bamboos, looking out to the open sea.

The sea was silent. A broad line of fire, as though drawn by Nature with a great ruler, joined the shore to the horizon, which was just touched by the setting sun. To right and left of this path the sea and the island lay in dark-green peace.

Lydia rose without effort from the deckchair on the cliff. The

slow, long-drawn perfection of her movements was due rather
to the load on her spirit than to the physical change caused by
the advanced stage of pregnancy.

Lydia's beauty was ennobled and intensified by suffering.
She still endured the unendurable in silence. Thus stood the
battle in which, every day and every hour, she came nearer to
death, while in her womb was growing a new life.

As a continent cannot overcome the natural law by which
after high day it sinks into night, so Lydia could not overcome
the horror, profoundly connected with the idea that she had
been her brother's mistress. Yet she still struggled; for love,
too, was not to be overcome.

The shock Marie experienced at sight of Lydia gave place
immediately to pain at the thought of adding to her suffering
by telling her of her mother's death. She could not strike the
note of intimacy; she talked so much and so confusedly of unimportant domestic matters, without saying a word of Madame
Leskov's condition, that Lydia, with the sharpened instinct of
one accustomed to sorrow, divined the answer to her question
before she asked it.

She sat down at the table beside her maid. "What has happened, Marie?"

And as the girl dropped her head on her arms and burst into
tears:

"Is my mother dead?"

Lydia saw by a movement of the top of her head that the
weeping woman had nodded.

"But your mother looked different, quite different, and more
contented than ever in her life." Fresh tears flowed from Marie's
eyes. When she could see again, Lydia was no longer in the
room.

She took her nightly path towards the shore; the two powers
accompanied her. The night was clear. Bush and tree still retained the basic tone of their color, and even the contours of
distant groups of trees nestled softly against the sky. The sea
was greater under the night.

She sat down as usual on a bench at the edge of the deep
cliff. Her head fell back with exhaustion. It was too much. She

needed help, an outstretched hand. If she could only lean on Constantine. Her weak lips quivered.

Love, that seizes any means to gain its ends, used this lull in the struggle to seduce the exhausted woman. Lydia leaned on Constantine, who was sitting beside her on the bench. She felt no horror, for Constantine was not her brother. He explained to her exactly why it was that he could not be her brother.

"If I were, should we love each other so infinitely? Impossible!"

That was convincing.

"Since I love you, Constantine, you cannot be my brother. . . . How wonderfully simple that is!"

She surrendered herself to waves of emotion in his arms; she kissed the bare spot behind his ear. All resistance was broken.

"I didn't want to show myself to you." She placed his hand on her body, so that he should feel the movements of the child. "I didn't want you to see me for another two months, my dearest. . . . But how could I endure it!" she said aloud, and thus gave the colloquy a turn towards warmth and simplicity.

His groping hand found the child; he kept his listening glance fixed on hers. "It's moving. Now it's moving."

"Is that beautiful?" She saw the delight in his eyes.

"Which will you love most," he asked, "the child or me?"

It came again, her hesitant smile. He caught it with his lips and turned it into bliss.

She sank unresisting beneath his kiss, and in her surrender her eyes grew wet with tears; love and her great longing conquered, but in a disguised and self-deceiving form.

Out of black nothingness, from far away, a thin, unbearably white-hot ray came shooting towards Lydia. Wrenched to her feet by the abrupt return of the horrible idea that she had belonged to her brother, she thrust him away from her and fell in a heap on the edge of the high cliff.

She knew that she had only to withdraw her supporting hand to be hurled down sixty feet. The conflict between the two equal forces had begun again.

The following morning she made her preparations to go to

Berlin and enter a nursing home. They left at midday. The horror accompanied her.

Her love and craving for Constantine remained cunningly in the background, leaving the field to Nature. And Nature proceeded vigorously with her work, which in ten days had to be completed, taking no heed of the horror, and therefore working in the cause of love.

Midwives and nurses, rosy and smiling, were flitting to and fro in the nursing home. Several times a day and several times a night a child was brought into the world amidst cries of pain that penetrated through the padded doors; nerve-racked fathers stood about in the corridors, learning to wait, and the nurses answered their questions always with the same smile; young mothers, exhausted, white as the beds in which they lay, listened blissfully to the first cry of their new-born babes. It was a place of pain, hope and birth, and every thought and feeling, every interest, every smile centered on the same thing. Even Lydia could not isolate herself from this atmosphere, for it filled the whole house.

Lydia lay for twenty-four hours in labor. She no longer wished to show that she was brave. Even the midwife would not maintain her professional smile, and the doctor was considering whether he could postpone action any longer without endangering Lydia's life.

The minute came when the life of mother and child hung on his sure hands and power of quick decision. Lydia was carried to the operating room; a single wild cry of agony, as long as breath would last, was borne down the corridor.

In face of life and death shame vanishes: Lydia screamed. She screamed with all the strength she had left, and she had no strength left. Her strength had been consumed by pain, but she still lived, still screamed; in raging, burning pains she sought for some other source of strength, for she was utterly exhausted; she screamed: "For you, Constantine, for you!" She borrowed strength from him. She screamed, while the pain tore her to pieces: "For you! For you!" Else she would have died.

The danger was immediate; the doctor swore; a woman's body reared up, and its writhings ceased only when the doctor, who disapproved of anaesthetics in such cases, was at last compelled by her agony to give her an anaesthetic.

"Are you there, Constantine? Are you there? . . . You are there! . . ."

The sister was holding the child in her trembling hands.

An hour after the delivery, Marie was allowed to enter the room. Benumbed by what she saw, she crept with frequent pauses to the bed. Lydia's eyes were still closed, her hair matted with sweat. Her whole face, grey and mottled, was twitching, and the feebly open mouth whimpered with fluttering breath. A devastated human being, who had suffered too much.

Her eyelids lifted. Marie never forgot that look. The mouth twisted plaintively, like that of a crying child: "What have they done to me?"

Marie could only kiss her moist hand. "It's all over now."

"Stay with me, Constantine, my Constantine!"

"Yes, I'll stay."

"For you! For you."

Constantine did not guess what had happened there for his sake, nor what was still happening. He did not know what his wife could endure out of her love for him.

For the next few days Lydia was not allowed to move. Her face became a human mask again. But she seemed neither to think nor to feel. It had been too much. She acknowledged their ministrations only with an absent glance.

When the doctor came to her and cried, with the fresh vigor of his professional optimism: "Well, what do you think of the boy now? A splendid fellow, isn't he?"—she smiled politely. But when he took up the child to lay it beside her, she recoiled in self-defense and closed her eyes.

The child was not in Lydia's room at night. It was brought in very morning, and Marie washed it, dressed it in fresh things and laid it down to sleep again. Lydia had not yet heard its voice. It was a particularly quiet child, and slept twenty-two hours of the day.

Nothing had been prepared. Marie went out to buy the little petticoat, woolen shoes and jacket. Lydia had slept long and peacefully, and when she woke, she took the mirror and found

that the doctor had been right. Her appearance exactly cor-
responded with her pleasant bodily feelings. She was pleased
with herself that morning; she had an actual, bodily feeling of
being rich in vital energy; she was calm and firm and sure, as
though she only needed to give the order and life would begin
anew. She stood before a new beginning and gave herself the
pleasure of postponing it.

It seemed there was no need for anxiety on account of the
child. It had inherited excellent qualities. She did not yet feel
any interest in it, but neither did she feel repulsion. No, there
was no actual repulsion, only indifference.

She took up the glass again and put her hair in order. It had
already been washed. Her eyes were clear. So the matter of the
child was settled. Now she could again devote herself to her
chief concern. She needed only to write him or telegraph or put
through a trunk call—for he must still be in Zurich—or, of
course, she could still wait. Many alternatives! Or she could go
to him. She was rich; she could take her choice. Like a woman
with a whole wardrobe full of new clothes. It was sweet to
choose, and to take one's time over it.

What if she went to Zurich, suddenly entered the room
where he was, and fell into his arms without a word. . . . And
the horror?—For he was still her brother! Why was the horror
no longer with her? She had done nothing to drive it away!
. . . Oh, if only he were there, her lover, if only he were
there now! How she would offer herself to his kisses!

How changed she was! She felt the change in every limb. Her
hold on life was quite calm and sure, and much firmer. Constantine and she were alone in the world, of course, quite alone;
but to make up for that their happiness was much, much
greater. It was soothing. She closed her eyes.

At first, although she heard it, the thin cry of the child did
not penetrate to her consciousness, so absorbed was she by the
rich feeling, of which that thin cry was a part. Not till it grew
louder and acquired a plaintive note did she open her eyes and
listen.

A day or so before, in a quiet, opportune moment, Marie
had said suddenly: "Herr Constantine is in a dreadful state.

Quite wasted away! He looks ten years older. I can't understand why you're treating him like this!" Love had slipped
cunningly into her pity and, thus disguised, had settled down
firmly in Lydia's heart. Now, in turn, her mother love slipped
into her pity and in this way reached her heart.

She turned her head. There, in the corner, was a little,
white-covered portable cradle. She could not look in; the edge
was too high. There was nothing else in the world but that thin,
plaintive cry. She listened, deeply moved. The waves of pity
following in quick succession, poured tempestuously through
her, till love burst open like a blossom in her heart.

Perhaps he was hungry? Marie was not there. It had all come
apparently of itself—just as the horror had apparently gone of
itself. She got up. Three steps to the cradle, still hesitant, a little nervous as to how to approach this great joy. Then she saw
it; the little, well-formed head, lying on its side, the little
mouth twisted piteously and reproachfully.

Two trembling hands, that had not yet learned their work,
lifted the child with too great care from the cradle. Her hot
eyes looked at it; her heart beat high. She could not take in at
one glance the thousand details, all unaccountably magical. She
had to say something. She could not help it. "Oh, my sweet,
sweet, sweet baby! Oh, my pet!" She carried her prize to the
bed.

What happened now was beyond belief! Scarcely had she
drawn her nightdress down over her breast, when the little
mouth pushed impetuously forward and seized it, thrusting
and sucking. Incredible that he could do that already! Incredible!

Did she imagine it? Or was it real? It was not imagination:
The little, blue eyes, wonderfully formed, looked up at her
now and then as the baby sucked, looked up with profound
meaning, as though to say: Now it is all right.

Marie, who had quietly opened the door, stole back into the
corridor again. "Everything will come right now." She was not
surprised, that afternoon, when Lydia asked for pen and paper; she knew whom the letter was for.

It was hard to know how to address him. "Dear Constantine?"

No, it was not so simple as that! Lydia had to learn that to be happy with Constantine in imagination was a very different matter from re-establishing direct relations with him by writing a letter. This was a form of reality, and it weighed heavily. A crowd of impetuous feelings of the most varied kind pressed forward to be explained and communicated, and much that was inexplicable had to be set down in words.

Meanwhile Constantine was sitting at his writing table in Zurich, inactive, as he had been for months, waiting, thinking, staring at the grain of the wood in the table top. He knew every vein of it. He thought and thought; he thought of Lydia. He bent his head till it touched the table. There was a certain spot where he could see in the grain the face of his beloved.

Lydia took a fresh sheet of paper. She closed her eyes and talked with Constantine. That was wonderful; now she could easily say: "My splendid lover!" And his answer enraptured her. But when she began the letter again with "My love!" she found the words impossible.

Then she placed the pen resolutely in the hand of her happiness and left it to write the letter for itself. But when she read through what was written, it seemed false to her. The foundation of suffering was missing.

"I left you in Trieste because—" She could not go on. Whatever she wrote, the mere fact of writing to him was equivalent to a willingness to be with him again. That was what he would think, when he received a letter from her.

"You knew four weeks before me that I—"

Six crumpled sheets of notepaper were lying on the coverlet.

"Although you knew that—"

"Sir—How could you dare to conceal from me for four weeks—"

She felt of a sudden that this was the style in which she could write to him. Reproaches! He had treated her badly, even disgracefully. She talked herself into a rage. And then, suddenly, her pen began to fly over the paper.

She could not have expressed to him her complex state of

mind by writing the clear, simple truth: "I love you. Come to me!" But in that tangle of reproaches, from which flashed out many a hidden endearment, like strawberries from a disorder of green leaves, she was best able to portray the conglomerate, accumulated experiences of those six months, and to write them out of her heart.

At the end of the letter, she had actually started to write that there was now, unfortunately, a child—but she started back with a sudden sense of reverence for that precious life. That would have been sin! She could not write that. Not that! Her baby was not a misfortune. It was an incredibly great good fortune. She preferred not to mention the child.

It arrived hidden among newspapers, a dozen circulars and thick catalogues from motor-car manufacturers. Stephan turned the slim, longish envelope over and over, weighed it in his hand, smelt it, he divined something. The shape! That shape! It was not a business letter. And what man would use a long, narrow envelope, for which the letter must be folded three times? Stephan did not know Lydia's writing.

But Constantine knew it. The look on his face was one that Stephan never forgot: Constantine recoiled as though from the sudden flash of a drawn knife. The letter fell to the floor. It is the way of the Japanese, when bathing, to jump out of ice-cold water into boiling hot: they can do it. Constantine could not. The letter had first to go away, to retreat a thousand miles, and then slowly to approach him again. In the meantime Stephan had picked it up and handed it to him. As he did so, he put his hand on Constantine's shoulder, without a word. Only his friendly heart spoke from his eyes.

He looked at Stephan, asking if it were possible. A mistake would have killed him. Stephan went out of the room, with his quiet face. Constantine laid the letter, unopened, on his writing table.

He had no need to read it. It mattered not what it said. First, she was still alive, and second, she had written to him. He knew, oh, he knew, what that meant.

If anyone had dared to offer him the treasures of the world in exchange for one word of that letter, he would have murdered him. For he must read each word, each single word, a thousand times.

The angler must be quiet, or he catches no fish. . . . So she had overcome her pride! Her wayward pride! She had written to him!

Suddenly the tears rose, and all was veiled in blue as he read: "Sir!"

He smiled entranced, and yet suppressed sobs were shaking him. "Oh, Lydia, proud spirit!"

And how would he begin his reply?—"My Lydia, dearest wife!"

"How could you dare to conceal from me for four weeks that you are my brother? Base! It was base of you!"

His happiness was full to overflowing. He had to speak, he needed someone. "Stephan, Stephan she's abusing me!" He wrenched open the window and shouted into the garden: "She's abusing me! Do you hear, Stephan? She's abusing me."

Lydia had crossed out a passage, and then the letter went on: "In Zurich you found out everything and then came back and played that disgraceful trick on me when I was standing on the balcony. Oh, how base you are!"

But the passage she had crossed out was still legible; it was the same as the one that followed, except that at first she had written the intimate "Du" instead of the formal "Sir." The "Du" was canceled with a stroke of especial strength.

Yet in the very next sentence her heart had run away with her again, and she had written the word "Du": "I shall never forget that you did that."

But he did not need such proof; he needed no more proof of any kind; he knew everything.

Out of the broken man a young man rose, of seven-and-twenty, who knew not what to do with his happiness and over-flowing energy. Something must happen! He could not work. Not now! But something must happen.

First he spent three days reading the letter. He knew it by heart. He read and read. Every character, every stroke was precious.

As he read, he saw Lydia in his mind, in Trieste. Something must happen! He went to Trieste. For it was there he had last been with Lydia.

8

A telegraph boy with a red pouch at his side jumped from his bicycle outside the villa and wheeled it into the garden, which lay in the early sunshine of a moist May morning. He gave the telegram to Constantine himself, who went into the house and at once ordered his trunks to be packed, saying that he was going away for a considerable time. Not till then did he open the telegram. He found it contained nothing but the address of an island in the Adriatic.

His feelings resembled a mighty chorale from which a high jubilant aria attempts to rise. In order to move to the rhythm of that sustained melody, he would have had to put skates on his feet and to move slowly in wide, sweeping curves. As he walked through the house he moved his shoulders a little in that manner, so that the jubilant aria should not begin too soon.

How easy, how beautiful and marvelous the waiting was now —for he knew with certainty that fulfillment was coming, and it would last a whole lifetime.

Lydia took their nearness for granted. She prepared for their meeting with a mind of noble calm. She knew that no word of explanation would be necessary. There were no more obstructions. Even her pride she needed no longer. Fate had created a reality to threaten their lives, and by the supreme power of love it had been transformed into happiness. Yet her shy heart throbbed faster at the thought of the great reunion, and surrendered itself time and again to the throb of her yearning.

She carried her yearning for her lover into the nursery, to her little man, now three months old. He had already learned to laugh but could only reach his highest note when he kicked out with both legs. Here she proved that two quite different kinds of happiness can find place at once in the same heart.

She had to lift him up and press his little head against her cheek. "My baby, oh, my baby!" And it was given to her to experience the unnameable, purling sweetness of that happiness, and at the same time to look with a surging heart at the Constantine who stood before her.

Whom should she thank? Whom? Whom? She had to kneel down and thank fate, who had ordained that her lover should be her brother, and her brother her lover.

What would have happened if they had grown up together, had seen each other day by day, united, perhaps, only as brother and sister? She did not want to think of it. It was unthinkable not to be Constantine's beloved! Fate had ordained it so, and eternal thanks were due to fate.

It was a long way from Zurich to Trieste. Very long! But there were railway lines. At the booking office one paid money and received a ticket, then the train came in; it began to gather speed, the conductor came: "Tickets, please!— Thank you!" And all the time the train rushed on to any tune one cared to hum for it. Constantine hummed several, and the train joined in them all.

It was important which frock she chose. Oh, yes! Nothing was unimportant. Yellow! But white would do as well. Just simple white! Girlish white! No one, not even the shrewdest observer would find in her any indication that she was a mother. She had got rid of the four pounds.

She must not think that anything would escape his notice. Once she had thought, quite wrongly, that he had not noticed the line of her nostrils. Nothing escaped him. Of course she must make her toilet with such extreme care that it would look as if it had been done in a minute.

And how would it be when she saw him, saw him again! When he came up to her? How would she feel? Throb, throb, throb, answered her heart.

The wait at the frontier was terrible. A whole hour. And yet it was very pleasant to walk up and down the waiting room, to go to the buffet and eat nothing. For who could have eaten? Yes, very, very pleasant to wait! At last even that hour came to an end, and then the train flew on, straight as an arrow, through the flat countryside.

We'll live on a remote plateau among the hills, where no one is and no one ever will be, thought Constantine. He was boarding the little motor boat that took the travelers from the steamer and carried them to the island, while the steamer itself went on to Venice. Fate can have nothing else in store for us. Fate brought us together to destroy us and we have conquered it. Conquered fate!

Perhaps he wouldn't come by this steamer after all. . . . Then he would come by the next. How calm she was!

Then she saw him: he was standing up in the motor boat. And he saw Lydia on the shore, detached from her surroundings. She was so familiar to him in bearing and appearance, that it was almost as if he had gone out half an hour before for a motor-boat trip and was just returning to her. Both bowed their heads—she in her own characteristic way. He saw it.

So Lydia went to the landing steps, up which he was coming. The sight of him only deepened the great calm within her, and the same feeling was in him. They shook each other by the hand.

"You are so brown!" Her smile matched her words.

"I've been traveling about the world; I've been in Egypt."

It was almost the same conversation as had taken place a year before, when they first met in the Tiergarten in Berlin, and this time also the words had a deeper meaning.

They said no more. They walked across the square; he even looked round.

As Lydia's steps turned slightly towards the right, he realized that she was going to pass the hotel. In accordance with the melodious harmony of their feelings, he turned aside with her down the woodland path.

They walked on, absorbed in themselves and each other's company, full of a sense of well-deserved happiness. They could have talked, but they were silent. Their hearts spoke to each other. Now and then a glance at hair and brow or at the other's precious form—new stuff for hearts' dialogue!

At home in our garden I kissed a tree because it took your shape in the twilight, so deep was my longing. "How many rooms are there in your villa?"

I shall never be able to tell you how much I love you, my Constantine. Never! "Eight. You'll have a very nice work-room." If I were able to express it, my love would not be so immeasurably deep.

"Does it overlook the garden?" What a walk she has! How deliciously she places her feet!

"Yes, the garden and the sea!" And her heart said: He is shining. Oh, how I love him! "The kitchen's in the basement."

It was rather like what Constantine had proposed in Trieste: Two people walking side by side through the wood; two mouths speaking of outward things while hearts were giving themselves. The tension was extreme, and only the certainty that each belonged eternally to the other made the tension bearable.

They drew near to the other side of the island, where the villa stood. The sea drew a blue ribbon through the green of the trees.

"This is where we live."

A long, white house, as low as a hidden fort, almost entirely concealed by the thick bushes that protected it on all sides. But he looked at Lydia's pointing forefinger, because the tip bent upwards so gracefully and was pink where the sun shone through it.

She went in front of him through a gate overgrown with creepers. Between her black hair and the edge of her black dress was her white neck, slightly bent, as though bowed before the lord of her heart.

And now, as she walked before him through the garden, her hips swaying vitally, he saw again the exciting flow of her legs, and the hollows of her knees, that had made him captive exactly a year before.

In the doorway, she stopped: "I wish you happiness in this house." Her smile faded into gravity; she looked at him for a long while, and in her glance the fate of both was perfected. It was like a mute prayer, and Lydia ended it with a soft,

womanly smile. They went into the house; both felt the significance of their entry.

"Now I must tell you something; I couldn't tell it you
before. . . . I'm no longer alone." She spoke as to an old
friend, who had formerly been a frequent guest, but had not
yet been informed of the addition to the family. But he did not
understand.

"I have a child." Again that look that came from the heart
and middle of fate.

He felt as though someone had told him of the existence in
the world of something that was not and could not be there.
Only in dreams do such impossible things become suddenly possible. But he was not dreaming. "What? What?" Even the most
intelligent man may look stupid in a moment of astonishment.

Lydia succeeded in suppressing a smile.

"A boy! He's three months old." She had grown grave, for
gravity and reverence dwell near together.

At first he felt a blow on his heart: in a fraction of a second
he realized the Odyssey of suffering through which Lydia had
passed. Then from some far, far corner of his emotional life a
fresh and novel joy came with frolic step towards him. Lydia
saw the young joy leap from his eyes.

"But that's impossible. A child? A child?"

After all there can be moments of too much joy in the world,
when a man immersed in happiness gasps for breath like one
drowning.

"I'll show him to you."

The pride shone, openly confessed, in her eyes.

"Good," he said, and it sounded out of place. He moved
doubtfully away from the doorpost, and followed her hesitat-
ingly along the hall.

But she was used to hurrying to the nursery; she was there
before him, and had to wait. Her smile ushered him into the
room and over to the cradle, which was covered in white
muslin.

First he only saw a little arm waving to and fro.

Of course one can't take hold of that. One can't take hold of
it. . . . One can't take hold of a miracle, he thought, trying

to steady himself. But he failed. This new joy had not yet cleared a path down which it could proceed unhindered to Constantine's heart.

He bent down, looked up at Lydia: "It's laughing," he said, in surprise.

"It always laughs at people."

He shook his head in bewilderment. He took the little fingers in his hand, looked at the tiny nails, five, well-formed finger-nails.

The child accepted his touch as a caress. It crowed aloud in pure joy of living, and thus cleared at one stroke a path for the new joy to reach Constantine's surging heart.

He could not speak. When she made a movement towards the door, he followed reluctantly, and even in the hall, he was still walking on tiptoe.

"Of course I can't grasp it all at once—"

"There's no need to apologize." Lydia put out her hand; she wanted to give him time. "Supper at ten, if that suits you."

He did not let go her hand: "—And I thank you."

The bloom of her smile helped him over his embarrassment.

He could do nothing but go into the room, sit down, press his fist on the table, get up and walk about. Finally he pressed his forehead against the wall, entirely without thought or purpose.

Marie waited at table. Lydia spoke to her only with her eyes, and Marie understood that speech.

Both were prepared for the incomparable, unique experience that hour would bring. Now she was sitting opposite him, his wife, his sister, the mother of his child, but in reality a young woman of faultless beauty, over whom he possessed no rights of intimacy. His wise heart counseled him to act thus, both in word and look.

Lydia had invited this sunburned man to supper, for whose sake even the grief at the death of her mother had passed her by. She had invited him to supper, no more and no less. They had not yet reached the beginning of a new relationship.

They spoke only trivial words. In those six solitary months

each had told the other everything, thousands and thousands of times.

Coffee was served in the drawing room, on a little table beside the divan where Lydia was reclining. Constantine was separated from her by the whole room; he was leaning against the wall opposite her.

Suddenly—a quick glance of understanding passed between them—they realized that their present situation, both inwardly and outwardly, was similar to that in the hotel in Unter den Linden a year before, that evening when Lydia had lain on the ottoman, floating in rapture, before generously affording him the first love night.

Yet, in spite of Lydia's victorious battle with the inscrutable something, which her feminine courage had destroyed, they were further from each other now than they had been a year ago. For the fact that they were brother and sister lifted them to a dangerous and magical plane, where the play of love was governed by unknown laws that arose from its own nature.

Once more Lydia was forced to learn that to exchange a loving glance with her brother in reality was an incomparably weightier thing than complete surrender in imagination. She did not move.

With a lover's instinct Constantine felt that if Lydia was to take a step across the borderline into a new oneness with him, she must do it alone. Words could not help, and a silent caress from his hand might as easily prove to her that it was all impossible. That would have been her death.

For long minutes she lay perfectly motionless, still as a corpse and beautiful.

He did not dare to act. Even when she rose and left the room without word or look, he did not follow and he did not move. He heard a door close in the distance.

In the half darkness of the drawing room—the only light came from the tall standard lamp beside the divan—Constantine was leaning motionless against the wall, taut in every nerve, as though confronted by a great danger which the faintest movement on his part would transform into a catastrophe.

Even now, as she sat on the bed in her room, undressing, with trembling knees, she could call her brother to her in imagination and give him her lips.

But reality was inflexible.

Constantine heard a faint click and saw the door handle move. The door opened.

Her nightdress reached to her feet. She came in, white and rigid, a walking corpse. Then he was beside her.

As he saw her face in the light of the lamp, pity guided his hand and he switched off the light.

He felt a slight pressure on his breast and yielded to it; Lydia raised her head and switched on the light again. Melting surrender in her face, and round her mouth a smile still bound to pain, though it was bedded in tenderness, she threw her arms round his neck and, with eyes fixed on his, took him to herself.